# Interdisciplinary Research Topics in
# URBAN ENGINEERING

**A Report by the
Urban Engineering Study Committee
of the
American Society for Engineering Education**

Dwight M. Baumann, Committee Chairman
Stephen L. Dickerson, Faculty Adviser
Bruce B. Lusignan, Faculty Adviser
William M. Hafferty, Report Editor
Richard W. Hess, Report Editor
Robert G. McGregor, Report Editor

This study was supported by Grant GK-15688 from the
Engineering Division of the National Science Foundation

Published by the
American Society for Engineering Education
Washington, D. C.

**October 1969**

# TABLE OF CONTENTS

# FOREWORD

This report is the result of a summer project conducted under a grant from the National Science Foundation, Engineering Systems Program of the Engineering Division, to the American Society for Engineering Education (ASEE). The project was staffed by three engineering graduate students: Robert McGregor, William Hafferty, and Richard Hess from MIT, Stanford, and Georgia Tech, respectively. They compiled the information in Chapters III through VI while working full time for three months under the supervision of a Faculty Steering Committee; Professors Dwight M. Baumann of MIT, Chairman; Bruce B. Lusignan of Stanford; and Stephen L. Dickerson of Georgia Tech; who also contributed the background information for Chapters I and II. Leslie B. Williams, Executive Secretary of the American Society for Engineering Education, served as Project Administrator, assisted by Susanne P. Flynn of the ASEE staff. The excellent guidance and support of the entire ASEE staff is gratefully acknowledged. Without their cooperation and administrative efforts, the task of preparing this document would have been much more difficult if not impossible.

We are also indebted to Elias Schutzman and Lewis G. Mayfield of the National Science Foundation for their guidance and suggestions in support of this effort. We are also indebted to Frances M. Pentecost,

Librarian of the NSF Library, for her dedicated assistance. In addition, we thank all the other members of the Government agencies who many times went far beyond what was expected in sharing their expertise, so that the substance of this report could be prepared for use in engineering schools across the country. Certainly it is upon these dedicated professionals from the Government sector that we have relied for most of the information presented. A complete list of these persons is given in Appendix C.

Our primary goal was to collect and organize as much useful and timely information as possible in the allotted time. We were particularly interested in those ideas and publications that were important in the current planning of public officials. Our guideline was to, as much as possible, collect the information that would be useful to our colleagues who do not have immediate access to the Washington, D. C., community. We attempted also to emphasize those sources of information that would perhaps be unfamiliar to the university student. By the same logic we do not reference many of the standard publications that are available in college bookstores.

This project is in many respects a follow-on to a preliminary study also sponsored by NSF and undertaken by Edward J. Jaramillo, Jr., and George A. Kladnick of Stanford University in the summer of 1968. Their project covered a somewhat broader scope and established much of the groundwork for this report. The 1968 Stanford study was conceived and directed by Dr. William B. Bollay, Visiting Professor of Aeronautics and Astronautics at Stanford University. Dr. Bollay was also involved in the planning for this summer's effort and encouraged us to undertake the study. We owe him special thanks for his role in furthering the interdisciplinary systems engineering approach.

In addition, we wish to thank Ella H. Wright, editor of the Journal of Engineering Education, Joan Stallard, and Merry Falconer of the ASEE publications staff for their valuable assistance in compiling the final document and also Helen Saleeby for her typing efforts.

The Urban Engineering
Study Committee

Someday boy, this will all be yours!

# INTRODUCTION

Engineers and scientists have long been active in resolving engineering and research problems associated with the urban sector. Many of these problems have accepted solutions as old as civilization itself. Recently, there has been considerable, renewed emphasis on the problems confronting the Nation's metropolitan areas. The increasing pace of urbanization, the special problems of minority groups, poverty, and the financial dilemma of the central city all contribute to the milieu. Some who vociferously assail the ills of our urban society may possess genuine concern; certainly, the partial success of recent protests has boosted their efforts. In an era of widespread discontent, surely much of society is beginning to suspect that it has been short-changed by technologists in some important civilian areas.

The same American who witnessed the trip to the moon finds he cannot get downtown conveniently. The underprivileged see billions of dollars spent on what are to them very abstract and often irrelevant projects, while their severe needs go seemingly unnoticed. It is relatively easy to place blame but quite difficult to find real solutions. In all of this travail, there lies a new challenge to engineering, science, and the entire technological community.

As our society seeks to reallocate its resources, it will be important that workable technological solutions and technologists capable of changing their theories into reality become available. On the other side of this same coin, the technological community must take the initiative to find effective solutions and then convince society that it needs these carefully considered remedies. It is to these purposes that this report is addressed.

The basic issues at this time appear to be ones of emphasis and approach. There now seems to be a growing public impatience to address the problems of the city in some of the massive and systematic ways that have been applied to the space program. We must realize that this phenomenon is also driven in part by the fact that there currently exists a technological capacity, developed through the vast space and defense funding phases, that is in search of a problem. It must also be apparent that it is often easier to agree on the solution to problems that are somewhat exotic or remote to our daily existence than to act on what seems to be local and mundane.

However, this hardly diminishes the potential gains from proper application of the lessons learned in other programs. The net result of these factors is renewed emphasis on technology as it could and should be applied to the city. We have chosen to call this area of endeavor "urban engineering." This is equivalent to the use of the terms "agricultural engineering" or "aeronautical engineering" to describe application of technology to the solution of complicated and interrelated problems, either by studies of the individual problems or by integrated studies considering many problem areas simultaneously.

In this document, we additionally stress the term "interdisciplinary" to note that an extensive technological capability alone will not be sufficient in dealing with the urban environment. The problems of the city cut across traditional professional interests and abilities. The effective "urban engineer" will, of necessity, expand his capabilities, not only into related engineering and physical science disciplines, but into the social sciences, law, and administrative sciences as well. More precisely, he will be part of a team of professionals from diverse discipline contributing to a thorough evaluation and comprehensive solution to urban problems.

The primary purpose of this report is to assist in the development at universities of interdisciplinary systems engineering research in the delineated area of urban engineering. To this end, several complex urban problem areas, annotated bibliographies, and directory information is presented in this publication to aid in the initiation of projects for both experienced and inexperienced groups.

The topic areas presented in the following chapters do not, by any means, encompass all of the problems related to urban living; nor can they possibly include more than an abbreviated outline of areas where extensive research is needed. Rather, they are included on the assumption that they are at least representative of the major concerns facing planners in the three critical areas of Urban Transportation, Urban

Housing and the Urban Environment, and that they demonstrate the integrated approach required in dealing with large urban problems.

The major topics listed were chosen primarily: (1) for their appropriateness for study by interdisciplinary systems teams; (2) because they suggest several contributing problem areas where in-depth research is desirable; (3) because they are considered to be of primary importance by Federal officials; and (4) because they could be isolated, however broadly, as distinct topic areas.

This series of interdisciplinary research topics should be read primarily as a "shopping list." Individual topics are only examples of possible approaches to the general problem and may be appropriately modified to realistically reflect conditions of a target locality, the researchers' interests, or available personnel.

The three general problem areas of Urban Transportation, Urban Housing, and the Urban Environment (Chapters III, IV, and V, respectively) are each organized into four sections:

Section A presents an overview of the elements of the general problem and a discussion of relevant history, current emphasis, and national policies.

Section B presents the specific interdisciplinary research topics, each of which is organized into four subsections: "The Problem"; "State-of-the-Art" with respect to current and proposed programs, legislation, appropriations, public and private research activities, and technology; "Participating Personnel and Organizations"; and "Contributing Problem Areas."

We use the notation (ref. 1) to refer the reader to specific numbered references in Sections D of Chapters III, IV, and V.

"Participating Personnel and Organizations" attempts to single out agencies, officials, and other organizations specifically involved with the topic and who might be able to provide further information and data. We also use the notation (pos. A) to refer the reader to particular officials listed in Sections C -- along with their addresses and telephone numbers -- who might have an active interest in the specific topic area.

"Contributing Problem Areas" includes aspects of the interdisciplinary research problem which are (1) appropriate for in-depth research at the thesis level, and (2) must be suitably resolved in dealing with the larger systems design.

Section C presents a list and description of agencies in the Washington, D.C. area concerned with the general problem, along with the names, addresses, and telephones of knowledgeable officials within those agencies. Due to the limitations of time and manpower, it was not possible to contact all or most of the principals involved with the problems of urban housing, transportation, and the urban environment. With a few exceptions, our contacts were restricted to persons in Federal agencies. Interviewees are denoted by asterisks.

We have also listed the names of several officials who were not directly interviewed, but whose positions suggest an intimate knowledge of particular topics.

In many instances, these officials are available for further contact or have volunteered their willingness to address systems engineering courses on particular problems. In all cases, however, such future activities remain the prerogative of the individual.

Section D of each chapter includes an annotated bibliography which, while somewhat extensive, by no means represents an exhaustive search of the literature on urban problems. It does include, however, some of the most current and extensive references presently available and in use in the Washington, D.C. area. It should be noted that many of the documents referenced are published by the Government Printing Office; others, particularly studies by private contractors for the Federal agencies, should be obtained from the Clearinghouse for Federal Scientific and Technical Information.

In addition, Chapter VI discusses general information sources in the Washington, D.C. area and procedures for obtaining timely Federal publications and gaining access to particular information services.

The authors of this report have all been associated with interdisciplinary systems design projects at their respective universities. Though the basic approach is essentially the same, the formats for these courses at the various universities differ somewhat. Chapter II

discusses the basic format and course philosophy, as well as some of

the specific projects that have been undertaken.

## II. INTERDISCIPLINARY SYSTEMS ENGINEERING IN THE UNIVERSITY

# INTERDISCIPLINARY SYSTEMS ENGINEERING
## IN THE UNIVERSITY

## INTRODUCTION

Recently a number of universities have instituted a unique kind of systems engineering course. These courses originally focused on problems related to aerospace activities but many have expanded to consider problems more closely related to man's domestic needs. Two goals of this document are to encourage more of these existing courses to investigate problems in the urban sector and to encourage more schools to institute new interdisciplinary systems courses, preferably also in the urban engineering area. The first goal is supported mainly by the succeeding chapters, which provide much of the background information needed for developing an interdisciplinary project in urban engineering. The second goal, encouraging information of new approaches to interdisciplinary research, design, and development is supported by this chapter, which seeks to outline the general goals of the interdisciplinary systems engineering courses, the experience many universities are having with them, and details of their organization and conduct. Further background on the systems engineering courses is contained in two earlier articles by Professors Baumann, Bollay, and Lusignan reproduced in this report as Appendix B.

## HISTORY OF COURSES

A number of Engineering Colleges are now offering courses which are descendants of the original efforts of the Massachusetts Institute of Technology to establish a graduate course in interdisciplinary systems engineering. The first course at MIT was conducted during the Spring Semester of 1963 under the auspices of several departments of the School of Engineering. Early courses tended to be aerospace-related both at MIT and elsewhere. During the Summer of 1965, the National Aeronautics and Space Administration sponsored the first Summer Faculty Institute in Systems Engineering, which has as one of its goals the promotion of project-oriented interdisciplinary design courses. A number of NASA centers now offer similar Institutes.

A summary of the college courses is given in Table I[*] and a summary of the NASA programs is given in Table II[*]. While Table II is complete, Table I is probably somewhat incomplete since we are unable to contact all engineering schools during this survey. We purposely have not included the numerous departmental senior project courses, but inadvertently may have missed interdisciplinary systems engineering courses similar to those listed.

## PURPOSE OF THE COURSES

The solution of today's broad systems problems requires teams of individuals each of whom ideally is expert in his own specialty area

---

[*] Tables I and II are both presented at the end of this Chapter.

but also has a broad understanding of the other areas involved in the problem. An exclusive specialist has difficulty in understanding his role in the solution of the broad problem and in conveying the results of his efforts to others involved in the study. An exclusive generalist on the other hand can combine existing knowledge but lacks the ability to extend the state of knowledge in a specific area. With both general understanding and specific expertise, a study team member can understand what is required from his area and invent and analyze the systems to meet those requirements.

The hardest part of the job of helping the student to be an expert in a particular field is done by the normal curriculum in colleges. The remaining part of the job is accomplished very effectively by the interdisciplinary systems engineering courses.

The principal academic aim of the courses is thus to teach the student to understand other areas involved in broad systems problems and enable him to work efficiently with other members of an interdisciplinary team.

A second academic aim is to overcome a shortcoming in the student's education in his own major. Most courses enable a student to understand and choose the appropriate relationship or theory to answer a specific question. But they give him little guidance in deciding what questions are important to ask, what is the critical parameter, and how approximate one can be in estimating an answer. This subject is best treated in a project course, and interdisciplinary systems engineering courses are very efficient project courses.

A third benefit which students derive from the courses is an extremely intensive and timely view of the world in which they plan to pursue their careers. The problems, existing groups seeking to solve the problems, and the methods currently being used are brought out. This exposure has significantly affected the careers of many students who have participated in past courses.

The fourth major benefits of the systems courses is to society in general. The topics chosen for study concern real problems and the students studies, supported by the experience of guest speakers, have made tangible contributions to the solutions of these problems. These contributions are directed to those outside the university by publication of a detailed report of the students' results. In a significant number of cases, the work on an interdisciplinary systems course has directly resulted in the initiation of new research projects. These have ranged from individual thesis research to larger projects. The Metran study undertaken at MIT is an example of the latter.

## THE COURSE AND THE CURRICULUM

The length of the systems courses varies from university to university. For those on the semester system it usually occupies one semester; two quarters are typical for universities on the quarter system. However, some courses have been run in only one quarter, while others have used three quarters or two semesters. The academic credit ranges from three to five units, with some offering the students a choice of the number of units credit. We must admit, however, that one of the most prevalent complaints about the courses is that they do absorb a lot of time for the instruction staff, and those students who become exceptionally interested find that they may spend almost full time on the course. The relative measures of effort vs. value are, of course, a continuous topic of debate by all concerned. It could be that the most significant part of the course is the development of judgment as to "what" and "how much."

The courses are all interdisciplinary to some degree, some drawing students from two or more departments within engineering, others drawing students from schools outside engineering as well. Enrollment has run from about 15 to as high as 80.

The courses fit the school's curricular requirements in many ways. Some are used to satisfy requirements for senior or master's theses. In other schools they are one of several optional courses under the general heading of "systems engineering." Where the course is broadly interdisciplinary, enrollment is used to satisfy out-of-department requirements; and in some cases, students enroll under independent study course numbers in their own departments.

The courses summarized in Table I naturally vary from school to school; however, the purposes of all of them are similar and the course formats have much in common.  The description that follows, with minor exceptions, is common to all of them.

## CHOICE OF STUDY TOPIC

As can be seen by Table I, a large number of topics have been studied by the systems engineering courses.  A number of factors are taken into account in selecting these topics.  The nature of the problem must be selected to match the specialty areas of the students expected to enroll, and the scope must match the expected number of students and the time span of the course.  In addition, the problem should be of timely interest; this will ensure a ready source of guest speakers and give assurance to the students that their hard work can be of real use. When the problem chosen involves the design of a system in the geographical area of the university, speakers and information sources are even more readily available.

The urban topic areas outlined in the following chapters include a wide variety of problems of varying scope.  Since the accepted procedure is not to repeat a project, these will be suitable topics for new and old interdisciplinary systems engineering courses.

## GUEST SPEAKERS AND CONSULTANTS

Background information is provided to the students by a series of

10-20 talks given during the first half of the course. The series contains general talks which outline the broad problem area and the various approaches being considered for solution. It also includes specialty talks which describe activity in each area that is important to the solution. These specialty talks acquaint all the students with the capabilities and limitations of each area and give the students majoring in that specific area a more general view of the common professional practice. (It is assumed that the students have a competent understanding of the sophisticated analytical tools of their chosen major or can acquire the necessary understanding by individual consultation with professors in their departments.)

The speakers are drawn from within the university, from other universities and from government and industry. Since the chosen topics are of real concern to society, there is always a plentiful source of expert speakers willing and anxious to talk to the student team. The speakers are also informally available to individual students during their visit. In addition, students often contact the speakers and many other experts for individual consultation throughout the course.

## STUDENT ORGANIZATION

After an initial orientation phase of a few weeks, the students form into individual groups, each responsible for a different part of the overall design problem. Depending on the size of the class, there are from three to six groups, each with six to twelve members.

Responsibility for information acquisition and analysis within a group is further divided among group members to avoid duplication of effort.

Responsibility for direction of the study lies with student leaders selected by the students themselves. Usually each group selects a leader and the class as a whole, or the group leaders, select a project manager. These leaders meet regularly to establish coordination between groups and to guide the overall study. In some courses, new sets of leaders are selected two or three times during the course to give more students the leadership experience.

As the study progresses, interface subgroups form, sometimes informally, sometimes by appointment of the group leaders. Composed of members of several groups, these subgroups work out detailed coordination between groups.

At one time some courses had students principally interested in management form a separate group responsible for coordination of the study. However, this group usually lacked understanding of the other groups' activities and thus lost their confidence and the ability to manage the study. Now most courses have these students join a primary group. Usually they emerge as student-selected group leaders or as members of interface subgroups, but now with a better understanding of the problems and with the support of their groups.

## COURSE SEQUENCE

By their nature, complex systems studies are parallel efforts. Since each group needs to use the other's findings to reach its own conclusions, all must start at the same time using guesses as to what others' conclusions will be. These guesses and analyses are repeated by the groups many times during the study, with successive cycles, starting with more accurate guesses as analyses get more and more complete.

Despite these many cycles, there are three phases of the study that can be identified as rough milestones to help the students time their activities. In the first phase, most effort is spent finding and inventing all the alternative solutions to the problems, rejecting the few that are obviously inferior, and determining what information will be needed to choose between the remaining alternatives. In the second phase, information is gathered and analyses made to select the best alternatives. In the final phase, detailed designs of the best alternatives are completed and the final reports are prepared.

Except for the end of the last phase, the divisions between phases are not clearly marked. Much actual design is done during the first two phases as part of the selection process, and a few alternatives are not chosen until detailed designs of nearly equal alternatives are completed in the third phase. Despite this, most courses find it useful to divide the time into these phases and have presentations to the class by each group at the end of the first and second phase. This serves as another useful intergroup coordination mechanism and also provides an appropriate time to select new group leaders.

## FINAL REPORTS

In all courses a formal presentation is given at the end of the final phase. The speakers, experts the students have contacted, and other persons interested in the topic area are all invited to this presentation and are asked to question the students and their results. Needless to say this "final exam" is more stimulating to the students than the more normal course examinations.

In addition to this final verbal presentation, the students also publish an extensive written report. Organization of the report is started in the second phase and serves as another useful coordination mechanism during the last phase of the course. The contributions are carefully edited during the weeks following the course. These reports run from 200 to 500 pages and form the principal contribution of the course outside the university. The result of the students' theoretical competence, imagination, and enthusiasm and the experts' practical experience usually combine to produce reports of high quality.

## FACULTY AND GRADES

The courses are staffed by several faculty, one principally in charge (about a half-time teaching load) and the others serving as advisers to the individual groups, about one-sixth time load. The faculty does guide the study to a considerable degree, but usually by working closely as advisers to the student group leaders. In addition they determine grades for the students. Grades normally are quite liberal, as is usually the case with project courses, and are derived from the students' contribution to the final report, participation in the group's design efforts, and performance as coordinator or group leader if appropriate.

## COURSE COSTS

In addition to the salaries of the faculty and secretary and their overhead, the course has the expenses of the final report and the speakers. Industry speakers usually donate their time and cover their own travel expenses, but travel is usually required for speakers from other universities and often for government representatives in low budget years. Costs vary from institution to institution, but at Stanford, which has a fairly elaborate course, the cost per student falls above most graduate lecture courses but below most laboratory courses.

# TABLE I

## Systems Design Courses

| Institution | Coordinating Professor | Course | Projects | Comments |
|---|---|---|---|---|
| California State Polytechnic College San Luis Obispo, Cal. 93401 | Al Andreoli Aeronautical Engrg. | Engr. 438, 439 Systems Engineering | 1969-Transportation System serving Calif. Poly's campus | Two quarters, senior level |
| University of Dayton Dayton, Ohio 45409 | Robert Mott Technical Institute Mechanical Engrg. Technology Dept. 513/229-4216 | MTI 400 Design of Systems | Start Fall 1969 - Low cost satellite tracking antenna system | One trimester, senior level. 3 credit hrs Students from mechanical, electronic, industrial, and chemical engrg. technology |
| Georgia Institute of Technology Atlanta, Georgia 30332 | Stephen Dickerson Mechanical Engrg. 404/873-4211 Ext. 5149 | A. E. 655-656 Complex systems Design E. E. 655-656 Complex Systems Design M. E. 655-656 Complex Systems Design | 1967-DART-Downtown transportation system 1968-SEERS-Earth resources satellite 1969-Interurban air transportation for continental United States | Two quarters, graduate level |
| University of Houston Houston, Texas 77004 | Rudy Motard Chemical Engrg. | EGR 761-762 Engrg. systems design | Start Fall 1969 - An integrated Data Processing and Computing Facility for a University | One semester project with 3 hours credit Required for Master of Science - Systems Engrg. |
| Massachusetts Institute of Tech. Cambridge Massachusetts 02139 | William Bollay Aero and Astrodynamics (Visiting) William Seifert Electrical Engineering Civil Engineering Dwight Baumann Mechanical Engineering Sigfried Breunning Civil Engineering (Visiting) Paul Sandorff Aero and Astro-dynamics | 16. 74 Advanced Space System Engrg. (Sandorff,Li,Miller) 1. 16 J Special Studies in Systems Engrg. (Seifert) 2. 191J Special Studies in Systems Engrg. (Baumann) 6. 604J Special Studies in Systems Engrg. (Seifert) 13. 47 J Special Studies in Systems Engrg. (Frankel) 17. 818 J Special Studies in Systems Engrg. (Wood) | 1963-MITROS-Equatorial weather satellite system (Bollay) 1964-AOAO-Advanced orbiting astronomical observatory (Sandorff) 1965-ARES-Manned Mars Mission (Sandorff) 1965-The Glideway System*-High-speed ground transportation for the NE corridor (Baumann) 1966-NERO*-Near earth rescue and operations system (Sandorff) 1966-Metran*-Evolutionary transportation system for a metropolitan area (Baumann) 1967-ICARUS*- Earth-meteorite collision avoidance system (Sandorff) 1967-Project Romulus*-A new sub-city in Boston harbor for 100,000 people (Breuning) 1968-GALILEO*-First interstellar probe (Sandorff) 1968-Bosporus*-A combined airport and seaport for Boston harbor (Seifert) 1969-LURE - Plans for utilizing the moon's surface (Sandorff) 1969-Project Nomad*-Northern Alaska oil, mineral and area development (Seifert) 1969-Personal Capsule System-A horizontal and vertical elevator system for dense urban areas (Baumann) | One semester, 12/hrs week (3 semester hours). Numerous other departments and course numbers have been involved depending on specific project. A permanent committee, chaired by Prof. Seifert and consisting of the staff in charge of the courses with Suffix J, is responsible for overall program direction. After 1965, two project options were undertaken --- one in Aero and Astrodynamics and the second in the area of transportation or urban engineering. * Reports available from MIT Press |
| The University of Michigan Ann Arbor, Michigan 48104 | Wilbur Nelson Aerospace Engineering 313/764-4319 | AE 483 Aerospace System Design | 1965-POSSUM - Meteorology satellite -PLUMMET - Mars Lander 1966-MEDIUM - Meteorology satellite 1967-SPECTRUM - Solar Probe -STRATUM - Meteorology satellite 1968-MISSAC - Educational FM satellite for South America -OBSERVER - Earth resources satellite 1969-UMPIRE - Jupiter Probe | One semester senior level elective Four credit hours mostly aerospace engineers |
| Oregon State University Corvallis, Oregon 97331 | Robert E. Wilson Mechanical Engineering 503/754-2218 | ME 505 Ocean Systems Engineering | Beginning in Winter 1970 | Two quarters, three credit hours, graduate level |
| Stanford University Stanford, California 94305 | William Bollay (1964) Aeronautical Engineering Bruce Lusignan (1965,...) Electrical Engrg. 415/321-3300, Ext. 394 | Engr. 235AB Systems Engineering I. E. 235AB Systems Engineering A. A. 235AB Systems Engineering M. E. 235AB Systems Engineering E. E. 383AB Systems Engineering | 1964-SWAMI-Satellite relayed balloon, buoy weather system 1965-SAMPLER-Mars orbitor plus landers 1966-SPINMAP-Satellite weather system using remote sensing, computer data reduction 1967-ASCEND-Educational TV for Brazil, India, Indonesia 1968-DEMETER-Earth resources satellite system and ground system 1969-SEAMART-General Ocean Development, resource exploration system | Well developed program with up to 80 students on projects with many law, business, economics majors as well as science and engineering. Two quarters, graduate level. Three credit hours in 235A, 3 to 5 in 235B |
| The University of Tulsa Tulsa, Oklahoma 74104 | Ross McDonald Associate Dean of Engineering 918/939-6351 | Aero 4293 Multidiscipline Systems Design ME 4293 Multidiscipline Systems Design | 1968-VECTOR-Vibration evaluation by computer for turbojet overhaul reduction 1969-Offshore oil exploration submersible vehicle | Required senior level course for ME and Aero students |
| University of Washington Seattle, Washington 98105 | Juris Vagners Aeronautics and Astronautics 206/543-6532 | Run as special problem in 1969 | Exploration and utilization of undersea mountain (Cobb Seamount) off the coast of Washington | Three quarters three credits per quarter senior level |
| University of West Florida Corpus Christi Center U. S. Naval Air Station Corpus Christi, Texas 78419 | Walter H. Jones Aeronautical Systems | AE 691 Systems Synthesis | Start Fall 1969 - Space rescue vehicle | Students are Navy. M. S. students. One-and-a-half quarters, five quarter hours credit, thesis substitute Offered four times per year. |
| University of West Virginia Morgantown, West Virginia 26506 | Emil Steinhardt Mechanical Engineering 304/293-3980 | ME 280 Systems Design | 1967-STRIDE-Educational TV for India by Satellite 1968-Earth Resources Satellite 1969-STAR '73-Educational TV for Appalachia by Satellite | One semester, graduate level, three credit hours. |

## TABLE II

## NASA-ASEE Summer Faculty Institutes in System Engineering

| Institutions | Co-Directors | Projects |
|---|---|---|
| Stanford University<br>Stanford,<br>California 94305<br><br>Ames Research Center, NASA<br>Moffett Field<br>California 94035 | Dr. William Bollay<br>Department of Aeronautics<br>and Astronautics<br><br>Mr. John V. Foster<br>Director of Development | 1965 - ICARUS - 0.1 AU solar probe<br><br>1967 - SAINT - Syncronous communications satellite system<br><br>1968 - MOONLAB - Permanent manned moon base for last quarter of 20th Century<br><br>1969 - MAT - Study of a metropolitan air transit system (San Francisco Bay Area) |
| University of Houston<br>Houston<br>Texas 77004 | Dr. C. J. Huang<br>Cullen College of Engineering (U of H) | 1967 - SERV - Astronaut rescue vehicle<br><br>1968 - SSV - Servicing vehicle for repair, re-supply, maintenance of orbiting satellite<br><br>1969 - LLV - Unmanned lunar lander for support of manned missions |
| Auburn University<br>Auburn, Alabama 36830<br><br>University of Alabama<br>University, Alabama<br><br>Marshall Space Flight Center<br>Huntsville, Alabama | Dr. R. I. Vachon<br>Mechanical Engineering<br>Department (Auburn)<br><br>Mr. Herman Hamby<br>(MSFC) | 1967 - JOVE - Jupiter Orbiter<br><br><br>1969 - STARLAB - Orbital manned spacestation |
| Old Dominion College<br>Norfolk, Virginia 23508<br><br>Langley Research Center<br>Hampton, Virginia | Dr. G. L. Goglia<br>Thermal Engineering<br>Department<br><br>Dr. John Duberg<br>Associate Director | 1968 - EDUSAT - Educational television satellite system for the United States<br><br>1969 - Earth resources survey system |

# III. URBAN TRANSPORTATION

# SECTION A

## ELEMENTS OF THE URBAN TRANSPORTATION PROBLEM

### HISTORY

Cities have been the traditional centers of manufacturing, retailing, distribution, and such social services as public schooling, health care, and government. For centuries they have lured people from agrarian life and smaller communities with promises of economic betterment or a more congenial social setting. In particular, cities have continually provided an expanding market for low-skilled jobs. As more and more foreign immigrants and refugees from American farms migrated to U. S. cities to fill these positions, urban populations grew and strained against established boundaries, thus prompting those who could afford the longer journey to relocate near the urban fringe and commute to the old city center. This exodus naturally followed existing transportation arteries and caused cities to expand first along rivers and canals, then along railroad lines, and finally along highways and streets.

As metropolitan areas grew in size and became more heterogeneous, the unskilled and poor tended to concentrate in the city center around industrial complexes, while the managerial and skilled workers dispersed to the outlying suburbs. Gradually, industry and retail businesses began to follow the people to the urban fringe, but white collar and administrative jobs, relying on close cooperation and good communication, remained in the central city. This commercial migration is illustrated by Social Security data on employment in Standard Metropolitan Statistical Areas (SMSA) with more than one county. In these SMSA's, total employment increased 13% from 1959 to 1965 in the central or main urban county, but it increased 22% in the suburban counties. From 1960 to 1965, about one-half of all new construction expenditures in SMSA's for business purposes occurred outside the central cities. Percentages outside the central cities for major business categories were: industrial 62%; commercial stores 52%; and office buildings 27% (ref. 66a, p. 9). The result was that many suburbanite-held jobs were still located in the city while the unskilled worker, who could not afford to move out of the central city area, was being forced to commute to a job on the city's fringe or join the unemployed.

Therefore, the need for a highly flexible urban transportation system that could be used for business as well as for pleasure was established. The flexibility provided by the automobile has traditionally seemed to satisfy this need. This fact is substantiated by the 1960 Census figures which showed that 67% of all employed persons living in the Nation's metropolitan areas traveled to work in automobiles. In addition, motor vehicles presently account for approximately 91% of our intercity passenger mileage and 20% of the ton-miles of goods movements (ref. 85, p. 76).

## URBAN TRANSPORTATION TODAY

In many ways, the automobile has served the urban area well and should continue as the principal element in urban transportation systems for some time to come. For long-range intercity trips and for most trips in low-density urban areas, the automobile will retain its dominant position. However, our reliance on the automobile has also resulted in some very significant social costs. For instance, it was estimated (ref. 85, p. 81) that 142 million tons of pollutants were discharged into the atmosphere of the United States during 1966, and approximately 60% of this total was attributed to motor vehicles. Also, automobile accidents result in more than 4,000,000 injuries annually, including over 52,000 fatalities, and this figure has increased at a rate of more than 5% a year. Automobile-based urban transportation systems typically result in congestion which means a daily loss of time to the traveler. The only "solutions" to congestion have typically been quantity approaches such as more and bigger highways which involve expensive landtaking and tend to divide and destroy existing neighborhoods.

Despite its flexibility, the automobile-based transportation system does not suitably serve all metropolitan transportation needs. In particular, the auto-based transportation system does not adequately serve the poor, the handicapped, the secondary worker, the elderly, and the young. Figure A-1 (ref. 66a, p. 15) below shows the automobile ownership within income groups for 1966 and points out the fact that 76% of the households with annual incomes of less than $1,000 owned no car.

Moreover, less than one-half of all families with incomes under $4,000, one-half of all Negro households, and one-half of all households with heads over 65 years old own no automobiles. Even among families owning automobiles, the family car is frequently tied up in the home-to-work trip and essentially isolates other members of the family.

### Figure A-1
### AUTOMOBILE OWNERSHIP WITHIN INCOME GROUPS, 1966

| | percentage distribution of spending units* | | |
| --- | --- | --- | --- |
| | owns 1 automobile | owns 2 or more | owns no automobile |
| all spending units | 54% | 25% | 21% |
| money income before taxes** | | | |
| under $1,000 ................ | 21 | 3 | 76 |
| $1,000-$1,999 ............. | 28 | 3 | 69 |
| $2,000-$2,999 ............. | 51 | 3 | 46 |
| $3,000-$3,999 ............. | 61 | 6 | 33 |
| $4,000-$4,999 ............. | 65 | 11 | 24 |
| $5,000-$5,999 ............. | 68 | 16 | 16 |
| $6,000-$7,499 ............. | 68 | 21 | 11 |
| $7,500-$9,999 ............. | 63 | 30 | 7 |
| $10,000-$14,999 ........... | 50 | 46 | 4 |
| $15,000 and over ........... | 35 | 60 | 5 |

*A spending unit consists of all persons living in the same dwelling and related by blood, marriage, or adoption, who pool their income for major items of expenses. Some families contain two or more spending units.

**Money income for previous year.

Source: Survey of Consumer Finances, conducted by the Survey Research Center of the University of Michigan.

The secondary wage earner in a family must also depend on the automobile for transportation to and from work, but only a few of these families have a second car. For example, 49% of white families have two or more wage-earners, but only 28% have two cars; 55% of all Negro families have two or more wage earners, but only 10% own two cars. The result is that a substantial number of these secondary wage earners must depend on someone else for a ride to work, which reduces their freedom to change jobs and limits either their job location or their place of residence.

Without access to a car, the urban traveler must rely on a public mass transportation system, but these systems have not developed adequately in response to changing urban conditions. Significant changes in land use and large population shifts have not altered the routes accordingly. In 1945, New York, Chicago, Philadelphia, and Boston had rail rapid transit lines with a total of 1,222 miles of track. Now, with the inclusion of Cleveland's new line, the total trackage nationally is only 1,255 miles. According to American Transit Association figures, 2,891 of the 9,273 subway and elevated cars in operation in 1966 were also in operation in 1940. This lack of modernization contributed to a 40-fold decline in nation-wide rail transportation patronage from 9.5 billion passengers in 1945 to a mere 0.38 billion in 1966. During this same period of time bus revenue has indicated a passenger decline from about 8.5 billion to about 4. billion (ref. 66a).

The shifting of the urban population, the decreased use of public mass transportation, the increased mobility of the urbanite, and the increased reliance on the automobile all signify the evolution of urban

transportation into an auto-based system which, by itself, does not

adequately serve the entire urban community and has significant social

costs associated with it. As these social costs increase and the

unserved urban travelers become more vocal, the need for new ap-

proaches and new solutions to urban transportation problems will

increase.

## A NEW APPROACH

Any new approach to urban transportation problems must take all

eight problem areas outlined in Tomorrow's Transportation (ref. 66a,

pp. 6-7) into account:

1.  Equality of Access to Urban Opportunity

    Present urban transportation tends to immobilize and
    isolate nondrivers.

2.  Quality of Service

    Public transit service too often is characterized by excessive
    walking distances to and from stations, poor connections and
    transfers, infrequent service, unreliability, slow speed and
    delays, crowding, noise, lack of comfort, and a lack of infor-
    mation for the rider's use. Moreover, passengers too often
    are exposed to dangers to personal safety while awaiting
    service. These deficiencies lead to a loss of patronage and
    a further decline in service for the remaining passengers.

3.  Congestion

    Congestion results in daily loss of time to the traveler.

4.  Efficient Use of Equipment and Facilities

    Increased efficiency and greater economy through better

management and organizational techniques -- including cost control, scheduling, and routing, experimentation in marketing and new routes -- is necessary to satisfy urban transportation requirements at minimum cost.

5. Efficient Use of Land

Transportation rights-of-way require extensive amounts of urban land, and compete with other important uses of the urban land resource. More rational urban land use made possible by new forms of transportation may achieve greater total transportation services for the amounts of land required.

6. Urban Pollution

Air, noise, and aesthetic pollution from all current modes of urban transportation are far too high, degrading unnecessarily the quality of the urban environment.

7. Urban Development Options

Transportation investments can be used creatively in the orderly development of urban areas. Urban transportation service should provide for choice in living styles and in locations as well as choice among modes of transportation. New town settlements, as well as other concentrations of urban growth, could be feasible options for land development patterns with improved intraurban transportation services.

8. Institutional Framework and Implementation

An improved institutional framework -- legal, financial, governmental and intergovernmental -- is needed to eliminate rigidities and anachronisms which prevent the adoption of new technologies and methods.

These eight problem areas effectively dissect "the urban transportation problem" and also serve as a check-list against which the total benefits anticipated from new transportation systems and subsystems can be measured.

The problem areas listed above also illustrate that "the urban transportation problem" consists of a very complex mixture of human, sociological, political, economic, and technological problems. The exclusion of any one of these areas or disciplines in a design effort would surely result in a failure to achieve a realistic solution. Therefore, a broad interdisciplinary systems approach seems to hold the greatest hope in the quest for urban transportation solutions.

In the following section, an outline of topics suitable for interdisciplinary systems studies is presented along with an indication of the governmental agencies and personnel interested in these areas. A bibliography, including a large number of annotated entries, is also included to aid an interdisciplinary design team in initiating its study. This outline obviously is not a complete list of all urban transportation problems, but does represent some of the most important. It is hoped that these suggested topics will be studied as large systems design problems and will indicate areas where detailed research and development is required.

# SECTION B

## INTERDISCIPLINARY RESEARCH TOPICS IN URBAN TRANSPORTATION

1. A Comprehensive Transportation Information System

2. A Methodology for Identifying and Evaluating Alternatives in Urban Transportation

3. The Integration of Current and Proposed Modes into a Complete Urban Transportation System

4. An Evolutionary Highway/Street System for Increased Capacity, Service and Safety

5. The Design and Staging of an Automated Highway System

6. An Evolutionary Transportation System to Serve Greater Metropolitan Areas

7. A Solution to the Downtown Parking Problem

8. Pedestrian Transport Aids for Major Activity Centers

9. Joint Development of Transportation Rights-of-Way

10. An Evolutionary Goods Movement System for the Central City

11. The Design of an Evolutionary Highway Vehicle

# 1. A COMPREHENSIVE TRANSPORTATION INFORMATION SYSTEM

## THE PROBLEM

In the Transportation Planning process, commonly involving large capital commitments, information which supports analysis, forecasting, and evaluation of decision-making is critical. Existing data sources are characterized by significant gaps, fragmentation, and incompatibilities. Therefore, it is desirable that a system be conceived and implemented which would provide useful data to transportation planners. Useful implies consistency of data, geographic and modal compatibility, an ability to discriminate in the data retrieved, and completeness of the data base (ref. 27, 51).

The requirement that transportation data be collected for the 200 largest urban areas was outlined in the Federal Highway Administration Policies and Procedures Memo 50-9 (ref. 43). This program has resulted in a number of regional and urban plans (ref. 4, 22, 67), funded in part through Section 701 of the Housing Act (ref. 14), and represents the most functionally oriented of all urban statistical efforts. Unfortunately, there are large discrepancies in the format and scope of this data base and other Federal statistical programs (ref. 57, 65), (pos. B, F, G, ). To remedy this shortcoming, the Department of Transportation (DOT) has recently requested that Congress support the development of a national transportation information system (ref. 37). The proposal calls for a 5-year, $35.6 million effort in system development, extensive surveys, and supporting research and development to provide useful data on:

a. Flow - Information on the flows of persons and goods for all modes, with characteristics of trips and travelers.

b. Activities - Information on the activities which generate the flows (data on populations, industries, land uses, etc.).

c. Channels - Information on the channels that carry the flows of persons and goods (data on transportation networks, terminals, services, safety procedures, etc.).

There is, therefore, a continuing need and a new incentive for the design of a comprehensive transportation information system.

## STATE-OF-THE-ART

At present, some 30 Federal agencies and hundreds of state and local governments and industrial organizations gather transportation information in varying forms. The statistical support for the individual urban plans mentioned above and other significant data is collected under the auspices of the DOT; Bureau of Public Roads is empowered by the Federal Highway Act of 1968 (ref. 41) to allot 1.5% of the Federal Highway money (approximately $34.5 million/year) to research in the various states. As expected, all of the research pertains to road transportation modes. Highway Research and Development Studies Using Federal-Aid Research and Planning Funds (ref. 19) summarizes research in progress and gives lists of published reports, many of which are pertinent to the field of transportation information.

Transportation information systems on a regional scale are being developed and tested for New York State (ref. 67), and a DOT pilot study is proposed for the Northeast Corridor (ref. 1). Significant advancements are also being made in regional information processing systems (ref. 74).

Standard references which contain considerable, statistical data of significance to transportation studies have been compiled by the Bureau of the Census (ref. 10, 11) and by the Transportation Association of America (ref. 81). Various, special-purpose, statistical sources exist on highways (ref. 17), aviation (ref. 26, 35), rail, maritime and commerce, all of which are listed in Statistical Services of the U. S. Government (ref. 9).

Various new technologies may also be appropriate to transportation data collection and maintenance, including remote sensing and surveillance (pos. N).

## PARTICIPATING PERSONNEL AND ORGANIZATIONS

Federal interest in transportation information is concentrated within DOT. Immediate concern for an overall information systems rests with recently established Office of Transportation Information Planning within the Office of the Secretary (pos. F, G).

Data management, processing, retrieval, and dissemination is relatively well-developed in both NASA and the Department of Defense, and some of the techniques and principles may be adaptable to the transportation areas.

## CONTRIBUTING PROBLEM AREAS

(a) Standardize definitions (and codes) for data items on all geographic levels and across all modes for such items as trip, shipment, commodity shipped, travel time, waiting time, travel cost, weight of shipments, value of shipments, mode, link, capacity variables, equipment types, accidents, mainenance, etc.

(b) Develop transportation "indices" which, when measured, would signify relative degree of personnel/commodity movement.

(c) Determine specifically those types of data which will yield the most appropriate and complete information about urban transportation and specify collection requirements.

### Urban Transportation Information Projects

Define specifically and develop methodology for the collection of:

(a) Urban person travel data: origin-destination, including travel time, cost, distance, trip purpose; mode of transport; socio-economic characteristics of traveler; origin-destination land use.

(b) Urban goods movement data: origin-destination, including shipment times, cost, distance, commodity type, weight, density, mode of transportation used; characteristics of shipper/receiver; origin-destination land use.

(c) Urban transportation facilities data: for networks and terminals, on a link-mode basis, to include travel time, delay time, waiting time, travel costs, capacity variables, traffic volumes, carrier schedules, etc.

### Monitoring Technology

Develop new techniques and design new equipment for obtaining and recording transportation data (pos. J, N).

## Design of a Comprehensive Data Collection and Processing System

(a) Integration of the various component data systems and specification of inputs and outputs.

(b) Adaptation of existing computer software packages, development of new systems, etc.

(c) Provision for geo-coding and commodity coding of data.

(d) Planning for the dissemination of information in the form of tapes, tabulations, maps, charts, etc.

## 2.  A METHODOLOGY FOR IDENTIFYING AND EVALUATING ALTERNATIVES IN URBAN TRANSPORTATION

### THE PROBLEM

At the present time, planners are severely limited in their ability to predict the evolving demands for transportation and to measure the consequences of new transportation system investments.  There is only meager quantitative understanding of the underlying social and economic factors which tend to make one transportation mode dominant over others, one right-of-way more suitable than the rest, or one system better than competing alternatives.  In part, this is due to the lack of a valid and complete methodology for a reliable, benefit-oriented evaluation of alternative systems and transportation plans.

In order to provide more reliable measures and methods for transportation planning and decision-making, a research effort is required that will define the fundamental social and economic factors which underline the use of transportation and develop a consistent methodology for simultaneously dealing with all relevant factors in evaluating transportation alternatives.  Most critical is that individual analytic methodologies be first improved and then integrated into a comprehensive evaluative package, applicable to various localities and across all modes of travel (ref. 13, 66j), (pos. B, I, BB).

## STATE-OF-THE-ART

Various analytical methodologies currently exist for demand-projection and economic forecasting, since demand studies typically constitute the initial stage in any urban or regional transportation plan (ref. 4, 22, 68). Assisted by the "1.5%" provision, the 1968 Highway Act (ref. 42), the Bureau of Public Roads (BPR) encourages development of planning techniques on the local level and has spelled out an extensive Federal effort in its National Program of Research and Development (ref. 13). Research project areas have been outlined specifically for the purpose of defining requirements for highway transportation, but also invite study which permits general evaluation of transportation alternatives (ref. 13, 21). On-going research pertinent to these project areas is reported in (ref. 19, 54).

The 1968 New Systems Study Project, conducted for the Deparment of Housing and Urban Development (HUD), addressed itself to specific evaluative techniques such as demand analysis (ref. 66n), performance evaluation, economic comparison, modal analysis, and system modeling and attempted to specify in detail needed research in these areas (ref. 66d, 66f, 66j). The Proceedings of the Modal Choice and Transit Planning Conference (ref. 62) outlines future developments in transit modeling, and the General Research Corporation has published a useful collection of specific studies (ref. 47). Computer application in the economic modeling of transit systems is reported in (ref. 80), and extensive work has been done by Alan M. Voorhees and Associates, Inc. in developing an overall computerized transit planning package (ref. 86).

## PARTICIPATING PERSONNEL AND ORGANIZATIONS

Within the Department of Transportation (DOT), both the BPR and the Urban Mass Transit Administration (UMTA) are directly concerned with evaluation and planning methodologies for the urban area (pos. I, L, P, Z, BB), while the Office of Economics and Systems Analysis and Transportation Information Planning have a peripheral interest (pos. A, F). State and Metropolitan Planning Agencies, as well as State Highway Departments, may also possess localized transportation models and considerable forecasting experience. The Highway Research Board has displayed interest in this area and may have a detailed knowledge of the state-of-the-art (ref. 54). Not to be overlooked are the private planning firms and research groups which are actively engaged in predictive and evaluative survey work (ref. 4, 47, 66d, 66f, 66n, 86).

## CONTRIBUTING PROBLEM AREAS

The development of a complete methodology for assessing alternatives in urban transportation is a formidable task. More likely, advances in several related areas will contribute to the evolution of a set of refined methodologies which, when assimilated, will provide a comprehensive tool.

## Analysis of the Functions of Transportation

To define analytically the underlying functions which determine the need for, performance of, and constraints on movement. In order to provide a rational basis for the design and evaluation of existing and novel systems of transportation, a complete analytical design of transportation requires a theoretical framework, which treats the functional requirements of transportation, the physical performance characteristics, and the physical and environmental constraints. The objective is to develop a general theory of transportation which will allow specification of systems to meet definite requirements with predetermined properties and known performance characteristics (ref. 6).

## Factors Underlying Choice of Transportation

(a) To determine the criteria that determine transport preferences by the individual.

(b) To develop methods of measuring these preferences. Improved modal split analysis is greatly desired (ref. 66f).

## Forecasting Transportation Use Demand

(a) To develop a methodology for accurately forecasting transportation demand by mode.

(b) To evaluate the impact on demand that the introduction of new transport facilities may have (ref. 66n).

## Economic Models of Urban Transport Efficiency

(a) To develop economic models that simulate the present structural characteristics of a metropolitan economy and its interrelationships with transportation components.

(b)  The development and integration of submodels on:

- transportation demand
- motivational response
- cost

## Evaluation of the Total Impact of Transportation Location

(a)  To identify all relevant parameters in locating transportation facilities including social, economic, aesthetic, and convenience considerations.

(b)  To appropriately quantify these parameters and model their interrelations.  Cost/benefit evaluations on a comprehensive scale should be the ultimate objective.

## 3. THE INTEGRATION OF CURRENT AND PROPOSED MODES INTO A COMPLETE URBAN TRANSPORTATION SYSTEM

### THE PROBLEM

An integrated transportation system should function to interconnect all elements of the urban area and facilitate the flow of people and goods. This concept implies the existence of alternative travel modes, mode interchange points, and readily available service along travel corridors which connect geographic areas between which a variety of service capabilities are desired. In this way, the particular requirements for travel and associated costs will be commensurate with the needs and economic activity levels of the various elements in the population, and the opportunities to satisfy travel requirements will be maximized. Chinitz appropriately emphasizes the importance of considering the whole transportation system when trying to assess total costs and benefits of subsystem components (ref. 25).

This is a problem which, for the most part, is locality dependent. To tailor an integrated transportation system to a specific urban area requires in-depth analyses of the geographic, demographic, and economic characteristics of that locale. This preliminary process is adequately demonstrated in (ref. 68) and has been developed in the preceding topic area. Appropriate project topics for interdisciplinary study in transportation systems integration might include:

a. Development of complete transportation systems for specific metropolitan areas.

b. Development of a complete transportation system for a new town.

c. Design of an evolutionary "modemixing" terminal facility.

These topics definitely imply a "total-design" approach, involving land-use considerations and socio-economic comparison of total costs and benefits. Moreover, this final integration of modes must also rank as a primary consideration in developing the individual subsystems outlined in the following topic areas.

STATE-OF-THE-ART

In a sense, each existing urban transportation system is an integration of modes. Of greatest interest are those cities which attempt to fuse the new and the old. A most ambitious effort has been made by Litton Industries to conceptualize an integrated transportation network for the State of California (ref. 59). Cornell Aeronautical Laboratory's Metrotran - 2000 synthesizes multiple transportation modes into complete systems for two types of generic city, using data from Buffalo, New York (ref. 29), while J. F. Curtin applies the same approach with respect to downtown Rochester (ref. 31). An excellent example of comprehensive transportation planning has been performed by Simpson and Curtin for the San Francisco Bay Area — particularly since it follows in the wake of the progressive BART development (ref. 75).

Stanford Research Institute, in its contribution to the Department of Housing and Urban Development (HUD) New Systems Study Project, developed generalized concepts for a family of transportation systems to meet the needs of the different sectors of the urban environment (ref. 66p). Other New Systems Studies discuss evolutionary concepts which could be incorporated into an urban network (ref. 24, 56, 66g) and the expected characteristics of future cities (ref. 25) and travel (ref. 46).

## PARTICIPATING PERSONNEL AND ORGANIZATIONS

Much of the responsibility for an integrated urban transportation system belongs to State, regional, or municipal governments; these should be the first sources consulted with respect to on-going planning in particular localities. On the Federal level, the Urban Mass Transportation Administration (UMTA), Office of Program Planning (pos. Z), and the Bureau of Public Roads (BPR), Office of Planning (pos. P), are most likely to be involved in comprehensive planning ventures. Private contractors should not be neglected as additional sources of information. In addition, HUD is responsible for ensuring that the planning and development of urban transportation is integrated with the overall comprehensive development of the urban areas in which the systems will be operating.

## CONTRIBUTING PROBLEM AREAS

### Individual Transportation Modes

Advances in specific methods of transportation are of primary importance. The individual modes are dealt with in their own right, as major problem areas in Topics 4, 5, 6, 8, and 11 of this section.

## Modal Interchange Modes

To design evolutionary, modal interchange facilities to speed passenger flow and reduce inconvenience. As suggested above, a "mode-mixing" terminal can be an appropriate systems design project.

## Administrative Framework

To develop an efficient municipal administrative structure to control integrated transportation systems — particularly when the user area includes several distinct municipalities.

## Minimization of Social Liabilities of the Transportation System

(a) To minimize pollution resulting from the transportation system -- both air and noise pollution (pos. H). Also see Chapter V, Topics 1 and 3.

(b) To develop an implementation plan which minimizes disruption of existing transportation links and urban neighborhoods. Relocation of displaced households, traffic bottlenecks, and construction scheduling must all be considered.

# 4. AN EVOLUTIONARY HIGHWAY/STREET SYSTEM FOR INCREASED CAPACITY, SERVICE AND SAFETY

## THE PROBLEM

In its National Program of Research and Development for Highway Transportation (ref. 13), the Bureau of Public Roads (BPR) has pointed to three high-priority areas as being of greatest significance to the development of efficient transportation as a means of achieving social and economic growth at both the local and national level:

1. Highway Safety
2. Urban Transportation
3. Reduction in Costs of Construction and Maintenance.

Inherent in the Bureau's mission is the conviction that the manually-operated vehicle will continue to be the main component of the national transportation network for several more decades and that immediate innovations are desperately needed.

At present, more than 90% of the personnel travel in this country moves on rubber-tired vehicles. In 1968, nearly 100 million drivers operated approximately 82.8 million autos and 17.1 million trucks over 3.7 million miles of road -- totaling some 1 trillion, 10 billion vehicle miles. The estimates for 1975 include a staggering 117 million vehicles and 1.2 trillion vehicle miles. Federal assistance for highways during 1968 amounted to $1.435 billion, matched equally by the recipient states. In short, unless a radical new mode of transportation wins national acceptance and speedy implementation, the Nation and its cities will be faced with more vehicles, greater congestion, and a plethora of expensive problems (ref. 12).

Two thrusts are possible, both of which must be attempted: to increase the capacity of urban streets and highways, and to make them better, safer, more efficient, and less congested. Upon completion of the 42,500 mile Interstate Highway Program, the major emphasis is expected to be toward a "fine-tuning" of the basic roadway system (pos. J). It is hoped that the implementation of evolutionary road concepts -- the application of component analysis and design, improved highway layout and structure, and the introduction of electronics technology in the development of traffic advisory, command, and control systems -- will produce substantial gains in reducing urban traffic congestion and hazardous conditions. This is the primary thrust of BPR's National R&D Plan; work currently in progress is extensive, with seven major goals outlined and twenty-eight specific projects defined (ref. 13, 21). Some is being conducted by the Bureau, part by private institutions, and the rest by the states under the 1.5% provision of the 1968 Highway Act (ref. 42, 42). Most of these efforts are reported in (ref. 19, 54).

Several projects suggest themselves as being appropriate for developing new and evolutionary concepts for highway transportation:

    a.    The design of a highway/street system for a specific urban locality.

b. The design of a highway/street system for a new community.

c. The design of a highway/street system to cope specifically with heavy suburban-metropolitan flow.

In all cases, analytical considerations raised in preceding sections must be taken into account (Topic 2). Interrelatedness with other transportation modes (Topic 3) and the total land usage (Topic 9) are also contingent factors. One further aspect of any highway development is the relocation of homes and businesses as provided for in the 1968 Act (ref. 36, 42, 14).

## STATE-OF-THE-ART

Federal legislation now requires that each state use at least 1.5% of its annual Federal-Aid Highway fund allotment for planning, research, and development (ref. 14). All states have made studies of their highway needs, which have included forecasting of future traffic, inventorying roads, streets, and their deficiencies, formulating and recommending appropriate system classifications, and long-range improvement plans with means of financing them (ref. 2, 68).

A comprehensive, continuing, transportation planning process is also being carried on cooperatively by the State highway departments in every sizable urban area in the Nation (ref. 4, 22, 43). These studies forecast the population, economics and social growth, and change in the urban area; predict future land use and travel patterns; plan optimal highway/street layouts; and attempt to integrate highway transport with other modes. Twenty examples of current freeway innovations may be found in (ref. 3). Specific statistical data describing highway transport appears in (ref. 17).

As described above, BPR supervises most of the on-going Federal research, development, and demonstration efforts in highway transportation, including analysis and development of forecasting techniques, methods for increasing capacity, control and safety in traffic movement, and the development of new materials and structural concepts (ref. 13, 19, 21). It has also embarked upon a new $200 million per year urban Traffic Operations Program to Increase Capacity and Safety (TOPICS); this activity promotes the use of traffic engineering techniques to step up the flow of traffic by making better use of existing streets (ref. 23), (pos. V). Several current projects attempt to utilize new electronics and communications technology to these ends; a stranded motorist aid system, freeway merging control systems, an experimental route guidance system, passing-aid devices, computer-aided urban traffic control (ref. 7), and evolutionary traffic sensing and surveillance techniques (ref. 19, 54, 66i), (pos. N).

Considerable research is also underway in an attempt to describe the varied characteristics and travel requirements of future metropolitan areas and to provide the types of innovation in highway travel to meet those needs (ref. 28, 30, 46, 76, 78, 89). HUD's New Systems Studies Project also paid attention to such integral components of highway travel as bus system innovations and traffic control, which are summarized in Tomorrow's Transportation (ref. 66a).

## PARTICIPATING PERSONNEL AND ORGANIZATIONS

The Federal Highway Administration (FHWA) within the Department of Transportation (DOT) has primary Federal responsibility for the Nation's highway/street transportation network and is divided into the Bureaus of Motor Carrier Safety, National Highway Safety, and Public Roads. Three offices within BPR share the major interest in evolutionary highway developments and components:

1. Planning (pos. P)
2. Right-of-Way and Location (pos. S)
3. Research and Development (pos. I, J), which supervises all Bureau R&D activities

A further subdivision of the BPR research effort is achieved within the Office of R&D. Economics and Requirements Division is concerned primarily with the social and economic impact of highways (pos. L). Structures and Applied Mechanics Division deals with bridge and pavement design construction and maintenance (pos. M). Materials Division is interested in materials properties, specifications, testing, and quality control (pos. K). Engineering Systems Division is investigating the application of computers and highspeed data processing to the engineering design process (pos. O). Traffic Systems Division is concerned basically with traffic flow problems and particularly with the application of communications technology to aid vehicle operators (pos. N).

State highway departments are the next most prolific source of developmental work, and local planning commissions are active with regard to the planning and maintenance of city streets and urban freeways.

The Highway Research Board of the National Research Council is also charged to stimulate and coordinate highway research and, through its Highway Research Information Service (HIRS), (ref. 53), provides a systematic means with computer capability to keep track of research under way throughout the world and publishes research findings that should be made known to administrators, engineers and researchers (ref. 54).

## CONTRIBUTING PROBLEM AREAS

### Analytic Definition of Complex Traffic Movements

A necessary prerequisite to the practical solution of traffic flow problems is to provide definitions for the nature of traffic flow in homogeneous streams and networks (pos. Z).

(a) Stream Flow: To define in analytical terms the nature of traffic flow for a general class of moving elements.

(b) Network Flow: To define the characteristic equations of network flow for a general set of movement systems.

(c) To develop reliable models for urban arterial simulation, grid network simulation, and stream-network interaction.

### Analysis and Innovation with Respect to Highway System Components

(a) To determine the constituents and physical structure of the materials which control the behavior of highway systems (pos. K).

(b)   To develop mathematical equations and digital simulation
techniques which properly reflect the influence of non-linear
and elastic elements in the dynamics of highway pavement
and structural systems (pos. M, O).

(c)   The driving process:

- Define the processes by which a driver locates
  himself with reference to other vehicles and to
  the highway

- Describe the information handling and decision-
  making process involved in the driving task

- Define the mechanics of driver control of vehicular
  position in time and space (pos. N)

## The Development of Methods and Devices for Increasing Capacity, Control, and Safety in Traffic Movement

The efficient movement and control of traffic is the ultimate

determinant for the adequacy of a highway/street system design.

Major obstacles at present are: merging areas and other bottle-

necks on high-speed highways; intersections in the urban network

(pos. N).   The following is a detailed list of suggestions on which

follow-up research could significantly improve traffic flow condi-

tions within urban areas:

(a)   Provide greater understanding and alternative solutions for
eliminating accidents at urban intersections:

- Develop informational display and control systems
  for alerting drivers of impending hazards

(b)   Improve utilization of high-speed highways:

- Provide geometric design requirements such as
  gradient, curvature, and sight distance to
  minimize turbulence in flow.

- Investigate exclusive lane or right-of-way concepts

- Develop effective merging control systems to improve the efficiency and safety of interchange operations

- Develop novel highway configurations for the urban area.

(c) Improve performance under adverse environmental conditions

(d) Enable more efficient flow on city streets:

- Determine urban street layout design for optimal flow

- Investigate operational solutions such as one-way streets, limited access, etc.

- Design a more efficient intersection concept

- Determine the most effective forms and location of informational aids

- Develop methodology and hardware for directing flow smoothly through the urban grid

(e) Develop evolutionary techniques and equipment for traffic sensing and surveillance and road monitoring.

## 5. THE DESIGN AND STAGING OF AN AUTOMATED HIGHWAY SYSTEM

### THE PROBLEM

Automated highways, in the generic sense can improve the capacity, comfort, travel time, and safety of individual transportation systems for both urban and intercity travel situations, while simultaneously reducing the right-of-way space required. To meet these objectives, speed must be increased while headway between vehicles is reduced.

Varying degrees of automation are, of course, possible. A moderate approach is to provide devices which aid the driver in his customary task. The distinguishing characteristic of a fully automated throughway is that the operator may relinquish all direct manual control of his vehicle from entrance to egress.

Several variations on the "automated highway" theme have been suggested:

  a. Individually-powered vehicles with an electronic guidance system incorporated into the conventional roadway. This system emits pathway directional signals which are picked up by sensors in the vehicle for servo-control of steering, acceleration, and braking (ref. 28, 29).

  b. Individually-powered, dual-mode systems in which a low-powered, wheeled vehicle designed for manual operation on the urban street system can also enter an exclusive guideway where it obtains additional power and automatic guidance for high-speed mode (ref. 28, 29, 49, 66g).

  c. Pallet-type systems in which the conventional automobile is transported by automatic conveyance (ref. 66a).

Preliminary to vehicle and channel considerations are critical projections of future highway travel demand (ref. 46, 76, 89) and a thorough evaluation of highway versus public mass transit alternatives. Equally important is a viable implementation plan which allows for automating existing thoroughfares and constructing new routes with a minimum of disruptive effects.

## STATE-OF-THE-ART

The Bureau of Public Roads (BPR) has applied the first of the three preceding definitions to the "automated highway" concept, but, at the present time, has no program directed exclusively toward this goal (pos. I, N). The Bureau's primary emphasis is in the area of driver aids and, in this capacity, has spurred technological development in the direction of completely automating the driving process. Work is being undertaken in remote sensing techniques, automation of freeway entrance ramps, and electronic route guidance techniques which are outlined in (ref. 13, 21); specific projects are reported in (ref. 19, 54).

Numerous concepts for an automated highway system have been conceived by private institutions. Cornell Aeronautical Laboratory has investigated several variations, including a dual-mode Urbmobile (ref. 29, 66g). MIT's Glideway System (ref. 49) and the Alden Starrcar represent early design efforts in automated transport.

Component technology is now perhaps the most promising field for further immediate advances. Details of the traffic pacer system, a means of guiding vehicles electronically through urban networks, are reported in (ref. 7), and research needs with regard to guideway components are outlined in several of the Department of Housing and Urban Development's New Systems Studies (ref. 66a, 66g) and in (ref. 24). General Electric Co. has also performed an extensive survey of control technology for the New Systems Study Project (ref. 66j).

## PARTICIPATING PERSONNEL AND ORGANIZATIONS

Though not a principal objective, the "automated highway" is of interest to the Bureau of Public Roads, Office of Research and Development (pos. I, N), and considerable work in component technology has been done under its auspices. The Urban Mass Transportation Administration (UMTA) also shares an interest in the concept, particularly when guideway considerations are introduced (pos. BB). State and local agencies are not likely to be independently involved in development of automated highways due to the magnitude of the undertaking.

Other sources of information are the several private research organizations, which have dealt with the concept (ref. 21, 24, 66g) and, of course, the automobile industry.

## CONTRIBUTING PROBLEM AREAS

Research and development are desperately needed in component technology for both electronic and guideway-controlled systems.

## Automated Highway Components

(a) Advanced guideway components: power transmission facility, surface structure, etc.

(b) Routing and flow control systems.

(c) Electronic transponding equipment for non-guideway control.

(d) Reliable gap prediction and merge control devices.

(e) Evolutionary power systems for the automated vehicle, such as the linear induction motor.

## Logistics

(a) Evaluate private ownership versus rental of automated highway vehicles.

(b) Investigate various financing schemes, both for capital construction and maintenance.

(c) Develop a "minimum-disruption" staging plan for implementing the automated highway.

# 6. AN EVOLUTIONARY TRANSPORTATION SYSTEM TO SERVE GREATER METROPOLITAN AREAS

## THE PROBLEM

New concepts in urban transportation must produce innovative systems, capable of coping with 20th Century needs (ref. 66n). Adequate transit service within both residential and downtown areas requires a flexible public transportation system which can react rapidly to shifting population densities and employment patterns. The Carnegie-Mellon Transportation Research Institute has termed such a system as being "geometrically flexible" in comparison to the conventional fixed-rail systems of today which are often limited by restrictive grade and track curvature criteria (ref. 24).

In the years ahead, increased area coverage of residential and business districts implies greater route mileage than is economically justifiable with conventional rapid transit systems. The automobile cannot provide the solution because of its formidable cost to low-income workers, its inability to be of service to the aged or infirm, and its lamentable contribution to today's congestion, noise, and pollution problems.

It is essential, therefore, to provide an evolutionary form of public transportation which both caters to the individual rider and reduces intraurban trip times (ref. 66c). "Evolutionary" requires that the transportation system be developed in stages (ref. 66s), and that every stage be financially, politically, and socially viable (ref. 66s).

## STATE-OF-THE-ART

Proposals for new rapid transit modes have come from numerous sources (ref. 66q). One range of alternatives has focused on improving current public mass transportation concepts, while another has proposed lighter and smaller vehicles with close headways which provide a high-capacity capability during peak hours.

The former approach has yielded transportation systems which operate conventionally in terms of utilizing trains of cars which run along predetermined routes and have fixed schedules. The following summaries describe transportation systems of this type.

### Public Mass Transit Systems

(a) Metro: This refers to subway systems currently in operation in Paris and Montreal which utilize rubber tires and other characteristically progressive features envisioned for guided vehicles (ref. 24, p. 203).

(b) Transit Expressway: This concept features all-electric, fully-automatic, minimum weight, single or multiple trains which operate on an exclusive right-of-way, in either an elevated at-grade, or subway mode, as dictated by environmental and economic considerations. An existing demonstration project is operating in South Park, Pittsburgh, through the combined efforts of the Department of Housing and Urban Development and the Allegheny County Port Authority; the system development was done by Westinghouse Corporation (ref. 48, 64, 66a, 88).

(c) Monorail: This consept utilizes a single set of wheels on a single rail. Existing systems include:

   . ALWEG - an overriding monorail with full-scale operational lines in Tokyo, Japan.

· SAFEGE - a suspended monorail designed in France, with a one-mile test track operating at Chateauneuf-sur-Loire, south of Paris. General Electric owns SAFEGE rights in the United States (ref. 24, p. 218).

(d) Dial-A-Bus: A computer-scheduled, demand-activated vehicle; a hybrid between bus and taxi. Present UMTA sponsored studies include a related project of a subscription service bus in Flint, Michigan, and Project CARS, a computer aided routing system, at MIT (ref. 31, 66a, 66k, 66s) (pos. BB).

(e) Gravity Vacuum Transit (GVT) Train System: This concept involves people-carrying cylinders in pneumatic tubes; specifically, the system consists of steel tubes buried in the ground through which steel-wheeled trains will travel, driven by gravity and air pressure. GVT is still in the conceptual phase, but has been proposed as a possible transit system for airport access links and the Boston-to-Washington Northeast Corridor (ref. 39). The Tube Transit Corporation is presently conducting development work.

(f) Bay Area Rapid Transit (BART): A fully-automatic train system for the San Francisco Bay Area for which contract bidders were encouraged to develop new concepts that would meet performance objectives at lower cost than conventional railway systems. Construction is progressing on 75 miles of double track railroad, below ground and above, with auxiliary facilities. General engineering consultants to BART are Parsons Brinkerhoff-Tudor-Bechtel (ref. 70, 71).

(g) Northeast Corridor Project: This project envisions a high-speed, intercity, rail transit for the Washington-New York-Boston corridor; using electrically-powered, air supported vehicles operating at 350 mph. The concept is still in the drawing-board stages. Though no construction contracts have been awarded, the Government-sponsored research expenditure has been somewhat less than $75 million. The Department of Transportation, Office of High-Speed Ground Transportation, has been active in promoting demonstration projects in the corridor (pos. X, Y).

The systems discussed above have all been "operationally conventional". With the exception of Dial-A-Bus, they are public mass transportation systems utilizing trains of cars and operating on a guideway.

An alternative concept in developing evolutionary transportation systems has been an extremely flexible vehicle, available on instant demand, which can compete with automobile transportation. The following systems are innovative proposals to meet flexibility requirements for a personalized mass transportation system.

Personal Vehicle Systems

(a) Minicar: Small electric cars for use as feeder vehicles between transit stations located throughout the metropolitan area; rental of such vehicles is a possibility. Present technology makes such cars feasible, but no total system proposal has been drawn up and accepted by the Government as yet.

(b) Dual-Mode: Individual, rented, ticketed, or personally-owned vehicles; driven manually on the present street system with propulsion from internal storage batteries or automatically-controlled and steered on a guideway with external propulsion from a power rail. Proposed dual-mode systems are:

- Starrcar, a product of Alden Self-Transit Systems Corp.

- Commucar, a concept arising from an MIT student systems design course, also see Metran (ref. 31).

- "Dual-Mode" vehicle, a prototype designed, built, and currently undergoing testing at MIT.

- Urbmobile, a concept developed by Cornell Aeronautical Laboratory (ref. 29).

(c) Personal Capsule (PERC): A fully-automated transportation system of two and four passenger vehicles operating on a network of exclusive guideways with vertical motion capability. The concept resulted from an MIT student transportation systems design study Project Metran (ref. 31, 60).

## PARTICIPATING PERSONNEL AND ORGANIZATIONS

According to the Urban Mass Transportation Act of 1964, DOT's Urban Mass Transportation Administration is authorized to undertake research, development, and demonstration projects in all phases of urban mass transportation, including the development, testing, and demonstration of new facilities, equipment, techniques, and methods (ref. 38).

UMTA has recently compiled a catalog which summarizes all projects to which it has contributed support through June of 1969 (ref. 83). Copies of all reports completed under UMTA's auspices and further information on individual projects may be obtained by writing UMTA, the author of the report, or the Clearinghouse for Federal, Scientific, and Technical Information in Springfield, Virginia 22151.

The Urban Mass Transportation Act of 1964 (ref. 14), also authorized a new program of Federal grants to local authorities for capital improvements and to private institutions for research, development, and demonstration projects in all phases of urban mass transportation. Such funding totalled $177 million in Fiscal Year 1969. Amendments to the Act of 1964, approved September 8, 1966, included the creation of three new programs, authorizing grants for technical studies, managerial training, and research and training in urban transportation problems. Brochures and sample formats which give information on grant application procedure are obtainable directly from UMTA.

Early next year, 1970, UMTA will make available a program guide of its primary research interests.

CONTRIBUTING PROBLEM AREAS

Since the inclusion of this topic area has been intended primarily to stimulate the design of complete evolutionary transportation systems for metropolitan areas, the emphasis has been primarily on the general systems concept, rather than on supporting hardware or logistical considerations. The full systems design, however, should include the following aspects:

Integration With Existing Systems

The new transportation facility should be fully compatible with existing modes and with proposed systems. It should also provide for the most effective utilization of other urban networks. See Topic 3 for a more complete discussion.

Staging of Construction and Implementation

Develop an implementation plan for introducing the evolutionary system which minimizes disruptive effects — relocation, congestion, confusion — and maximizes economical considerations.

Financing and Administrative Control

New and more equitable means are required for financing both capital and operating costs and for management of the transit system:

(a) Investigate the feasibility of a "Transit Trust Fund" as a mechanism for supporting continued transit development.

(b)  Devise new administration mechanisms for controlling joint-city or joint-county urban transportation systems.

## Joint Development Concept

The transit system must be planned in terms of future growth trends for the surrounding area:

(a)  Feasibility studies for renewal projects in conjunction with construction of the main transportation system.

(b)  Joint use of transit rights-of-way for both contiguous land and air space.

## Supporting Facilities

The primary transit links must be developed in conjunction with adequate terminal facilities, mode interchange points, and automobile access and parking plans.

## Social Assets and Liabilities

Critical in the design and layout of the transit system is the reduction of its potential for air and noise pollution; its ability to provide extraordinary services to disadvantaged groups; its accessibility by all urban, socio-economic groups; and its aesthetic quality.

## 7. A SOLUTION TO THE DOWNTOWN PARKING PROBLEM

### THE PROBLEM

The 1960 Census disclosed that at least 67% of the employed persons living in metropolitan areas travel to work by automobile. Once in the downtown area, these and other vehicles must be parked; and the space available for this purpose is being placed at a higher and higher premium. Although current space cannot be readily used for more productive purposes, it is nonetheless imperative that this space prove sufficient for all vehicles desiring access to the city center. Within well-planned downtown areas like Philadelphia, 8% of all floor space (including ground areas but excluding streets) is devoted to off-street parking, while highly automobile-dominated cities like Los Angeles must devote up to 15% of their downtown floor area to vehicle storage (ref. 77).

Several approaches to this problem have been suggested. The use of Federal-Aid Highway Funds has been authorized for the construction of public parking facilities on the fringe of downtown business districts (ref. 12, 42) to create an incentive for keeping automobiles out of the central urban core. The fringe parking program, coordinated with efficient bus or rail transportation, would relieve congestion on both the downtown streets and the highways leading to the center of the city. Parking in the fringe areas would also motivate mass transit systems to improve their service, which would, in turn, encourage more motorists to use public transportation. Such facilities, designed to serve an urban area of more than 50,000 population, must be located outside the central business district and planned in conjunction with existing or other proposed public systems.

The alternate approach is to permit the flow of vehicles into the central core and attack the problem directly by providing adequate parking facilities to handle them. Of course, many related consider-ations must be included such as effective land use, traffic flow around facilities, integration with other means of conveyance (Topic 3), and joint use of transportation corridors (Topic 9).

## STATE-OF-THE-ART

A quantitative definition of the problem is found in several statis-tical sources (ref. 17, 81). The fringe parking program is being con-ducted primarily by the Bureau of Public Roads (BPR) which will share the cost of parking facilities equally with State highway departments. A three-year demonstration project has been authorized and a small number of pilot projects will be developed and evaluated. Little actual R&D effort is being conducted at present, but a few on-going projects are reported in (ref. 19). Other studies performed by the Highway Research Board (HRB) are found in (ref. 53, 54).

Most of the additional parking spaces developed in recent years have been in the form of garage facilities. Recent trends include self-parking units, multi-deck parking structures in larger cities, construction of dual-purpose facilities to divide land costs among several activities, more uniform hourly-fee scheduling to encourage short-term parking, etc. These and other developments are comprehensively reported by Wilbur Smith and Associates in Parking in the City Center (ref. 77) and are placed in their proper perspective in Transportation and Parking for Tomorrow's Cities (ref. 78). The Department of Housing and Urban Development's New Systems Study Project deals briefly with the parking problem in (ref. 66s) and examples of particular innovations are reported in (ref. 6, 30, 55).

The joint land-use concept is particularly appropriate with respect to parking facilities. It is defined and developed by Barton-Aschman Associates, Inc. in (ref. 5). Topic 9 in this section gives a brief account of possible future projects.

## PARTICIPATING PERSONNEL AND ORGANIZATIONS

As outlined above, the BPR is involved in the development of fringe parking facilities (pos. I, P). However, the primary responsibility in this area belongs to local planning agencies and, to some extent, to State highway departments. Most developments are locality-dependent, but Wilbur Smith and Associates has demonstrated a comprehensive involvement with the urban parking problem in general. The HRB also publishes reports (ref. 53, 54) from time to time containing pertinent studies on parking concepts.

## CONTRIBUTING PROBLEM AREAS

### Background Studies

(a) Relate parking needs to size, activity, and economic use of the downtown center.

(b) Develop innovative schemes for financing and maintaining parking facilities.

(c) Analyze traffic flow characteristics around existing and proposed parking facilities.

### Planning and Control

(a) Develop novel schemes to encourage/discourage parking in the central core.

(b) Develop joint land-use concepts which would maximize the productivity of downtown land area.

(c) Integrate planning for pedestrian movement with the development of parking facilities (see Topic 8).

### Facilities

(a) Evolutionary hardware for control of parking facilities.

(b) Evolutionary design for garages and lots.

## 8. PEDESTRIAN TRANSPORT AIDS FOR MAJOR ACTIVITY CENTERS

## THE PROBLEM

During the past decade, metropolitan areas have witnessed the birth, rapid development, and expansion of major activity centers -- the most notable being shopping centers and airports -- of enormous size and occupying extensive land space. The air travel industry has doubled its passenger capacity and quadrupled its freight mileage since 1960, thus requiring additional facility construction and stepped-up efficiency at airports throughout the Nation (ref. 35). In both downtown and suburban areas, stores of every conceivable type have been centrally located in shopping malls to afford a variety of easily-accessible services to residents of the neighboring communities. Due to the increasing size of such major activity centers, the movement of people within them becomes a problem of significant proportion -- particularly since considerable distances between destinations are involved, and walking becomes a time-consuming effort.

Parking facilities must also be planned for and, by necessity, are often remotely located from the activity center itself. Transporting baggage and purchased goods within these centers and to and from parking garages is an added element of the pedestrian transport problem, especially at facilities such as airports where rapid and efficient baggage handling is critical.

## STATE-OF-THE-ART

Conventional concepts for pedestrian transport aids, which have undergone testing and implementation in selected major activity centers, include escalators, moving belts (installed at certain airport terminals), and small trains of motorized vehicles, containing from two to five cars (such as the "people movers" operating on shopping malls at Miami Beach).

The Philadelphia Penn Center subway plaza, contiguous to the suburban station of the Penn Central Railroad, is one of the most successful developments employing a separated pedestrian walkway concept. Similarly, the San Francisco Civic Center pedestrian mezzanine connects shopping facilities and station access on the upper level with Bay Area Rapid Transit train cars on the lower level.

The Batelle Institute facilities in Geneva are currently developing a conveyor belt "walk" for use in some large airport terminals. The belt moves at 1.5 mph at the point where passengers step on, but then accelerates to 11 mph after a collapsed cabin, with fold-out walls and seats, emerges from a compartment beneath the floor.

A current evolutionary concept, which has been on the drawing board for over five years now, is that of a fully-automatic, pedestrian transit railway, located either at ground level or on an elevated guideway (ref. 31).

Small personal vehicles, which operate independently (two

passengers per vehicle) but can be linked together for transporting greater numbers, ferry people between parking facilities and the activity center as well as within the center (ref. 60). A prototype has not yet been built, but several design proposals do exist.

Baggage handling systems between parking areas and major transportation terminals are non-existant. Automated baggage handling within terminals typically consists of moving belts between ticket desks and dock facilities outside the building, where the luggage is placed on a wagon to await further delivery. Otherwise, porters remain as the traditional source of transport for personal baggage. One solution has been to place rollers or wheels on suitcases so that luggage can at least be pulled along instead of carried.

At shopping centers, goods are packaged for customers while they wait, after which the packages must be transported to parked vehicles. Grocery stores have developed automobile pick-up facilities for purchased goods so that hauling bags or boxes from the store to the car is eliminated. The partial success of these systems is reflected in increased customer convenience, but they typically fail to appreciably speed service. Most department stores offer a customer pick-up service, but such facilities rarely exist at drive-in locations where purchased merchandise can easily be loaded onto waiting vehicles.

## SUPPORTING PERSONNEL AND ORGANIZATIONS

Airport officials are specifically concerned with the movement of people and freight within terminal facility areas. Projects directed toward this problem can often receive considerable information and support by contacting local airport authorities in each metropolitan area. The same holds for all other major transportation terminals in urban areas.

Major shopping centers likewise have hired personnel whose prime concern is the flow of people and goods within these areas. Contacting them can lead to relevant information on past studies and proposals for pedestrian transport aids.

At the Federal level, the Department of Housing and Urban Development contracted with the Batelle Memorial Institute to provide a comprehensive, up-to-date report on all moving-way transportation systems for pedestrians (ref. 66d). Additional information on the current development of pedestrian transport aids can be obtained from the Urban Mass Transportation Administration (UMTA) (pos. AA, BB).

## CONTRIBUTING PROBLEM AREAS

### Baggage Handling Aids

Increased automation of existing baggage handling systems within major activity centers:

(a) Baggage handling at airports and other transportation terminals.

(b) Car pick-up services afforded by shopping center, department, and grocery stores.

## Control Mechanisms

The application of mechanical devices to pedestrian ways to enhance the speed and flow of traffic:

(a) Automated information systems.

(b) Changing walkway levels for different destinations.

(c) Separating rights-of-way at intersections.

(d) Minimizing pedestrian climbing and descending.

(e) Employing ramps as an alternative to stairways.

# 9. THE JOINT DEVELOPMENT OF TRANSPORTATION RIGHTS-OF-WAY

## THE PROBLEM

As we rebuild the Nation's cities, we are faced with the very real limits of money, space, and time (ref. 11, 82). Limited funds require that dollars be used for dual purposes. Intense competition for space in the hearts of our cities points out that urban land must be more efficiently used. Statistics indicate that by the end of this century, America's accelerating urban sprawl will be characterized by a doubling of the population and a 50% increase in the total urban land area. The 5.5% of the Nation's land space which has been urbanized will rise to 7.7%, according to Bureau of Public Roads calculations.

The concept of joint development (ref. 33) is one way in which cities can provide housing, parks, and other facilities simultaneously with the construction of future urban freeways and other transportation links in less space and with less cost (ref. 45).

The economics of land acquisition and use show that in areas where the greatest demand for space exists, the land required for multiple purposes can be acquired for little more than the cost of land for freeway uses alone.[1] A city could acquire entire blocks on the route of a planned

---

[1] Bureau of Public Roads' studies have shown that the cost of acquiring whole city blocks is comparable to the cost of acquiring freeway rights-of-way, including severance damage payments to owners of affected properties (ref. 5), (pos. S).

freeway, sell to the highway department the space needed for the freeway, and still have valuable land available for other development at a fraction of the cost of acquiring it alone.

Other studies (ref. 20) conducted by the Bureau of Public Roads (BPR) have shown that only one block of new housing is required for replacement of three blocks of typical row or tenement housing in blighted urban areas, thus making two out of three blocks available for additional development such as parks, schools, or play grounds.

The objective of the joint development concept is to stimulate local programs through which cities can meet the needs of growth by combining their land-use development with planned freeway or other transportation system construction. The next step in this new program is to formulate joint development proposals for those urban areas where the location of transit facilities and redevelopment of the local area around existing freeways can be planned hand-in-hand.

STATE-OF-THE-ART

Of the 3.7 million miles of roadway in the United States, the $50 billion Interstate and National Defense Highway System has accounted for 27,000 miles of completed urban freeways. During the next few years, $10 billion remains to be spent on 2,500 more miles of city highways, which suggests that opportunities for employing joint development concepts should be readily available.

Many additional miles of roadway will be built under other Federal, State, and local activities, of which the ABC Highway program ranks foremost. Through this particular program, the Federal Government makes outlays of $1 billion per year through the Department of Public Works in each State toward development of:

a.   Federal aid primary highways (goal - 350,000 miles).

b.   Federal aid secondary highways (goal - 750,000 miles).

c.   Urban connections.

The Nation's massive freeway program (ref. 3), affecting almost all of our major cities, thus represents an immediate opportunity for joint urban development.

The most recent efforts to apply the joint development concept can be found in an informational report compiled by BPR's Environmental Development Division (ref. 20). Published documents are available concerning joint development projects currently underway in the cities of Phoenix, Arizona (ref. 58), and Washington, D.C. (ref. 73).

At present, the BPR is working with the Nation's cities, through their State Highway Departments and other Federal agencies, to seek new uses of the joint development concept and to achieve maximum use of that part of urban land which must be devoted to highway transportation. The most widespread application of current joint development concepts can be seen in the use of space under elevated freeways and the construction of plazas and shopping centers above major intraurban expressways.

Possibly the most comprehensive existing bibliography on the state-of-the-art for joint development projects and studies has been compiled in a circular memorandum from the BPR (pos. I) to the Regional Federal Highway Administrators and Division Engineers. This memorandum, entitled "Bibliography on Joint Urban Freeway Development", can be obtained from BPR's Office of Right-of-Way and Location (pos. S).

## PARTICIPATING PERSONNEL AND ORGANIZATIONS

The joint development concept and effort originated in the Department of Transportation's Federal Highway Administration (FHWA). Within the FHWA, the BPR has spearheaded the program through its Office of Right-of-Way and Location. A group within this office called the Environmental Development Division (pos. S, T) is directly concerned with the application of joint development and multiple land-use to the construction of urban freeways and can provide up-to-date information on related programs. In addition, BPR's policy permits the Environmental Development Division to provide whatever assistance is within its power (lectures, movies, slides, and panel discussions) to schools which undertake joint development and multiple land-use projects.

Relevant legislation and policy memoranda supporting the joint development program include the following:

a. Federal Highway Act of 1968 (ref. 42).

b. BPR's Interim Policy and Procedure Memorandum on Joint Development of Highway Corridor and Multiple Use of Roadway Properties (ref. 18).

c. BPR's Instructural Memorandum on Federal Participation in the Development of Multiple Use Facilities on the Highway Right-of-Way (ref. 15).

In addition, Department of Housing and Urban Development (HUD) "701" grants provide financial assistance in overall urban planning and reflect HUD's interest in beautification and improvement of the total urban environment (ref. 14).

## CONTRIBUTING PROBLEM AREAS

### The Joint Development Concept

(a) Define compatible land-use; specifically, identify those factors which characterize desirable urban transportation corridors in terms of land-usage.

(b) Index those critical variables which must be considered in the process of transportation corridor location and devise a method for evaluating them, especially non-costable items such as community values.

(c) Catalog the relevant factors and effects pertinent to existing highways established in local community areas.

- Factors: Ethnic composition of population, benefit-cost ratios, etc.

- Effects: Relocation of families, replacement housing, change in social attitudes, etc.

### Applications

(a) Propose redevelopment projects to replace current inefficient land-usage around existing highway corridors.

(b) Investigate landscaping around major urban freeways and determine its effect on the noise abatement problem.

-79-

(c) Make use of the space underneath current and proposed elevated urban freeways.

(d) Incorporate joint development considerations in planning for mass transit systems.

(e) Create new joint development concepts and designs for compatible land-usage in urban areas: e.g., heliports at major highway interchanges.

The Airport Access Link

Recent efforts in airport design and location have brought about the movement of airport terminals from local metropolitan areas to rural districts where population density is minimal. Dulles Airport which is located in Northern Virginia and serves the Washington, D. C., area, is a prime example.[2]

Airport access roads are comparable to major highways and will undoubtedly prompt the location of new industrial complexes and business concerns on the land adjacent to their corridors. An interesting joint development consideration is how to optimize the use and effectiveness of this airport access link for the benefit of the greater metropolitan area. A high-speed public transportation system is one possibility to look at, but more innovative ideas are called for.

---

2 Dulles airport is located twenty miles from the downtown D. C. area and the only means of travel to and from the terminal facility is via a limited access highway (ref. 2).

## 10. AN EVOLUTIONARY GOODS MOVEMENT SYSTEM FOR THE CENTRAL CITY

### THE PROBLEM

Urban transportation is the product of two demands -- personnel travel and goods movement. The movement of goods into, within, through, and out of the metropolitan area is critical to the economic prosperity of its inhabitants and to the city's welfare. Of necessity, the goods movement system of a city must function compatibly and evolve hand-in-hand with the developing public transportation systems.

Various forms of goods movement within the city contribute significantly to the congestion of downtown streets and to the problem of excessive noise (pos. H). Automatic, off-street goods delivery systems could bring considerable relief to these afflictions and could substantially increase the economic efficiency of doing business in major activity centers (ref. 66a).

However, there is presently a severe deficiency in goods movement data (as outlined in Topic 1). With only limited data on demand, trip origins and destinations, and real costs, it is only possible to reach an intuitive understanding of the present needs and alternatives. There is an urgent requirement for comprehensive data, for quantitative studies, and for detailed analyses to define and support the technological innovations which must be introduced.

## STATE-OF-THE-ART

Automation of materials movement systems has taken place within many modern factories and warehouses, but little has been done with respect to goods movement between buildings and between sectors of congested cities. Delivery systems such as conveyor belts, pneumatic tubes, and small automated cars exist in mining, manufacturing, and warehouse operations. In addition, elaborate data processing schemes are available for inventory control and delivery. An attractive approach, therefore, is to select and adapt such technologies to the movement of goods within the city center.

The potential also exists for combining the metropolitan goods delivery and personnel transport functions by using available public mass transit facilities for freight delivery during off-hours. The Post Office Department is presently investigating this concept as a means of facilitating urban mail delivery (ref. 72).

Containerization, or assembling goods into larger delivery units, is becoming increasingly common for both intercity and intraurban delivery. This facilitates the intermodal transfer of the packaged materials and permits uniformity in the design of delivery vehicles.

With regard to fundamental data on goods movement, numerous statistics are available from the Federal Government (ref. 8, 52). Schemes for collecting such information range from waybill surveys to the monitoring of truck license plates. Several statistical models currently exist for projecting person travel demand, but these have scarcely been applied to the goods movement operation.

The concept of an autoless central core for cities is also being investigated (ref. 29), and this scheme necessitates an alternative to the current truck-based delivery system.

In any case, an evolutionary goods movement system should effectively reduce downtown traffic congestion and incorporate new delivery modes and interchange facilities which will not hamper urban traffic flow patterns.

The full problem of goods movement -- specifically the problem of an adequate data base -- is excellently described by Battelle Institute in the Department of Housing and Urban Development's New Systems Study Project (ref. 66e).

## PARTICIPATING PERSONNEL AND ORGANIZATION

At the present time, there is little active participation on the Federal level in developing an automatic goods movement system. Latent interest might exist within the Department of Transportation or the Department of Commerce, but the Post Office Department appears closest to the immediate problem. Manufacturing and warehouse facilities would be the most appropriate sources of delivery system technology and scheduling know-how.

Independent delivery agencies such as United Parcel Service and

Railway Express Agency would also be familiar with scheduling, delivery techniques, and the characteristics of urban goods movement in general.

## CONTRIBUTING PROBLEM AREAS

Since little has actually been done in automating urban goods movement, the area is wide open for innovation.

### Data Base and Forecasting Techniques

(a) Develop a methodology for collecting, processing, and analyzing data on goods movement.

(b) Develop models for effectively projecting urban goods movement.

(c) Develop economic models of goods flow.

### Technological Innovations

(a) Develop new concepts in containerized transport, including transport components.

(b) Develop evolutionary delivery vehicles.

(c) Develop automatic scheduling and control devices.

### Operational Innovations

(a) Develop methods of using public conveyance to deliver goods and of scheduling this joint use.

(b) Investigate the feasibility and impact of restricted delivery ways, exclusive delivery hours, etc., in the central city.

# 11. THE DESIGN OF AN EVOLUTIONARY HIGHWAY VEHICLE

## THE PROBLEM

A prime example of the solid foundation which existing technology has provided in the field of transportation is the automobile, a flexible and speedy vehicle which satisfies a wide variety of travel needs. Mass production and utilization of this unique highway vehicle, however, have created a serious traffic congestion problem -- one which increasing car ownership can only worsen in the immediate future. Equally disturbing are the inherent problems of excessive noise, air pollution, and accidents, all of which are substantially attributable to the automobile.

A realistic projection shows that, despite the appeal of future evolutionary transit systems, the conventional highway vehicle of today will continue to provide the predominant form of urban transportation for at least the next decade. Simultaneously, however, these same highway vehicles, of which there are currently over 900 million on our Nation's highways, will continue to be the most significant source of air pollution. A resulting conclusion is that coexistence with the automobile necessitates immediate improvements in its technological components (ref. 66a).

## STATE-OF-THE-ART

One hopeful approach to the problem is to exploit the technology presently envisioned for transportation systems of the future. Evolutionary systems require many subsystems and components, some of which are already in a developmental stage and could be easily adapted to the present highway system.

What follows is a review of some promising technological components which require further investigation through research and development programs to determine advantages and feasibility for incorporation into the conventional highway vehicle.

### Automated Vehicle Monitoring and Control

The increasing number of vehicles on the Nation's highways can be handled with greater speed and safety if electronic devices are employed to make the routine control decisions.

(a) Proposed automatic vehicle monitoring (AVM) systems can control upward of one million vehicles continually and automatically by using a time-sharing scheme for both public and private vehicle operators.

(b) Prototypes of route guidance systems have been developed to facilitate urban traffic flow and increase trip comfort for the driver by directing vehicles over minimal time paths on a roadway network. Decisions are based upon a continuous information retrieval process regarding existing traffic conditions. A code system has been devised to classify each major intersection in the United States and electronic hardware for an experimental route guidance system is undergoing testing at two intersections in the Washington, D. C., area.

(c) Additional research and development work is being conducted in the areas of:

   - Overtaking and passing on the standard, two-lane highway.

   - The merging operation on the urban expressway.

   - A real-time traffic data sensing and control system (ref. 66i).

## Evolutionary Power Source and Energy Conversion Systems

The following list reflects the state-of-the-art in existing propulsion systems, some of which have become conventional, others which are in need of further development:

(a)  On-board prime movers for self-contained vehicles:

    .  Steam engine

    .  Diesel engine

    .  Gasoline engine

    .  Gas turbine

    .  Electromechanical energy storage devices: 1) battery power source for electrically propelled vehicle (only the lead-acid battery is at present technically feasible); 2) fuel cell.

(b)  Remote power sources:

    .  Electrified third rail (nominally 600 volts D. C.)

    .  Overhead distribution lines connected to power units by pantagraph (nominally 11,000 volts A. C.)

    .  Mechanical energy storage devices: 1) linear motor; 2) inertial energy system (Oerlikon Engineering Co.) (ref. 66d).

Considerable activity in the design of unconventionally-powered vehicles has been stimulated by the National Air Pollution Control Administration (NAPCA) in its search for the low-pollution passenger vehicle. Extensive studies of electrically-powered and other unconventional vehicles completed for NAPCA (see Chapter V, Topic 1).

Steam power is also being seriously investigated for private automobiles. Five private firms have submitted proposals to NAPCA in competition for a contract to design a practical passenger car steam engine: Planning Research Corp/STP Corp.; Battelle Memorial Institute; Continental Motors Corp.; Vought Aeronautical Division of Ling-Temco-Vought; and Thermo Electron Corp.

In addition, Lear Motors Corp. and Thermo-dynamics Systems, Inc., pioneers in modern steam-vehicle technology, have been chosen by the California Highway Patrol to install steam engines in patrol cars for year-long road tests. Both also hope to demonstrate steam technology with entries in the 1970 Indianapolis 500-mile race.

Complete information on propulsion system development can be found in (ref. 32, 66a, 66h, 66m).

New rapid transit systems under construction have tested several new concepts of power sources and propulsion equipment including a three phase, alternating current concept (ref. 64).

Under prime consideration at present is an efficient battery power source with respect to weight, range, and speed of the vehicle; such a source exists neither in the laboratory nor in a successful design stage.

## Exhaust Inhibitors

Five predominant concepts have been proposed, experimented with, and tested to some degree:

(a) Adjust the fuel and air to maintain a lean mixture.

(b) Add secondary air in the exhaust manifold to ignite the unburned products of combustion.

(c) Retard the spark to raise the exhaust manifold temperature, thus promoting additional combustion.

(d) Recycle part of the exhaust gases.

(e) Employ a catlytic type muffler.

A detailed account of the research conducted in connection with each of the above concepts is presented in Day and Zimmerman's study on potential near term improvements for the highway vehicle (ref. 66h).

## Evolutionary Suspension Systems

The five categories below provide a general idea of technological development in the field of highway vehicle suspension systems (ref. 66m):

(a) Passive suspension systems - spring-damper concept to act as a shock absorber; such elements have fixed characteristics.

(b) Adaptive suspension systems - a sensing device, added to the wheel-axle assembly, which measures incoming roadway disturbances and automatically alters the spring-damper characteristics to match the signal input.

(c) Active suspension system - a sensor on the wheel-axle assembly which reacts to guideway displacement and acceleration inputs by controlling active suspension elements in the form of linear or rotary activators which, in turn, alter body-suspension spacing.

(d) Scanning devices - mechanisms which scan the roadway ahead of the vehicle, predicting inputs prior to their occurrence.

(e) Air cushion vehicles (ACV) - propelled by turbines or air propellers; intensive development in France, England and the United States; specifically:

. French Aerotrain

. Military ACV vehicles

A study on air pad support applicability can be found in

(ref. 66d).

## PARTICIPATING PERSONNEL AND ORGANIZATIONS

The Traffic Systems Division of DOT's Office of Research and Development is directly involved in the application of electronics to traffic control problems (pos. N).

The Urban Mass Transportation Administration (UMTA) is similarly concerned with highway communications research to aid traffic control as a part of its wider scope of improved vehicle component technology.

Federal funding procedures for projects oriented toward improving today's highway vehicles have been outlined in Topic 4.

## CONTRIBUTING PROBLEM AREAS

### Design, Build, and Test

(a) A command and control device for safe, reliable vehicle guidance over any roadway.

(b) An automated route guidance system for conventional vehicles.

(c) A sufficient algorithm for solving mathematically the best route to take between two points on an urban grid.

## Propulsion

(a) A vehicle propulsion system to power vehicles with little or no resulting air pollution or noise.

(b) A practical, economically-feasible electric battery-powered vehicle (ref. 32).

## Suspension

A suspension system which improves vehicle comfort and

safety beyond current levels.

## Vehicle Design

(a) Design a vehicle which fills the gap between the limited capacity motor bus and the high capacity, but staggeringly expensive, rail-rapid transit system.

(b) Bus design with the following considerations -- larger, more spacious, quieter, more comfortable, easier ingress and egress, higher performance, lower operating cost.

(c) Redesign the standard PCC model street car, an outdated subway-surface vehicle.

(d) Develop the concept of an intermodal vehicle which can operate on both rail and road (possibly by conversion of its carriage equipment).

## SECTION C

## AGENCIES AND OFFICIALS CONCERNED
## WITH URBAN TRANSPORTATION

## 1.  DEPARTMENT OF TRANSPORTATION (DOT)

The United States Department of Transportation, established in
1966, brings under one roof activities formerly in more than 30 offices
throughout the Federal Government.  Operating with a combined annual
budget approaching $6 billion -- including $4 billion from the Highway
Trust Fund -- the Department is comprised of six operating administra-
tions which serve the various modes of transport:  Federal Aviation
Administration (FAA); Federal Highway Administration (FHWA);
Federal Railroad Administration (FRA); United States Coast Guard
(USCG); Urban Mass Transportation Administration (UMTA); Saint
Lawrence Seaway Development Corporation (SLS).

Certain agencies within the Department of Transportation have a
direct interest in the topics described in Section B.  They are outlined
below, with a partial list of persons specifically concerned with Urban
transportation problems.

## OFFICE OF THE SECRETARY

> 800 Independence Avenue, S. W.
> Washington, D. C.  20590
> Tel.  (202)  962-5503
> (General Information)

### Office of Economics and Systems Analysis

(A)       Ira Dye - Director
           Rm.  829
           800 Independence Avenue, S. W.
           Washington, D. C.  20590
           Tel.  (202)  962-0885

(B)*     Arthur L. Webster - Deputy Director
           (address and telephone as above)

(C)*     Joseph Stowers
           (address and telephone as above)

### Office of the Assistant Secretary for Research and Technology

(D)*     James E. Densmore - Deputy Assistant Secretary
           Rm.  800W
           (address as above)
           Tel.  (202)  962-8677
             (Coordination of R&D in various DOT agencies)

(E)*     Richard L. Strombotne
           Office of the Physical Sciences
           Rm.  840A
           (address as above)
           Tel.  (202)  962-7861
             (Propulsion Technology)

### Office of Transportation Information Planning

(F)       Robert E. Barraclough - Director
           Rm.  806
           (address as above)
           Tel.  (202)  962-8801

---

* Denotes interviewees

(G)*       Harley Unger
             Rm. 806B
             (address as above)
             Tel. (202) 962-8613

<u>Office of Noise Abatement</u>: Coordinates and directs noise abatement activities in all DOT agencies.

(H)*       Charles R. Foster - Director
             Rm. 801
             (address as above)
             Tel. (202) 962-5531

## BUREAU OF PUBLIC ROADS (BPR)

Federal Highway Administration
1717 H Street, N.W.
Washington, D.C. 20235
Tel. (202) 967-2526
   (General Information)

The Bureau of Public Roads, within the Federal Highway Administration, is the principal roadbuilding agency of the Federal Government and carries out the Government's program for Federal and Federal-aid Highway construction, administration, and research. Principal areas of interest include: Highway engineering (planning, design, construction, materials); traffic operations; bridges; hydraulic engineering; highway transportation; highway economics and financing; and urban planning.

The Bureau will answer general inquiries and refer technical inquiries. Both may be addressed to the above BPR address, c/o The Federal Highway Administration.

<u>Office of Research and Development</u>. The BPR Office of Research and Development has interests in many areas: Highway engineering;

highway construction and maintenance; highway structures; materials engineering; pavement design and analysis; bridge design and analysis; embankments and foundations; mechanistic behavior of materials under stress; dynamics of vehicular movement; traffic flow; accidents and safety; traffic movment and control; design and operating characteristics of highways and highway systems.

(I)*    C. F. Izzard - Director
        Rm. 501
        (BPR address as above)
        Tel. (202) 967-2121

(J)*    C. L. Shufflebarger - Science Advisor
        Rm. 507
        (BPR address as above)
        Tel. (202) 967-5563

(K)     W. J. Halstead - Chief
        Materials Division
        Rm. 101
        Fairbank Highway Research Station
        1000 N. Glebe Road
        Arlington, Va. 22201
        Tel. (703) 557-5201

(L)     G. W. Hartman - Chief
        Economics Requirement Division
        Rm. 651
        (BPR address as above)
        Tel. (202) 967-3285
          (Social and economic considerations in
           highway planning)

(M)     C. F. Scheffey - Chief
        Structural Applied Mechanics Division
        Rm. 202
        Fairbank Highway Research Station
        (address as above)
        (Tel. (703) 557-5287

(N)*    Dr. William W. Wolman - Chief
          Traffic Systems Division
          Rm. 207
          Fairbank Highway Research Station
          Tel. (703) 557-5221

(O)     L. R. Schureman - Chief
          Engineering Systems Division
          Rm. 221
          Fairbank Highway Research Station
          (address as above)
          Tel. (703) 557-5249
            (Application of computers to engineering design)

Office of Planning. This office concerns itself with the planning of

highway systems and with research necessary for improved planning

in all aspects of highway transportation.

(P)     G. E. Marple - Director
          Rm. 536
          (BPR address as above)
          Tel. (202) 967-4425

(Q)     Michael Lash - Deputy Associate Director
          Rm. 536
          (BPR address as above)
          Tel. (202) 967-4427

(R)*    William L. Mertz - Chief
          Urban Planning Division
          Rm. 552
          (address as above)
          Tel. (202) 967-4281

Office of Right-of-Way and Location. This office is concerned with

all aspects of highway location: Right-of-way appraisal and acquisi-

tion; socio-economic impact of highways; and multiple use of high-

way right-of-way corridors. This office includes the newly-formed

Environmental Development Division.

(S)*     David R. Levin - Deputy Director
          Rm. 834
          (BPR address as above)
          Tel. (202) 967-4333

(T)*     R. H. Kraft
          Environmental Development Division
          Rm. 824
          (BPR address as above)
          Tel. (202) 967-3778

(U)*     Harter M. Rupert
          Environmental Development Division
          Rm. 826
          (BPR address as above)
          Tel. (202) 967-3779

Office of Traffic Operations. This office is involved in activities related to traffic flow and control of traffic flow. It is primarily an operational division and works closely with State Highway Departments.

(V)*     Asriel Taragin - Chief
          Planning Division
          Rm. 206
          (BPR address as above)
          Tel. (202) 967-5381

(W)*     Arthur A. Carter
          Planning Division
          Rm. 228
          (BPR address as above)
          Tel. (202) 967-5381

## FEDERAL RAILROAD ADMINISTRATION (FRA)

400 - 6th Street, S.W.
Washington, D.C. 20591
Tel. (202) 962-5503
(General Information)

The newly-created Federal Railroad Administration is responsible for three on-going programs: The Federally-owned Alaska Railroad, the Bureau of Railroad Safety, and the Office of High-Speed Ground Transportation. The FRA is also charged with identifying the role of railroad transportation in the overall transportation system.

Office of High-Speed Ground Transportation. The primary concern of this office is maintaining mobility in those regions where population threatens to overtax existing and planned transportation facilities. The program's basic objective is to develop systems capable of moving large numbers of people at high speed with an economical use of space. Specific areas of interest include: Intercity and metropolitan high speed ground transportation systems; regional transportation systems engineering and economic research; transportation systems demonstrations.

(X)    Edward J. Ward - Chief
        Engineering Research and Development Division
        Rm. 216
        (FRA address as above)
        Tel. (202) 962-8712

(Y)    Dr. Paul W. Shuldiner
        Transport Systems Planning Division
        Rm. 213
        (FRA address as above)
        Tel. (202) 962-8845

## 2. HIGHWAY RESEARCH BOARD (HRB)

Division of Engineering
National Research Council
NAS/NAE
2101 Constitution Avenue, N. W.
Washington, D.C. 20418
Tel. (202) 393-8100

The Highway Research Board of the National Academy of Sciences/
National Academy of Engineering seeks to advance knowledge concerning
the nature and performance of transportation systems by stimulating
research and disseminating the information derived therefrom. The
HRB is concerned with all factors pertinent to the understanding, design,
and function of systems for the safe and efficient movement of people and
goods, including:

a. The planning, design, construction, operation and
   maintenance of transportation facilities and their
   components.

b. The economics, financing and administration of
   arrangements for providing transportation.

c. The interaction of transportation systems with the
   physical, economic, and social environment they
   are designed to serve.

# URBAN MASS TRANSPORTATION ADMINISTRATION (UMTA)

800 Independence Avenue, S. W.
Washington, D.C.  20590
Tel.  (202)  963-4573
(General Information)

On July 1, 1968, the President's Reorganization Plan No. 2 of 1968, transferred Federal programs assisting urban mass transportation from the Department of Housing and Urban Development to the Department of Transportation for execution by the newly-created Urban Mass Transportation Administration.  Thus, all major programs assisting urban transportation are consolidated in one Cabinet-level Department.

The purpose of the reorganization is to facilitate development of urban transportation that will -- (1)  Foster desired patterns of urban development;  (2)  Substantially improve the movement of people and goods in cities; and  (3)  Be compatible with national and regional transportation networks.  UMTA assists and promotes urban mass transportation systems through programs of financial aids to local public bodies and through directed research, development and demonstrations.

## Office of Program Planning

(Z)      Gordon M. Murray - Assistant Administrator
            Rm. 701
            (UMTA address above)
            Tel.  (202)  962-6294

(BB)*    Thomas H. Floyd - Director
            Division of Research Project Management
            Rm. 705
            (MTA address as above)
            Tel.  (202)  963-4206

1. Abt Associates, Regional Travel Survey for the Northeast Corridor, Cambridge, Mass., 1 April 1968.

A two-volume report submitted to the Office of Transportation Information Planning, U.S. Dept. of Transportation. This report outlines a data collection program designed to provide an information base for testing forecasting models of annual travel demand in the Northeast Corridor for automobile, bus, train, and air modes of transportation. The survey concentrates on information about travel between specific district pairs, rather than on origins and destinations alone. The second volume is the "Implementation Plan" for the Survey.

2. Abt Associates, Inc., Washington-Baltimore Airport Access Survey, Cambridge, Mass., 1967.

Origin, destination, access mode, and socio-economic data from airport users.

3. Automotive Safety Foundation, Urban Freeway Development in Twenty Major Cities, Washington, D.C., August 1964

Twenty selected major urban areas are surveyed from the standpoint of progress and distinguishing characteristics of each system. Many current developments in freeway planning and design are covered, including such variations as reversible roadways, joint use of right-of-way, and distinguishing geometric design developments.

4. Barton-Aschman Associates, Inc., A Transportation and Land Development Plan for the Indianapolis Region, A Summary Report, Oct. 1968.

A complete plan for the Indianapolis Region, including economic and travel characteristics, land use planning, and facilities for highway and public transit.

5. Barton-Aschman Associates, Inc., Joint Project Concept— Integrated Transportation Corridors, Prepared for the U.S. Dept. of Housing and Urban Development, Jan. 1968.

The Joint project concept is discussed as a particularly effective device for the implementation of comprehensive urban planning, and principally includes those types of joint projects which include a major transportation facility. The report is organized into four basic sections: (1) Basic objectives (2) Definition of the joint project concept (3) General exposition of techniques and methods to be used (4) An in-depth discussion of various aspects of the joint project, i.e. financing, engineering, and environmental factors.

6. Bay, P. N., "Innovations in a Downtown Parking Problem," Public Works, Vol. 98, Feb. 1967, p. 118.

Describes new parking facilities in San Mateo, Calif. Innovations include use of air rights, building under a tennis court, direct access to rear of stores, and convenient pedestrian easements.

7. Bierley, R. L., and Parkinson, J., The Traffic Pacer System, Research Laboratories, General Motors Corp., April 1963.

This paper summarizes studies recently completed to evaluate the "Traffic Pacer," one means of improving performance of streets with intersections. A control methodology is also discussed.

8. Bureau of Accounts, Interstate Commerce Commission, Cost of Transporting Freight by Class I and Class II Motor Common Carriers of General Commodities by Regions or Territories for the Year 1965, Interstate Commerce Commission Statement No. 7-66, 1966.

9. Bureau of the Budget, Statistical Services of the U.S. Government, Office of Statistical Standards, Bureau of the Budget, Executive Office of the President, U.S. Gov. Printing Office, Washington, D.C. 20402, Revised 1968.

Describes the organization and operation of the statistical system of the Federal Government, various forms of presentation, and the meaning of certain indicators. Principal statistical programs are outlined, and significant publications by each of the Federal agencies are listed and described.

10. Bureau of the Census, Bureau of the Census Catalog, U.S. Gov. Printing Office, Washington, D.C. 20402, Quarterly.

The Publications Section of the catalog lists available Bureau of the Census publications, while statistics stored on punched cards and magnetic tape are listed in the Unpublished Materials Section. The catalog is published quarterly with annual compilations.

11. Bureau of the Census, "Metropolitan Area Statistics", a reprint from Statistical Abstracts of the United States, 1968, U.S. Gov. Printing Office, Washington, D.C. 20402, September 1968.

Statistics from various Federal Government and private sources are presented here for areas officially defined as Standard Metropolitan Statistical Areas (SMSA's). Table 1 presents 166 items of information for the 110 SMSA's of 250,000 inhabitants or more in 1960; Table 2 includes 83 items for the remaining SMSA's. Such topics as population, housing, income, employment, business, etc. are documented.

12. Bureau of Public Roads, "America's Lifelines: Federal Aid for Highways," U.S. Gov. Printing Office, Wash. D.C. 20402, 1969.

Information brochure outlining the many aspects of the Federal Aid Highway Program. It describes both the mechanics of the Federal Aid program and the various projects currently in progress, such as interstate highways, ABC Program, fringe parking.

13. Bureau of Public Roads, "A National Program of Research and Development for Highway Transportation," Promulgated by B.P.R. Circular Memorandum of 20 Sept. 1965.

The official Dept. guidelines for research and development on the most urgent problems in the highway field. It outlines an extensive national program of 7 goals and 28 major projects, each of which evolved from a series of reviews of transportation. General objectives are listed for each of the problem areas and specific programs suggested. This document forms the basis for ongoing R&D in highway travel.

14. Bureau of Public Roads, Federal Laws, Regulations and Other Materials Relating to Highways, U.S. Gov. Printing Office, Wash. D.C., Dec. 1965.

A comprehensive listing of Federal legislation related to highways through December of 1965. Included in the volume are Title 23, U.S. Code-'Highways'; Highway laws not repealed by Title 23; Internal Revenue Code and Highway Trust Fund laws; regulations, standards, and statements of policy; bridge laws, labor laws, and contract laws; and other related material. An extensive subject cross-index is appended.

15. Bureau of Public Roads, Federal Participation in the Development of Multiple-Use Facilities on the Highway Right-of-Way, 8 Oct. 1968.

Instructional memorandum which discusses allowable Federal expenditures to provide for a variety of multiple uses of right-of-way properties.

16. Bureau of Public Roads, Freeways to Urban Development, Washington, D. C.

   A 7-page brochure that presents the joint development concept for urban freeways. The following points are covered: the Challenge, Economics, Efficient Land Use.

17. Bureau of Public Roads, Highway Statistics, U. S. Gov. Printing Office, Wash. D. C. 20402.

   Booklet published annually. Statistics by year and state on vehicle and driver registration, fuel consumption, expenditures of Federal-aid highway funds, highway maintenance costs, and state obligations; and by state, county, and municipality on tax receipts, disbursements, and road and street mileage.

18. Bureau of Public Roads, Joint Development of Highway Corridors and Multiple Use of Roadway Properties, Interim Procedural and Policy Memorandum 21-19, 17 Jan. 1969.

   This memorandum describes procedures to be followed in joint development planning activities related to new facilities on the Federal-Aid Highway systems within urban areas. It also outlines policies for Federal participation in the costs of such planning and in the implementation of the resulting joint development plans.

19. Bureau of Public Roads, Office of Research and Development, Highway Research and Development Studies Using Federal Aid Research and Planning Funds, U. S. Gov. Printing Office, Washington, D. C. 20402, Nov. 1968.

   A general summary of the R&D studies that are presently being conducted under the Office of R&D of the Bureau of Public Roads. The studies are listed by project subject area, by states. Each listing contains detailed information on the objectives of the study, the agency conducting the study, and the funding.

20. Bureau of Public Roads, Office of Right-of-Way and Location, Environmental Development Div., A Report on the Status of Multiple Land Use and Joint Development, Washington, D. C., 30 Sept 1968.

   An informational report of activities in the joint use development of federal-aid highway rights-of-way. The document is principally a photographic presentation of completed, continuing, and proposed projects in governmental and industrial use of highway rights-of-way.

21. Bureau of Public Roads, Task and Study Statements of the National Program for Research and Development in High way Transportation. U. S. Department of Commerce, Bureau of Public Roads, Office of Research and Development, August 1966.

   Available from Clearinghouse for Federal Scientific and Technical Information, Catalog No. PB. 174-888.

22. Bureau of Public Roads, Texas Highway Dept., & City of Amarillo, Amarillo Urban Transportation Plan, Washington, D. C., 1964.

   An extensive analysis of transportation needs and plan for future facilities for Amarillo, Texas. Volume I contains an extensive description of needs and travel characteristics, while Volume II describes the recommended ten-year transportation plan.

23. Bureau of Public Roads, "Urban Traffic Operations Program to Increase Capacity and Safety (TOPICS)," Policy and Procedure Memorandum 21-18, 17 Jan 1969.

24. Carnegie-Mellon University, Urban Rapid Transit Concepts and Evaluation, Transportation Research Institute, Pittsburgh, Pa., 1968.

   This study attempts to evaluate the concept of geometrically flexible transit systems and their probable application to transportation service within urban areas. The project includes the following areas of analysis: vehicle design, guideway technology, interface simulation, vehicle technology and systems. The configuration for the Pittsburgh central business district is used as a model. Both descriptive and technical information are included.

25. Chinitz, Benjamin, City and Suburb: The Economics of Metropolitan Growth, Prentice Hall, New Jersey, 1964.

26. Civil Aeronautics Board, "List of Publications," CAB Publications Section B22, Wash., D. C.

   An annual listing of CAB's statistical and other publications. Selections include: Air Carrier Traffic Statistics, CAB Chart Book of Airline Economic Trends, Comparative Selected Data for Local Air Carriers, Handbook of Airline Statistics.

27. Commerce Department Transportation Research, H. R. 5863, House Report 89-17, House Committee on Interstate and Foreign Commerce, Sub-Committee on Transportation and Aeronautics, 89th Congress, 1st Session, 30 June 1965.

   Proceedings of Congressional hearings on the proposed program for the improvement of transportation statistics; including extensive testimony by the Secretary of Commerce. Also includes an extended evaluation of existing data and information programs.

28. Cornell Aeronautical Laboratory, Inc., A Projection of Technology Applicable to the Future Highway System of the Boston-Washington Corridor, U. S. Department of Commerce, Washington, D. C. 20402, 2 Oct. 1964.

   The objectives of this study are: (1) to review the existing trends in highway-oriented technology, (2) to explore those aspects of existing trends and developments in the field that have exceptional merit, (3) to select certain innovations in component and systems concepts appropriate for further research. Topics included are vehicles, facilities, safety, traffic control, and air cushion vehicles. (Available from Clearinghouse for Federal Scientific and Technical Information.)

29. Cornell Aeronautical Laboratory, Inc., Metrotran-2000: A Study of Future Concepts in Metropolitan Transportation for the Year 2000, Transportation Research Dept., CAL, Cornell University, Buffalo, N. Y., Oct. 1967.

   This report deals with metropolitan or "megalopolitan" integrated transportation systems believed to represent those most likely to become a reality in applied technology by the year 2000. Included are discussions of the Generic City and synthesis of a balanced passenger transportation system for two urban areas, along with the development of such concepts as a "Modemixer" terminal, dual mode Urbmobile, futuristic intercity highway, high-speed rail, the Aquamotel, and the regional VTOL system.

30. Curtin, J. F., "Traffic-Transit-Parking in Downtown Rochester: Now to 1975," Highway Research Board Bulletin No. 293: Urban Transportation Planning, Highway Research Board, Wash. D. C., 1961.

   An Analysis of forthcoming demand in Rochester and possible ways of meeting that demand.

31. Danielson, Scott, ed., Project Metran: An Integrated Evolutionary Transportation System for Urban Areas, MIT Press, Cambridge, Mass., Spring Term 1966.

   Interdepartmental student project in systems engineering under the direction of Prof. Dwight M. Baumann at MIT.

# TRANSPORTATION

32.  Department of Health, Education, and Welfare, Power Systems for Electric Vehicles, Public Health Service, Cincinnati, Ohio, 1967.

A recount of a symposium held at Columbia University from April 6 to April 8, 1967. Attending the symposium were the National Center for Air Pollution Control, the Polytechnic Institute of Brooklyn, and Columbia University. The symposium's purpose was to provide a coordinated review of current research activities, define the present status of knowledge, and stimulate research related to power systems for electric vehicles.

33.  Department of Housing and Urban Development, Freeways to Urban Development, U. S. Gov. Printing Office, Wash., D. C. 20402, 1967.

34.  Department of Transportation Act, Public Law 89-670, 89th Congress, H. R. 15963, 15 Oct. 1966, U. S. Gov. Printing Office, Wash. D. C., 1966.

An act to establish a Department of Transportation and for other purposes.

35.  Department of Transportation, Federal Aviation Administration, F. A. A. Statistical Handbook of Aviation, U. S. Government Printing Office, Washington, D. C.  20402

The compendium of official statistical information on civil aviation activity in the United States. The twelve chapters include data on: The F. A. A. itself, airports, airport activity statistics, and U. S. civil air carrier operating data.

36.  Department of Transportation, Highway Relocation Assistance Study, U. S. Gov. Printing Office, Wash., D. C., 1967.

A study transmitted by the Secretary of Transportation to the Congress as required by the Federal Highway Act of 1966, 90th Congress, first session, Committee Print No. 9.

37.  Department of Transportation, Transportation Information, A report to the Committee on Appropriations, U. S. House of Representatives, May 1969.

The report includes an initial 5-year plan for meeting the critical transportation information needs of industry and government at national, state and local levels. Program provides for information on flows of people and goods, activities which generate flows, and the channels that carry these flows. The information collected would cover all modes of transportation. This reference includes: information needs analysis, plan details, implementation procedures, benefit analysis, possible future developments in transportation information.

38.  Department of Transportation, Urban Mass Transportation Act of 1964 and Related Laws (as amended through Nov. 1, 1968), Wash., D. C. 20590.

This departmental publication contains Mass Transportation Act of 1964, Reorganization Plan No. 2 of 1968, Public Facilities and Loans, Planned Area-wide Development, Land Acquisition and Relocation, Non-discrimination in Federally Assisted Programs, Public Parks, Recreation Areas, etc., and Declaration of Development Assistance Policy. Pertinent excerpts of the laws are given. An excellent summary of the legislative background.

39.  Edwards, L. K. and R. E. Skov, Baseline System Definition: Urban Gravity-Vacuum Transit, Tube Transit Corporation, Palo Alto, California, May 1968.

This report describes an urban Gravity-Vacuum Transit (GVT) System to provide a baseline for further study. It discusses the physical principles employed in GVT and shows details of the trains, tubes, tunnels, pump facilities, stations, turnaround, and maintenance facilities, and other aspects of the total system.

40.  Environmental Development Division, Literature References to Highways and their Environmental Considerations, Office of Right of Way and Location, Bureau of Public Roads, Wash. D. C. 20591, 1 July 1969.

A review of published material dealing with the mutual impacts of highway program and the environment. This comprehensive literature survey is subdivided into four parts: A bibliography (keyed and cross-referenced to six broad environmental considerations: urban, rural, social, economic, physical, esthetic), 52 items (individually reviewed by E. D. D. staff dealing with the environmental impact of highway facility), 85 abstracts, and a subject index.

41.  Federal-Aid Highway Act 1962, Public Law 87-866, 87th Congress, H. R. 12135, 23 October 1962, U. S. Government Printing Office, Washington, D. C., 1962.

An Act to authorize appropriations for Fiscal Years 1964 and 1965 for the construction of certain highways.

42.  Federal-Aid Highway Act of 1968, Public Law 90-495, 90th Congress, S. 3418, 23 Aug. 1968, U. S. Gov. Printing Office, Wash. D. C., 1968.

An act to authorize appropriations for the fiscal years 1970 and 1971 for the construction of certain highways in accordance with title 23 of the U. S. code. Requires consideration of socio-economic and environmental effects in planning.

43.  Federal Highway Administration, "Policy and Procedures Memorandum 50-9," Washington, D. C.

Outlines the policies and procedures to follow in collecting transportation data for the 200 largest metropolitan areas in the U. S. to use as one of the elements of comprehensive urban transportation planning.

44.  Franklin Institute Research Laboratories, A Selected and Annotated Survey of the Literature on Transportation: Status, Structure Characteristics, Problems and Proposed Solutions, Bibliographic Series No. 1, April 1968.

This annotated bibliography consists of the examination of the extensive published information on the status, the needs, the problems, and solutions to problems faced by several modes of transportation: railroads, highways, air transportation, pipelines, waterways, and urban transportation. It likewise covers the material on new technology as it relates to transportation, economics, intermodal relationships, legal aspects, safety, system automation, mathematical modeling, computer simulation, and land use aspects as these relate to transportation. There are 614 items included in this bibliography and arranged alphabetically by author. A detailed subject list is also provided at the beginning of the volume.

45.  The Freeway in the City, Principles of Planning and Design, U. S. Gov. Printing Office, Wash. D. C. 20402 ($3.00), 1968.

A report transmitted to the Secretary of Transportation that offers more than 170 specific recommendations for planning, locating, designing, and building highways. It is also intended as a guide for decision-makers in the federal, state, and local governments and for a broad section of the American public. Its purpose is to present a basic statement on the urban highway-- its problems and its possibilities. (G. P. O. Catalog No. TD 2.108: F87).

46.  Ganz, Alexander, Emerging Patterns of Urban Growth and Travel, Dept. of City and Regional Planning, MIT Press, Cambridge, Mass., Jan. 1968.

An attempt to predict the alterations in urban structure in the next twenty years and the consequent changes in urban travel patterns and required new systems.

47. General Research Corporation, Supplemental Studies of Urban Transportation Systems Analysis, Santa Barbara, Calif., Sept. 1968.

This volume reports on studies of alternative uses and travel demand, extended rail rapid transit systems in Boston, and improved modal split formulations. A valuable example of the use of systems analysis in transportation choice evaluation.

48. Gillespie, P. R., Transit Expressway Concept and Achievements, Westinghouse Electric Corporation, Pittsburgh, Pa., 1967.

49. The Glideway System— A High Speed Ground Transportation System in the Northeastern Corridor of the U.S., Mass. Instit. of Tech., Cambridge, Mass., 1965.

Final report of an interdisciplinary design project by students at M.I.T.

50. Gruen, Victor, The Heart of Our Cities, Simon and Schuster Publishers, New York, 1964.

Gruen gives a detailed presentation on all factors contributing to the demise of the central business districts (CBD) in our nation's cities. He also outlines and describes several projects undertaken by specific cities attempting to remedy the situation in the CBD.

51. High Speed Ground Transportation, S.1588, Senate Report 89-22, Senate Committee on Commerce, Subcommittee on Surface Transportation, 89th Congress, 1st Session, 16 June 1965.

52. Highway Research Board, "Freight Transportation," Highway Research Record, No. 82, Wash. D.C., 1965.

Contains nine reports on statistics on waterborne commerce; trucking data from the 1963 census of transportation; highway ton-mile data; obtaining quality data from carload waybills and other samples.

53. Highway Research Board, HRIS Abstracts, Wash. D.C., quarterly.

HRIS Abstracts is a quarterly publication compiled from the computer tape records of the Highway Research Information Service. Contains abstracts of research reports, papers published in technical journals, and articles selected from the open literature that were stored on the tape files during the preceding three months. Each issue contains a table of contents by subject and indexes by source, author, and authorized term. (Single copies $4.00; yearly subscription $15.00)

54. Highway Research Board, National Academy of Sciences, Highway Research in Progress, 2101 Constitution Ave., N.W., Wash., D.C., Jan. 1969.

A three-volume publication containing about 5700 summaries of research projects listed under 34 subject areas, including: Land Acquisition, Transportation Finance, Traffic Control and Operations, Urban Transportation Administration, Urban Community Values, Urban Land Use, and Urban Transportation Systems. Entries are obtained from individuals and sponsor agencies, Bureau of Public Roads, and the International Road Federation. Aside from project descriptions, the report includes dates, investigations, sponsors, and cost estimates. Authorized term, source, and investigator indices are provided. An excellent source book for ascertaining state-of-the art research in road transportation.

55. Highway Research Board, National Academy of Sciences, "Shopping Centers and Parking," Highway Research Record, No. 130, Wash. D.C., 1966.

Consists of three papers: two are concerned with traffic and parking requirements at large shopping centers, and the other is a study of fringe parking usage for transit riders in Wash., D.C.

56. Homburger, Wolfgang S., ed., Urban Mass Transit Planning, Institute of Transportation and Traffic Engineering, University of California, Berkeley, California 1967.

An anthology of papers related to mass transit planning used in a short course on "Urban Mass Transit Planning." Subjects include: Urban Growth Trends, Components in Urban Travel, Mass Transit Characteristics, Demonstration Study Results, and Case Studies for Twin Cities, San Francisco Bay Area, Cleveland, and Washington, D.C.

57. Improving Federal Transportation Statistics, House Report No. 1700, House Committee on Post Office and Civil Service, Subcommittee on Census and Government Statistics, 87th Congress, 2nd Session, 17 May 1962.

A general discussion of the transportation data problem with emphasis on the three major deficiencies in currently available transportation information.

58. Johannesen & Girand, The Papago Freeway, A Report Prepared for the Arizona State Highway Department, 1968.

A detailed account of the joint development project undertaken on a three-mile stretch of Phoenix, Arizona's east-west freeway. The report includes all phases of the project, from its initiation through alternative design proposals to the final stage of construction.

59. Litton Industries, Toward a Systems Approach for a California Integrated Transportation Network, Economic Development Division, Beverly Hills, Calif., 30 Dec. 1964.

An extensive study submitted to the California Division of Highways to specify the requirements for a work program to implement a systems approach in the design of an integrated transportation network. This document surveys transportation technology and spells out systems methodology.

60. McGregor, Robert G., ed., The Personal Capsule System, M.I.T., Cambridge, Mass. June 1969

The final report of an interdisciplinary design team of students at MIT. The project involved the design of a fully automatic public transportation system.

61. Metcalf, Kenneth Nolan, Transportation Information Sources, Gale Research Co., Book Tower, Detroit, Mich., 1965.

Annotated guide to publications, agencies, and other data sources concerning air, rail, water, road, and pipeline transportation.

62. Modal Choice and Transit Planning Conference, Proceedings of the Model Choice and Transit Planning Conference, Cleveland-Seven County Transportation-Land Use Studies, Cleveland, Ohio, May 1967.

A documentation of the conference proceedings including papers presented and discussions of these papers. Also an open discussion on the future development in transit modeling. Relates general evaluative methodologies to transit planning.

63. MPC Corporation, Report on Testing and Evaluation of the Transit Expressway, Mass Transportation Demonstration Project, Pittsburgh, Pa.15213, 20 Feb.1967.

This report covers the "Transit Expressway" mass transportation demonstration project installed in South Park in Pittsburgh, Pa. It also covers the test and evaluation program designed to determine the engineering, operating, and economic feasibility and public acceptance of "Transit Expressway". Observations, results, and evaluations of the results of the test program are also presented.

64. M.P.C. Corporation, Transit Expressway Report, Pittsburgh, Pa., 1967.

Comprehensive report and evaluation of the Transit Expressway system installed in the South Park, Pittsburgh area.

# TRANSPORTATION

65. National Academy of Sciences, National Research Council, Conference on Transportation Research, Publication 840, 2101 Constitution Ave., N. W., Wash., D. C., Aug. 1960.

A report issued by a special panel of experts in the National Academy of Sciences that met at Woods Hole, Mass. in Aug. 1960. This report develops a series of questions for the purpose of evaluation of the adequacy of current transportation data. It discusses both the types of data needed and the collection methodology.

66. New Systems Study, U. S. Dept. of Housing and Urban Development, Wash. D. C. 20410.

The 1966 amendments to the Urban Mass Transportation Act of 1964 directed the Secretary of Housing and Urban Development to undertake a project to study new transportation systems that would "carry people and goods within metropolitan areas speedily, safely, without polluting the air, and in a manner that will contribute to sound city planning." The next 19 references are the result of that 18-month study.

(a) Tomorrow's Transportation: New Systems for the Urban Future, U. S. Dept. of Housing and Urban Development, Office of Metropolitan Development, Urban Transportation Administration, U. S. Gov. Printing Office, Wash. D. C., 20402 ($1.75), 1968.

This is a summary of the results and recommendations of the 16 contractors involved in the "New Systems Study" on urban transportation. The following 16 references are the detailed technical reports submitted to HUD by each contractor. (Any of the following reports can be obtained from the Clearinghouse for Federal Scientific and Technical Information, 5285 Port Royal Road, Springfield, Virginia 22151. Hard cover copies can be obtained for $3 and microfiche copies for $0.65. The accession numbers are in the annotations below.)

(b) Abt Associates, Qualitative Aspects of Urban Personal Travel Demand, May 1968.

Clearinghouse accession no.: PB 179 745

(c) Barton-Aschman Associates, Guidelines for New Systems of Urban Transportation, May 1968.

A three-volume final report that contains:
Volume I - Urban Needs and Potentials. PB 179 333
Volume II - A Collection of Papers. PB 179 334
Volume III - Annotated Bibliography. PB 179 335

(d) Battelle Memorial Institute, Monographs on Possible Urban Transportation Research, Development, and Demonstration Projects, Jan. 1968.

This final report presents an inventory of potential RD&D propositions in the areas of component developments, systems developments, operational design methodology, and planning techniques. In addition, monographs are included on 18 special propositions meriting further delineation; land use, urban streets, transportation models, novel heat engines, etc. PB 178 279

(e) Battelle Memorial Institute, Urban Goods-Movement Demand, Oct. 1967.

This final report develops a methodology for conducting goods-movement studies as an integral part of the planning process. It is divided into 7 sections: (1) outline of a methodology for developing an urban goods-movement information system, (2) identification of the urban planning application of goods-movement data, (3) techniques for collecting, processing, and analyzing goods-movement data, (4) forms and procedures for implementation, (5) waste movements, (6) application of goods-movement information in the urban planning process, (7) additional research and development needs. Also includes an extensive bibliography and sketches of on-going research related to the field. PB 178 277

(f) Consad Research Corporation, Transit Usage Forecasting Techniques: A Review and New Directions, April 1968.

The scope of this final report includes a review, analysis, and evaluation of present modal split forecasting techniques; a review of relevant literature and special investigations: the identification of special deficiencies in the present transit usage forecasting techniques, and recommendations of methods for overcoming these deficiencies and improving the forecasting capabilities of modal split models. PB 178 436.

(g) Cornell Aeronautical Laboratories, Bi-Modal Urban Transportation System Study, March 1968.

A two-volume report that defines and describes a dual mode vehicle transportation system that is intended primarily for urban-suburban use. The "Urbmobile" is battery powered for street use and also operates on an exclusive, tracted guideway. This system is also compared with the pallet concept. Vol. I: PB 178 286; Vol. II: PB 179 192.

(h) Day and Zimmerman, Inc., Potential Near Term Improvements in Transportation, March 1968.

A study of ways to obtain improved results from existing transportation systems within a 6-month to 3-year timeframe. Considerations include vehicles and their components, pedestrians, rights-of-way, operations and administration. PB 178 278.

(i) General Electric Company, A Study of Command and Control Systems for Urban Transportation, Feb. 1968.

A three-part final report that covers: (1) Introduction-surveys command and control systems, (2) Candidate command and control systems for research, development, and demonstration, (3) a framework for evaluation of transportation systems. This report includes demand-actuated route transit, microelectronic intersection computer, automatically controlled guided vehicle. PB 178 281.

(j) General Motors Research Laboratories, New Systems Implementation Study, Feb. 1968.

A three-volume final report that develops recommendations for a program of research and development leading to the establishment of improved methods of analyzing the requirements for new transportation systems, their estimated performance and cost, and the socio-economic evaluation and comparison of such new systems. Volume I is a summary of conclusions. Volume II is concerned with methods for transportation planning and evaluation. Volume III contains seven case studies which illustrate the development of new systems in several urban environments. This volume also contains an extensive bibliography. Vol. I: PB 178 273; Vol. II: PB 178 274; Vol. III: PB 178 275.

(k) General Research Corp., Systems Analysis of Urban Transportation, Jan. 1968.

A four-volume final report: Vol. I- summary: Vol. II- cases for study; Vol. III- network flow analyses; Vol. IV- supporting analyses. Vol. I: PB 178 261; Vol. II: PB 178 262; Vol. III: PB 178 263; Vol. IV: PB 178 264.

(l) Midwest Research Institute, Special Transportation Requirements in Small Cities and Towns, May 1968.

Clearinghouse ac. no. PB 178 280.

(m) North American Rockwell Corporation, Frontiers of Technology Study, Jan. 1968.

A three-volume study of transportation subsystem technologies such as: propulsion, energy storage, command amd control, non-skid braking and traction, advanced suspension, non-contact power transmission, and air cushion technology. (Vol. I-summary; Vol. II- survey; Vol. III-implementation. ) Vol. I: PB 178 270; Vol. II: PB 178 271; Vol. III: PB 178 272.

(n) Peat, Marwick, Livingston and Co., Projection of Urban Personal Transportation Demand, March 1968.

This study develops functional relationships for estimating transportation demand for 1965, and for forecasting transportation demand for 1975 and 1985 for all urban areas in the U.S. The final objective was the recommendation of a continuing research program based upon existing needs discovered during various phases of the project. PB 178 276.

(o) Regional Economic Development Institute, Transportation Requirements and Effects of New Communities, May 1968.

Ac. no. PB 178 983

(p) Stanford Research Institute, Future Urban Transportation Systems: Descriptions, Evaluations, and Programs, March 1968.

A study to develop concepts for future systems or families of systems, employing advanced technology that can be introduced within 5 to 15 years. Five different families or generic classes of complementary systems are proposed and evaluated in an attempt to tailor systems to specific needs. PB 178 265.

(q) Stanford Research Institute, Future Urban Transportation Systems: Impacts on Urban Life and Form, March 1968.

Ac. no. PB 178 266.

(r) Transportation Research Institute, Latent Demand for Urban Transportation to Satisfy Urban and Social Needs Unmet by Existing Systems, May 1968.

Ac. no. PB 178 979.

(s) Westinghouse Air Brake Co., Wilbur Smith and Associates, and Institute of Public Administration, Study of Evolutionary Urban Transportation, Feb. 1968.

A comprehensive study to outline a program of research and development projects with short-term payoffs and to identify short-term improvements in urban transportation. Included in this report is information on future urban transport needs, institutional obstacles, and specific recommendations for research and development. Recommendations pertain to bus transit, parking, freight handling systems, wide area traffic control, transit information, etc. Vol. I: PB 178 267: Vol. II: PB 178 268: Vol. III: PB 178 269.

67. New York State Dept. of Transportation, Statewide Transportation Planning, Jan. 1969.

A report presented to the National Academy of Science, National Research Council, Highway Research Board. This report is a description of New York State's statewide policy, analytic techniques, and consequent transportation data requirements.

68. North American Aviation, Inc., California Integrated Transportation Study, Los Angeles Division, 15 Sept. 1965.

A 5-volume study for California covering seven major task areas: (1) Population Model Development (2) Econometric Model Development (3) Land Use Model Development (4) Transportation Demand Model Development (5) Transportation simulation Model Development (6) Evaluation Model Development (7) Supporting Studies.

69. Office of High-Speed Ground Transportation, Dept. of Transportation, Department of Transportation High-Speed Railroad Research and Development Program, Wash., D.C.

70. Parsons, Brinckenhoff, Tudor, Bechtel, Engineers, Engineering Report to the San Francisco Bay Area Rapid Transit District, June 1961.

Preliminary study outlinging the BART system.

71. Parsons, Brinckerhoff, Tudor, Bechtel, et. al., The Composite Report: Bay Area Rapid Transit, May 1962.

Reports submitted to SFBARTD describing the engineering, financial, and economic phases of the BART plan.

72. President's Commission on Postal Organization, Towards Postal Excellence, U.S. Gov. Printing Office, Washington, D.C. 20402, June 1968.

Report of the Kappel Commission analyzing postal organization and operations. Recommendations are included for a massive restructuring of the Postal Department and for the implementation of new methods and technologies, including new delivery modes.

73. Richardson, Gordon, and Assoc., Inner Loop Freeway System, Washington, D.C. — Southeast Freeway, Under-Structure Study 7th to 8th Streets, 3 Gateway Center, Pittsburgh, Pa. 15222, 14 May 1968.

Joint development study results for possible uses for the space under the viaduct structure carrying the Southeast freeway between 7th and 8th Streets in Washington, D.C. This report was prepared in cooperation with the U.S. Bureau of Public Roads. The scope of the investigation was limited to 3 alternative schemes. Cost estimates are also included.

74. Sawyer, Thomas E., Preliminary Design for a Regional Information System as an Integral Part of a Statewide System, TRW Systems Group, Redondo Beach, Calif., Aug. 1967.

A chiefly non-technical report discussing some of the on-going data processing developments and their application in the development of a Regional Information system. The emphasis here is on information systems in general.

75. Simpson and Curtin, Transportation Engineers, Coordinated Transit for the San Francisco Bay Area-- Now to 1975, Clearinghouse for Federal, Scientific, and Technical Information, Wash. D.C., Oct. 1967.

An excellent study of the overall transportation picture for the San Francisco Bay Area. In the wake of BART, this report strives to fuse new and old services into a system that will be progressive years from now.

# TRANSPORTATION

76. Smith (Wilbur) and Associates, Highway Travel in Washington-New York-Boston Megalopolis, U.S. Department of Commerce, Washington, D.C. 20402, 1963.

An over-all study related to existing and future highway travel in the corridor, including the development of a model for synthesizing current highway travel patterns. The study includes: description of the megalopolis and present highway travel; future travel; highways and the future of the megalopolis. (Available from Clearinghouse for Federal Scientific and Technical Information.)

77. Smith (Wilbur)& Associates, Parking in the City Center, for the Automobile Manufacturers' Association, May 1965.

A guide to all concerned with downtown parking, it cites the various factors contributing to downtown parking demands, economic contributions, and shows how the nation's cities can meet these demands through various private and public approaches. Extensive bibliography and case studies.

78. Smith (Wilbur) & Associates, Transportation and Parking for Tomorrow's Cities, New Haven, Conn., 1966.

This report was prepared for the Automobile Mfg. Assoc., and summarizes an in-depth study of the changing metropolis and its transportation requirements. Full recognition is given to the various social, economic, and environmental forces which influence growth and travel. This report focuses particularly on the downtown area and has an adequate section on the parking problem.

79. Spreiregen, Paul D., Urban Design: The Architecture of Towns and Cities, McGraw-Hill, New York, 1965.

An excellent account of the fundamentals of urban design. Included are discussions of the heritage of urban design, basic principles and techniques, esthetics, designing parts of the city, circulation, and regulation and control. An extensive bibliography is also presented.

80. Stewart, William B. and Mason, Ralph, "Computer Program Simulates Proposed Transit Systems and Evaluates Them Economically," Westinghouse Engineer, May 1968.

This article describes a program to permit speedy evaluations over a wide range of alternative yet interdependent choices. The technique is that of simulating a systems operation and the associated costs for each realistic and promising set of alternatives. Each set is evaluated over a term of years equal to the expected economic life of the system, and the program permits rapid appraisals of the relative effects of important variables.

81. Transportation Association of America, Transportation Facts and Trends, Washington, D.C., April 1968.

A statistical analysis showing the importance of and trends in transportation in the U.S. — including both for-hire and private carrier. A special appendix includes a methodology for data collection.

82. Tunnard, Christopher and Boris Pushkarev, Man-Made America: Chaos or Control?, Yale University Press, New Haven, 1963.

This inquiry into selected problems of Design in the Urbanized Landscape emphasizes the esthetic in landscape, dwellings, freeway form, industry, and recreation facilities. Both historical trends and future directions are outlined. An extensive bibliography is presented.

83. Urban Mass Transportation Administration, Directory of Research, Development, and Demonstration Projects, 800 Independence Ave., S.W., Wash., D.C., June 1969.

84. Urban Planning Division, Bureau of Public Roads, Urbanized Area Transportation Planning Program, Wash., D.C. 20591.

85. U.S. House of Representatives, Committee on Science and Astronautics, Science and Technology and the Cities, U.S. Gov. Printing Office, Wash. D.C. 20402 ($.70), 1969.

A compilation of 11 papers prepared for the tenth meeting of the panel on Science and Technology of the Committee on Science and Astronautics of the U.S. House of Representatives. The papers deal with human problems, urban environment, transportation, and economics of cities.

86. Voorhees (Alan M.) and Associates, Inc., Urban Mass Transit Planning Project: Factors Influencing Transit, October 1966.

The first of a series of technical reports that will be used to describe the development of a series of computer programs for transit planning. This volume sets forth the functional specifications which computer programs should satisfy to meet the full range of needs in transit planning.

87. Walker, W.J. and Howell, J.K., "Transit Expressway Medium Density Mass Transit System," ASME, 65-RR5, 7 April 1968.

A presentation of the Westinghouse "skybus" or Transit Expressway System, being developed under an HHFA demonstration grant. The system utilizes a rubber-tired, bus-like vehicle operating on an exclusive guideway, controlled by a central computer.

88. Westinghouse Electric Corporation, Capital Cost for Transit Expressway: Report No. 7-167-46, Pittsburgh, Pa., 1966.

89. Wolf, Robert A., "Elements of a Future Integrated Highway System Concept," Cornell Aeronautical Laboratories, Inc., March 1965.

A paper presented at the Transportation Research Seminar, held by the U.S. Dept. of Commerce.

S. danielson

SECTION A

ELEMENTS OF THE URBAN HOUSING PROBLEM

## THE HOUSING GOAL

In 1949 the 81st Congress passed a National Housing Act which called for "the realization as soon as feasible of the goal of a decent home and a suitable living environment for every American family". Nearly twenty years later, the 90th Congress found unequivocally that this objective "has not been fully realized for many of the Nation's lower income families" and reaffirmed the original national goal in its Housing and Urban Development Act of 1968 (ref. 74, p. 7).

On the basis of criteria established by the President's Committee on Urban Housing, it has been estimated that approximately 7.8 million American families cannot afford the present market prices for suitable housing. Studies undertaken for the Committee by General Electric's Center for Advanced Studies, TEMPO, concluded that U.S. households could reasonably be expected to allocate up to 20% of their total monthly incomes for shelter costs -- the national average being 15%, and 25% being the "hardship" standard established by the Federal Rent Supplements Program. 56% of these house-deficient families are urban dwellers, living in Standard Metropolitan Statistical Areas (SMSA) of 50,000 or more in population; about half of the house-poor are also "officially poor", with gross incomes below the $3,000 Federal poverty level (ref. 74, p. 8).

In the absence of a dynamic increase in housing availability or a major change in the rate of national economic growth, the number of house-poor families is expected to decrease only slightly in the next decade. About 7.5 million households will still be unable to afford market prices for standard housing in 1978. However, the proportion of these families which are urban residents will have increased to 60%. Classifying them demographically, TEMPO predicts that 70% of the house-poor families will be white; half will be elderly; and most will have two members or less. Of the non-white, house-poor families, only 27% will be elderly, and 43% will have two members or less. About one in four non-white families will require housing assistance compared with one in twelve white households (ref. 74, p. 9).

Additional TEMPO studies on the present condition of the Nation's total housing stock estimate that approximately 66 million units exist for the housing of 60 million households (ref. 74, p. 8). Although this suggests that there are more than enough dwelling spaces, at least 6.7 million and perhaps as many as 12 million units are substandard -- 4 million lack indoor plumbing, and 2.7 million are in dilapidated condition. 6.1 million units (standard and substandard) are overcrowded with more than one person to a room. At best, only about 2 million of the Nation's unoccupied housing units are considered to be in acceptable condition and

ready for occupancy -- the Nation's lowest available vacancy rate since

1958. Moreover, the concentration of deficient units is an added dimen-

sion to the housing problem since approximately 4 million dwellings are

crowded into major SMSA's (ref. 75).

If the Nation is to satisfactorily resolve its housing problem, it must

forthrightly address the dual questions of quantity and quality. On one

hand, there is the basic objective of supplying a sufficient number of

shelters at reasonable cost to provide choice, comfort, and mobility for

a rapidly growing population. On the other is the desire to upgrade the

quality of dwelling units available to disadvantaged segments of the popu-

lation. So long as there is a severe shortage of housing among all income

levels, the goal of meeting the housing needs of the poor will not only be

more difficult, but it is also unlikely that it will be politically, socially,

or economically obtainable.

To achieve both quantity and quality is a tall order -- one which the

President's Committee on Urban Housing declares must include the

building of 26 million housing units by 1978, including 6 to 8 million

Federally-subsidized dwellings for families requiring financial assistance.

13.4 million units will be needed to accommodate new families formed in

the next decade; 8.7 million units are expected to deteriorate and must

be replaced or rehabilitated; 3 million standard units that will be either

accidently destroyed or purposefully demolished for residential land use must be replaced; 1.6 million additional units will be required to provide sufficient vacancies for an increasingly mobile population (ref. 74, p. 8).

This represents no less than a 70% increase over the Nation's total housing production during the 1950's, which proceeded at the rate of nearly 1.5 million units per annum. The ten-year housing goal calls for a staggering 40% increase in the total current housing stock; by the end of the century, the Nation must produce more housing than it has done in its entire history. Dollar expenditures in the next decade will practically double the past ten years' total.

During 30 years of Federal housing activity, only 800,000 subsidized units have been completed. The President's Committee has recommended, and the 1968 Housing and Urban Development Act requires, that at least 6 million subsidized units be constructed in the next decade, at a Federal subsidy cost of some $2.8 billion.

Since the President's Committee submitted its report in December of 1968, the national housing outlook has continued to deteriorate. The Federal Government's efforts to combat inflation are forcing a steady decline in homebuilding; restrictions on the growth of the money supply have discouraged construction by about 30% in the first seven months of 1969. Barring a fast turnabout in the availability of money, the National Association of Home Builders predicts that annual production could fall to one million units or below -- frightfully short of the 2.6 million units per year required to meet the 10 year housing goal.

To supply 26 million units by 1978 - or to simply prevent falling even further behind - will require a concentrated effort on many fronts. Technical innovations, cost reduction programs, new concepts in financing and marketing are only a few. The Department of Housing and Urban Development (HUD) responded to the problem in June of 1969 with "Operation Breakthrough", a program designed to effectively increase housing production and control its costs by establishing a partnership between labor, industry, the financial community, home-builders, consumers, and Federal, State and local governments. It is hoped that the program will stimulate building and development systems capable of providing high-volume, rapid delivery of housing with improved environmental quality at costs that are within the reach of all families (ref. 27).

## THE HISTORICAL PERSPECTIVE

The housing sector of the U. S. Economy has traditionally been administered by a complex association of private enterprise and public responsibility. The first Federal housing assistance program was enacted in 1938; since then some 35 different Federal housing programs have been established to achieve a variety of ends. Many have had specific economic objectives -- to create jobs, to improve the tax base or central cities, to clear slums, or to aid the poor. But few projects have sought to directly increase the Nation's housing stock, and only a small number have attempted to provide decent houses for the disadvantaged. Frequently competing public works programs, relying heavily on the power of eminent domain, have actually effected net reductions in the supply of available housing in certain areas.

The brief history of Federal involvement in urban housing can best be characterized as a joint application of insurance and subsidy. Programs have been developed at various times to serve three broad income groups: families below the Federal poverty line; families above the poverty line but who would otherwise have to pay a disproportionate amount of their incomes for housing; and families able to pay the economic cost for standard housing under a Federal mortgage guarantee or insurance program. The programs which have enjoyed greatest success are those, such as FHA mortgage insurance, which channel the forces of existing economic institutions into formerly unproductive areas.

A Depression-era crisis in lending led to the establishment in 1932 of the Home Loan Bank System for the purpose of extending credit to member Savings and Loan Institutions through Federal Home Loan Banks. The Home Owner's Loan Corporation (HOLC) was entrusted with the power to buy mortgages threatened with foreclosures. The 1934 National Housing Act established a system of mortgage insurance to be administered by the Federal Housing Administration (FHA), and in 1938, the Federal National Mortgage Association (FNMA) became a secondary market for trading insured mortgages.

The U. S. Housing Act of 1937 established Public Housing as the first significant program of subsidized housing for low-income families. Development, ownership, and management of the projects was entrusted to local public agencies, and rents were minimized by a combination of Federal and local subsidies. Though the program was originally intended as a job-producing mechanism in the early Thirties, the emphasis rapidly shifted to that of housing the disavantaged.

The war years witnessed the development of a veteran's mortgage guarantee program administered by the Veterans Administration (VA). Patterned after the FHA concept, the VA program permitted veterans to borrow 100% of the housing purchase cost. The Housing Act of 1949 authorized a Public Housing program of 135,000 subsidized units to be constructed over 6 years. In addition, it established a separate slum clearance and urban development activity, which has since evolved into the Urban Renewal program, and encouraged increased participation of private enterprise.

Conservation and rehabilitation programs were attached to the Urban Renewal concept in the Housing Act of 1954 in order to broaden the scope of Federal redevelopment. The Act also required municipalities to maintain a "workable program" for community improvement in order to qualify for Federal assistance under Public Housing, Urban Renewal, and later programs. A liberalization of multifamily FHA terms was also included (FHA, Section 220) to attract the private sector into building middle-income housing in Urban Renewal areas.

The 1959 Housing Act broke the pattern which restricted development and operation of subsidized projects to public owners. It also authorized direct loans from the Federal Government to non-profit sponsors of rental projects for the elderly and the handicapped. Section 221(d)(3) of the Housing Act, the Below Market Interest Rate (BMIR) Program, expanded opportunities for private development of both single and multi-family dwellings.

In 1965 the Housing Act introduced two new subsidy techniques. The Rent Supplements program attempted to adjust housing subsidies to the needs of individual families, and the leasing program of Section 23 enabled local Public Housing authorities to subsidize rent in existing rental units. HUD was also established as a Cabinet level authority in 1965, and the next year it instituted the Model Cities program in an attempt to coordinate government policies, both physical and social, within defined neighborhoods.

The Housing and Urban Development Act of 1968 culminated a strong movement toward the use of housing subsidies for private dwellings. Section 235 Homeownership programs provided modest subsidies for low-income family home purchase. Section 236 provided for a new rental assistance program for families above the Public Housing income ceiling. Both programs relied heavily on private developers and private lenders, aided by Federal subsidies. FHA insurance was made more readily available in declining urban areas. The National Housing

Partnership, a contractual arrangement between public and private sectors, was designed to offer a well-financed source of management and technical know-how, a means for diversification, and the opportunity for cash returns and tax savings.

The private sector has not of itself developed much housing for low-income families because, until recent years, subsidies required to make such efforts attractive have been lacking. Assistance for low-income households has been embodied chiefly in Public Housing and Rent Supplements programs. "Turnkey" public housing, which allows builders to initiate the development of projects and sell the completed packages to local authorities, is presently involving the private sector more in this particular area. Aside from mortgage insurance, moderate-income families are presently aided by Section 235 Homeownership and Section 236, which replaces earlier BMIR programs.

Until the announcement of HUD's "Operation Breakthrough", there had been little effort to stimulate housing production on a broad scale. This new program marks a shift in the Federal Government's basically piecemeal approach to the housing problem. It does in fact recognize that there is a real and pressing need to do more than aid specific segments of the population. HUD is attempting in "Breakthrough" to ensure adequate housing for the entire Nation. The success or failure of this program will do much to define the condition of America's housing in the coming decade.

## CONSTRAINTS

Despite a pronounced national commitment and over three decades of Federal involvement in housing, there is considerably less than universal agreement that the goal of 26 million houses by 1978 will be realized. Various constraints are in evidence - some truly significant, others a traditional nuisance - which must be satisfactorily resolved before housing of sufficient quantity and quality can be made available. The aggregate costs of housing can also be reduced significantly if none of the avenues for savings is dismissed prematurely.

### The Homebuilding Industry

In its present form it is factionalized and highly localized, subject to constraints and eccentricities of local markets, widely varying building codes and local ordinances, and local labor practices. No single home-builder or group of home-builders produces more than a small percentage of the Nation's housing, though some firms hold dominant positions in specific areas of the country. Even Federal subsidy housing is developed and controlled by a conglomeration of firms, only a few of which engage in volume production. In total, there may be as many as 23 major public and private direct participants in the housing process and 17 major public and private sources of rules, laws, and practices of varying restrictiveness (ref. 74, p.10).

Though some innovations have been introduced, home-building technology has not advanced commensurate with housing needs. There

has been insufficient basic research on new concepts or on evolutionary
materials, scheduling, and testing. The urgent need for producing
housing in large quantities and at minimal cost cannot adequately be
fulfilled without a substantial facelifting of the industry itself.

## Building Codes

Unnecessary or conflicting provisions and restraints in locally-
administered codes add significantly to the costs of housing, cause construction delays and inhibit the use of creative designs and modern
materials. There are now four model national codes, but only about 15%
of all municipalities above 5,000 population have adopted and adequately
maintained them (ref. 67). This lack of uniformity in codes and standards
understandably works as a serious impediment to widespread marketing
of unconventional housing types. Appropriate changes in codes themselves
could lead to economy of scale with no loss in quality.

## Labor

Housing is a labor-intensive commodity, with that element contributing about 20% of total on-site construction costs. Total cumulative
labor cost, from raw material through finished product, has been estimated at 80% of the final housing construction cost. This results in part
from certain union restrictions and in part from the present characteristics of the construction process -- seasonality and migratory
employment. Though labor productivity in construction has shown some
increase since the war, it is estimated that 1.8 men are still required

for each man-year of productive work (ref. 74, p. 31). To achieve the national goal of 26 million homes calls for an increase by 1 million man-years in construction and homebuilding by 1975. Either a sufficiently large work force must be assembled or the present work force must become more productive.

## The Market

The market for housing is characterized by volatility and fragmentation. It is particularly sensitive to national financial conditions, local employment, and demographic changes. In particular areas, the demand may increase by 50% from one year to the next. Large-volume production of housing with related economies of scale cannot exist without a market of sufficient size and stability to support the required capital investment. "Operation Breakthrough" maintains, as one of its major objectives, the aggregation of a market large enough and suitably reliable to support volume production of housing.

## Financing

The traditional emphasis of home financing has been on ownership, which favors single family units and makes it difficult to develop the multifamily and multiuse structures commonly required in central cities for low-income families. Various types of financial mechanisms (mortgage insurance, rent and interest subsidies, etc.) have been developed on an ad hoc basis, toward various ends, with a minimum of coordination. The requirement that the housing unit itself serve as

collateral has worked to inhibit innovation in design and material.
Moreover, credit is generally unavailable to low-income buyers.

Housing finance has always been particularly sensitive to national
monetary policies, as is evidenced by FHA rates rising from 4.5% in
the 1940's to 7.8% in mid-1969. A 1% increase in interest rate on a
40-year mortgage for a $15,000 home raises the owner's monthly
outlay by more than $10 -- which equals a 13% increase in total develop-
ment and construction costs (ref. 74, p. 23). If the availability of
housing finance is to be stabilized, this dependency must be lessened;
but complicating the relationship is the fact that stimulating or damping
housing construction is, in itself, a significant tactic in national
monetary policy.

The goal of 26 million housing units by 1978 requires new levels of
investment in both subsidized and unsubsidized housing. New mortgage
funds must be attracted from other than the traditional sources, and
innovative financing concepts -- such as exist in the automobile market
-- must be investigated. In providing for low-income families, several
questions must be resolved: Who receives assistance and in what
amounts; what quality of subsidized units are to be built; where should
they be built; and who should own, develop, and manage the housing?

Land

The President's Committee on Urban Housing estimates that 6
million additional subsidized units will require at least a million net

acres of land. Assuming that most of these units will be located on urban fringes, associated, nonresidential facilities may require up to another million acres. Development of 20 million unsubsidized units and their supporting facilities could consume up to another 6 million acres. This represents a 60% increase on the current land acquisition rate (ref. 74, p. 25).

The price of raw land is the fastest rising element among all major housing costs, currently running at about 25% of the initial cost of single-family housing and 13% of the per unit cost of multi-family housing (ref. 74, p. 10). Between 1956 and 1966, the market value of privately owned land in the U. S. approximately doubled -- ordinary taxable real estate rising from $269 billion to $523 billion. This corresponds to an annual rise of 6. 9%. Urban land in particular increased 130% in value in the last decade (ref. 67).

Present difficulties include the lack of reasonable acquisition procedures, short of exercising eminent domain, and the lack of financing for large developments during land preparation and pre-construction stages. Tract acquisition, with contiguous land, is a prerequisite to volume construction; with sufficiently large parcels, there is greater flexibility in site planning, higher opportunity to achieve economies of scale, and increased likelihood of including full community facilities.

In many instances, the barrier of high land prices is institutional rather than economic; land availability is substantially limited by arbitrary policies on zoning and subdivision regulations. Population growth, community facilities and services, and the total community's commerce and industry create land values. Zoning laws based on archaic concepts of real estate or community development cannot reflect these values accurately.

New concepts in land use are imminent with large changes in traditional living densities and more effective utilization of less land. Zoning standards must be made to reflect new residential and community philosophies.

## Peripheral Housing Costs

The total costs of owning and maintaining housing are not accurately known. Rough estimates attribute about 25% of the monthly housing expenditures directly to the acquisition of land and buildings and 75% to interest, property tax, maintenance, etc.

Property taxes are the greatest operating expense in new housing projects. They must be constantly reviewed from the standpoint of efficiency and equity with which they allocate the cost of necessary public services. Taxes can provide the medium for major incentives and determinants for better housing and should be utilized accordingly.

Inadequate maintenance serves to accelerate the deterioration of the existing housing stock and, in this respect, its total economic cost is difficult to assess. There is at present no market mechanism which rewards maintenance by homeowners, nor are there adequate incentives to encourage maintenance of rental buildings.

Utilities are frequently the limiting factor in land acquisition and development. Utility rates and taxes are presently based on dispersed housing patterns and are not conducive to high-density developments required in urban centers.

A significant but intangible "cost" is that associated with relocation and disruption of the community in redevelopment and renewal activities. As of now, it has not been adequately assessed.

The Flow of Services

As important as the housing unit itself is the proximity of housing facilities to service areas---employment, education, commerce, recreation, meeting places, health care, and protection from fire, flooding, etc. This means that housing must be planned in conjunction with these services or developed where they are readily available. The provision of power and water, the prevention of noise, water, and air pollution, and facilities for disposal of solid waste are all integral components of the housing development.

The flow of services is particularly important with respect to low-income housing. There is a need for commerce and job-producing facilities within the immediate vicinity of subsidized housing, or at least adequate mobility for residents should be assured.

## Social Aspects

The problem of housing the Nation logically means housing individuals and families. Producing housing units is one matter; producing housing that people will accept and enjoy is another. It is not a certainty that those who build housing necessarily have the same concept of desirability as do potential residents. Public Housing stands as a lamentable example.

Much of the substandard housing is concentrated in central cities. Merely replacing these units is not sufficient in itself -- destruction of existing neighborhoods, relocation, and isolation too often result. But neither is it easy to overcome resistance to introducing low-income housing in moderate- and higher-income neighborhoods.

## AN APPROACH

Housing can simultaneously be defined as a physical product, part of a community, and a flow of services. Traditional approaches have stressed the structural aspect – housing as physical units to provide shelter and security. But it is now generally recognized that user needs go quite beyond the physical. They depend intimately on such considerations as housing location in relation to community services and employment, contiguous space and its use, population characteristics, recreation, and opportunities for social interaction. As much as possible, housing should be a medium which allows people to fulfill these needs.

Class and ethnic differences are considerable throughout the urban population and, with social patterns, are important inputs to the housing process. Some forms of housing and land use are better suited to certain life styles than others. The existing image of a house, defined by building codes and advocated by a majority of the middle-class population, is not necessarily so rated by people who will be using it. The "home-as-castle" concept has prevented housing from being considered a malleable product which is capable of adjustment to dynamic social and cultural patterns and needs.

An essential element in meeting variant needs is that of choice; as far as possible, housing users should be provided with adequate choices of where they would like to live, in what kind of housing, and between rental and ownership. A corollary is the fact that potential users must be afforded the power -- both social and economic -- to act on such choices. Perhaps the chief user need with respect to the housing process is the need to participate in that process by having an opportunity to exercise a choice of housing types and styles and be a part of the group which controls the environment.

The housing problem is particularly appropriate for attack by interdisciplinary systems teams, since neither a wholly-technical nor a technically-deficient approach will yield satisfactory solutions. Projects can be organized around particular constraint areas such as finance, land acquisition, housing codes, etc., with the intent of developing evolutionary mechanisms for lessening the effect of these constraints; or the study can focus on the development of a particular housing type and deal with the constraints as necessary elements of the problem. Perhaps the most realistic approach is to plan a strategy for housing and community development in a nearby urban area. In this case, the constraints are the real ones, and local authorities can offer needed guidance and information.

Section B which follows suggests areas of emphasis. The topics are sufficiently broad to be adaptable to specific localities, yet they indicate areas where advances are desperately needed. Systems projects might appropriately combine two or more topic areas in an overall development plan.

Two source references are particularly useful. Both were the result of extensive Executive studies — by the President's Committee on Urban Housing (ref. 74) and the National Commission on Urban Problems (ref. 67) — and are the latest and most comprehensive assessments of U. S. housing. Many of the preceding comments were extracted from them.

# SECTION B

## INTERDISCIPLINARY RESEARCH TOPICS IN URBAN HOUSING

1. An Information System for Improved Planning, Analysis and Evaluation in Urban Housing Development

2. The Development of New Housing: Single and Multifamily Dwelling Units

3. The Industrialization of Urban Housing

4. The Rehabilitation of Urban Housing

# 1. AN INFORMATION SYSTEM FOR IMPROVED PLANNING, ANALYSIS AND EVALUATION IN URBAN HOUSING DEVELOPMENT

## THE PROBLEM

In developing adequate housing for the Nation, a city, or a particular neighborhood, it is imperative that sufficient information be available for accurate demand forecasting and realistic evaluation of alternatives. Furthermore, new and more comprehensive techniques must be developed for reliably selecting among site, design, and program alternatives. Particularly in the case of subsidized and high-density developments, location and design must permit the maximum satisfaction to both user and community needs; design, construction methods, and materials should be the most appropriate for a given housing objective; and there must be an adequate assessment of total costs and benefits involved in meeting that objective.

Questions dealing with the factors influencing residence choice, the elements which constitute successful housing concepts, and the various types of services derived from housing are not fully answered. Recording systems are needed such that statistical data and quantitative and qualitative measures can be established on the characteristics of each project, the topologies of building types and of land development, the materials used, their method of production, and their incorporation into finished buildings. Other recording systems should provide comprehensive cost breakdowns, including building time and forecasts for length-of-life and maintenance costs. It should ultimately be possible to develop relationships between kinds of technical innovations and their success in impróving quality, reducing time of production, or reducing real costs (ref. 31). There is also a need to systematically record the social characteristics of new-housing users, their former living conditions, and their reactions to new housing environments. The need for such information is shared equally by metropolitan planners and national policymakers.

Because housing is very much a part of the complete urban system, it is appropriate to integrate housing information requirements with those of the total metropolitan planning function. On the municipal level, on-going planning programs are conducted under Section 701 of the Housing Act (ref. 47). A versatile municipal data collection and processing "package", providing demographic, economic, and community information, would be invaluable in assisting local governments with their long-term planning activities and would provide a standardized data base for interurban analysis and comparison. This might in turn lend order and consistency to the profusion of data presently being collected by various agencies which is relevant to urban housing development (ref. 7, 11).

STATE-OF-THE-ART

The TEMPO studies conducted for the President's Committee on Urban Housing illustrate types of data and evaluation techniques presently being employed to assess housing needs (ref. 75), while

accompanying studies represent sophisticated analyses of housing costs,

production efficiency, finance, manpower and land constraints. A great

deal has been written on the types of data needed in housing development

and urban planning (ref. 31, 45), and numerous authors have discussed

the importance of accurately determining user needs (ref. 3, 80).

Practically every major urban area maintains an active urban

planning program and an associated information system (ref. 64). The

Department of Housing and Urban Development (HUD) has published an

extensive document on the subject, including specific hardware and

software considerations (ref. 35). A detailed discussion of state-of-

the-art in automatic municipal data systems can be found in (ref. 1),

and the Council of Planning Librarians has published extensive bibliog-

raphies pertinent to municipal data processing systems (ref. 16, 18).

A certain study prepared for HUD defines in significant detail the types

of information, study techniques, and analytical methodologies specific

to urban housing (ref. 31).

Work has also been done in attempting to devise models of urban

development (ref. 44), but there is little evidence of modeling techniques

being successfully applied to the housing process in particular.

## PARTICIPATING PERSONNEL AND ORGANIZATIONS

Information is presently available in one form or another on

numerous aspects of housing. Several agencies of the Federal

Government are conducting on-going statistical programs related to the metropolitan environment in general and housing in particular. The Bureau of the Census is the most prolific source of demographic data (ref. 8, 10, 11). It also conducted the comprehensive Census of Housing: 1960 and compiles certain construction data (ref. 9). The Bureau of Labor Statistics collects data on urban employment and earnings (ref. 12) and provides statistics on housing rents to be used in the Consumer Price Index.

Of course, HUD publishes information on all aspects of housing (ref. 7) including: sales (ref. 26), social characteristics of residents (ref. 34), and financing (ref. 23). HUD is also extremely concerned with new concepts in housing and/or municipal information systems, particularly within the Office of the Assistant Secretary for Metropolitan Development.

The Urban Institute is seeking broad competence in evaluating urban action programs and is therefore quite interested in improved analytical techniques and concepts. Other data sources include professional associations such as the American Institute of Architecture and the National Association of Home Builders. Municipal governments should be able to provide information specific to their requirements and can demonstrate various data treatment techniques.

Data requirements can be ascertained from almost as many sources as there are users. Contact (pos. C) in HUD and (pos. N, O, P) at the

Urban Institute contributed some of the suggestions in the following section.

## CONTRIBUTING PROBLEM AREAS

Several of the items below suggest systems design projects involving large-scale information processing requirements. In addition, specific areas have been outlined in which existing data is insufficient, unreliable, or nonexistent. The development of effective statistical indicators to provide such critical information and workable programs for their collection is prerequisite to the creation of an operating data system.

### Development of a Complete Community Information Handling Package

A complete community information facility must have the capacity for obtaining and treating at least the following types of information:

(a) Physical Development: specifically, buildings in place by age, condition, type of structure, and usage; public and private supporting facilities such as roads, streets, highways, power-lines, sewers, water, etc.; open land use such as parks and recreation, agriculture, etc.; emphasis on permanent aspects of land use.

(b) Public Services: administrative data includes location of licenses issued, code enforcement proceedings, and other administrative actions that are specifically desirable and locatable; data involving persons and property include location of welfare cases, reportable health incidents, fires, crimes, and the identity of those involved in criminal incidents, births and deaths by place of residence.

(c) <u>Community Information</u>: population data include location by family, size, income, and social status, together with the location of special subgroups of the population, including children by age groups and school eligibility, the aged, the infirm, the chronically ill, and a number of other categories depending on the objectives of social programs currently in operation (ref. 35).

## Development of a Complete Information System to Aid Housing Development

The creation of an information system about housing users, their physical, social and psychological needs, their relationship to the housing process, and changes in these variables. Indications of positive or negative effects (social costs and benefits) of housing development should then be possible from a data base which includes:

(a) <u>Characteristics of the Resident</u>: demographic description of potential users, including ethnic groups, family size and structure, socio-economic status, sexes, ages, frequency of movement from one locality to another.

(b) <u>Characteristics of Housing Sites</u>: data on the availability and relationship of support services in the neighborhood, land use patterns, land prices, and trends.

(c) <u>Characteristics of Neighborhoods</u>: social interaction patterns, crime rates, and community cohesion. Similar data from neighborhoods vacated by users.

(d) <u>Characteristics of Existing Structures</u>: general housing type, design characteristics, and condition (code violations, state of deterioration, age, etc.).

(e) <u>Tenant-Management Relationships</u>: data on the rate of home ownership, rent and lease agreements, and maintenance responsibility.

(f) <u>Codes, Standards and Building Restrictions</u>: a compilation and priority-ordering of all legal restrictions in home construction, with enforcing agency and date. Community-wide adherence to such standards and code violations should be recorded.

## Improved Techniques for Analysis and Evaluation

With the aid of a sound data base, certain questions might be answered and evaluative methods improved:

(a) Determine the factors which influence people's choice of housing; predict what will best satisfy individual needs; and determine the key ingredients in successful housing designs and projects.

(b) Establish standards which assure that housing satisfies user needs but which are minimally restrictive; develop a "figure of merit" or indicator for evaluating the success of housing in satisfying those needs.

(c) Aggregate the complete monetary costs of housing; and determine the total social costs and benefits of housing alternatives.

(d) Determine how fixed utilities limit the flexibility of land use.

## Development of Innovative Techniques for Gathering and Processing Information Without Impinging on User Privacy

Information should be available at minimal cost and should require little active participation by the subject in supplying important data.

## 2. THE DEVELOPMENT OF NEW HOUSING: SINGLE AND MULTI-FAMILY DWELLING UNITS

## THE PROBLEM

Based upon extrapolations of the U. S. 1960 Census records, which provide the most recent comprehensive source of data on population, housing, and households (ref. 9, 10), the Department of Housing and Urban Development (HUD) has projected a national demand for at least 26 million housing units over the next decade. The housing construction industry has maintained an average output of 1.5 million units or less during the five years preceding 1969, with a less-than-adequate effort in meeting the low-cost housing need of low-income families (ref. 74). The problem, then, is to provide adequate, livable, and affordable housing for all families (ref. 47) -- especially those in the lower-income population groups (ref. 37) -- when volume production and effective performance by the construction industry itself are inhibited by a multitude of constraints (ref. 31, vol. II). Regardless of how efficiently the Nation conserves its existing stock of housing -- and it is not doing well at present -- a significant number of new dwellings must be supplied to meet its housing needs in the next decade.

The construction industry admittedly suffers from a variety of internal problems, including low working capital, antiquated management procedures (ref. 41, 73, 91), and intense competition among the different contracting firms. Topic 3 in this Section, "The

Industrialization of Urban Housing", will treat the homebuilding process and industry in greater detail.

Along with certain vagaries within the housing construction process, outdated zoning regulations and building codes have increased housing costs in an inflationary economy by placing dampers on innovative developments in structures and materials and on the uses of new building techniques by the construction industry. Prefabrication technology on a large scale has been particularly inhibited. Past inefficiencies and mismanagement of some Public Housing agencies have also added to the housing crisis by undercutting public confidence in the benefits promised by new low-cost housing projects. A general lack of knowledge about home users needs, especially among low-income groups, frequently renders certain urban housing developments ineffective and undesirable long before ground is ever broken for construction (ref. 31, vol. I; 3, 34).

If rapidly growing urban populations are to be adequately housed, in an environment that is both attractive and conducive to social and psychological well-being, new concepts in housing and community development are necessary. If potential residents are to be offered a reasonable choice as to how and where they will live, dwelling units must be made available in varying price ranges, in city centers and on urban fringes, in different mixes, and with full access to essential community services.

In particular, land acquisition in many urban areas is becoming prohibitively expensive to permit open space to remain unutilized or even developed with single-level construction. New high-density, multifamily developments are the only means of accommodating more people on less land. To prevent intolerable overcrowding of such multifamily dwelling complexes and gross overutilization of supporting facilities and service areas, careful planning and new approaches to high-density urban living are required.

This topic area is concerned primarily with the supply of new housing. Both single-family and multifamily dwellings are needed in the urban area; neither are currently being supplied economically or in sufficient quantity (ref. 67). Specific considerations related to the development of new housing are presented in Contributing Problem Areas. An appropriate interdisciplinary systems approach in this instance would be to ascertain the new housing needs for a given urban area, within a particular time frame, and to design a housing system which effectively meets these needs.

## STATE-OF-THE-ART

In new housing construction, the most recent building innovations have typically been those which are easily integrated with existing residential concepts and which take advantage of well-developed construction techniques (ref. 50, 70). Design flexibility has commonly been achieved through use of sub-core and service-wall approaches, the application of a prefabricated module technology, and high-rise developments employing successful European panel systems for large volume housing production. The state-of-the-art in building materials has advanced to include possible applications of plastics and fiberglass, the development of new on-site construction machinery, and revolutionary housing concepts such as a "stacked sack" system or the Dymaxion home and geodesic dome, both conceived by architect Buckminster Fuller (ref. 40). Unfortunately, however, no generally accepted methodology exists in the United States whereby innovations in housing technology can be routinely collected, certified, and made generally available to industry (ref. 31, vol. III, p. II-3). Foreign industry possesses a large body of tested technological data, some of which is applicable to U. S. housing needs and the construction industry. Innovations in building systems and materials are discussed more fully in Topic 3.

Whereas technological advancement does not necessarily reduce the price of new housing, cost reduction can readily be brought about by using less land, providing less floor space, cutting back on appliances, insulation, and other household items, and easing construction standards. The contributions of limited land availability and overly-restrictive building codes to the overall housing problem have been presented in sufficient detail in this topic area and in Section A. Cutting back on various household items or reducing floor space are design considerations which have been employed time and again in urban developments to reduce housing construction costs. The multifamily high-rise, which is based upon the partially successful population compaction technique of building vertically, is perhaps the single concept which combines high-density use of available land with reasonable housing services. Evolutionary concepts in urban residences are also beginning to employ the joint development of land, whereby housing can be less densely spaced, but simultaneously integrated with other community facilities that were formerly set apart. The most prominent effort in this area has been outlined in "Joint Development of Transportation Rights-of-Way", Topic 9 in Chapter III.

Clearly the most ambitious and comprehensive ventures in new housing construction have occurred in the development of new towns, wherein entire communities are conceived and built in a total planning process which considers all the interrelated aspects of transportation, housing, and the environment (ref. 68). Reston, Virginia, and Columbia, Maryland, are the two most prominent examples, both being supported by coordinated, public and private efforts (ref. 33).

The following paragraphs describe some of the major Federal Programs and projects concerned directly with new housing. Most of these efforts are being conducted principally by the Department of Housing and Urban Development (HUD).

## The "In-Cities" Project

In a series of published reports dated March 1969, HUD's
Office of Urban Technology and Research, within  the Office of the
Assistant Secretary for Research and Technology, released a
detailed presentation of information on the constraints which have
inhibited the introduction of innovations in the Nation's housing
production effort for low-income families.  This four-volume
series, entitled the In-Cities Experimental Housing Research and
Development Project, represents the completion of Phase I of a
two-phase HUD project and presents detailed facts on home user
needs, housing unit production constraints, building technologies,
and a study of eighty cities to determine their potential for use in
specific low-cost housing sub-experiments (ref. 31), (pos. C).
Phase I is intended to establish a conceptual framework for this
experimental housing project; Phase II, which is now in progress,
with contractual agreements established, calls for the actual
development of In-Cities demonstration projects.  Building Systems
Development, Abt Associates with Daniel, Mann, Johnson, and
Mendenhall, and the Westinghouse Electric Corporation have been
the contractors for Phase I.  In connection with Phase II, Kaiser
Engineers have prepared a collateral literature survey entitled
Information on and Evaluations of Innovations in Housing Design and
Construction Techniques as Applied to Low-Cost Housing (ref. 54).

It was completed in order to:

a. Determine the availability and quality of published materials concerned with cost-reducing innovations in the production of housing.

b. Examine its suitability for use as a control in the low-income housing subexperiments.

The reports of the "In-Cities" program provide the most current and comprehensive report on the state of existing housing design, technology, constraints, and alternatives for channeling future housing production efforts. (Also, see Appendix A)

"Operation Breakthrough"

HUD's most recent approach to spur volume housing production is embodied in the form of a program entitled "Operation Breakthrough" (ref. 27), developed and administered principally by the Office of the Assistant Secretary of Research and Technology (pos. A). The program's two major objectives are:

a. To determine the aggregate demand and need for housing and to identify the land available for such housing.

b. To stimulate the design, testing, evaluation, and prototype construction of innovative concepts by the housing industry and other elements of the private sector.

The first goal, market aggregation, will be achieved through joint efforts of Federal, State, and local governments. In June of 1969, the second goal was initialized in the form of a Request for Proposals (ref. 32) issued to firms and individuals interested in housing and building systems concepts which promise to supply eonomical housing in large volumes.

-143-

## Experimental Housing Projects

Of particular interest to HUD have been a variety of experimental housing projects, under the control of the Federal Housing Administration, to produce high quality, low-cost homes (ref. 29 ). Listed below are such projects with related references:

(a)    Ashburn, Georgia, and Parsons, Kansas, projects --
       mobile homes fixed on piers (ref. 36 ).

(b)    West Hollywood, Florida, project -- construction of very-
       low-price quonset huts on a Seminole Indian reservation.

(c)    Austin Oaks, Texas, project -- ten builders were contracted
       to construct separate low-income, single-family housing
       units in the price range of five to seven thousand dollars.
       The homes were completed in December 1968 (ref. 21 ).
       A report is expected in March 1970, by the University of
       Texas, which will evaluate the home dwellers' reactions
       to the project.

(d)    Fredella Village, Vicksburg, Mississippi -- 28 two-story,
       low-cost multi-family town houses; modularly constructed
       employing industrialized techniques (ref. 24 ).

These projects constitute a series of experiments in low-cost housing ($4, 000 to $7, 000, including land and financing) -- a range which conventional construction methods can't reach employing the best of existing industrialized production techniques.  HUD's basic aim in these projects is to investigate new materials and building techniques and to assess the cost reductions possible through relaxed construction codes and existing FHA standards (ref. 31, vol. I, p. VI-12 ).  The Architectural Division, within the office of the Assistant Secretary for Mortgage Credit and Federal Housing

Commissioner, has been involved in soliciting and coordinating many of these experiments (pos. I, J).

An extensive listing of completed and current experimental housing projects for both single and multi-family purposes is contained in (ref. 29).

## Federally-Sponsored Housing Corporations

In June of 1969, a Federally-sponsored national corporation to mobilize the private sector in low-income housing construction took shape with the establishment of the National Corporation for Housing Partnerships, under the direction of chairman Carter L. Burgess and president Ray A. Watt. With the underwriting of $50 million in stocks as the initial equity, approximately $2 billion in financing will be energized for the construction of low and moderate-income housing units. It is estimated that most of this will be applied toward achieving the Government's official goal of 600,000 Federally-subsidized housing units per year for the next decade.

## Technical Studies

HUD, through the restructured Federal Housing Adminstration (FHA), conducts much of its technological research within the Technical Studies Program by contracting with other government agencies, educational institutions, and research organizations to study the technical problems encountered in construction, design, and materials (pos. I, J). FHA's Experimental Housing Program stimulates the utilization and testing of advanced technology in housing by underwriting mortgages to housing projects involving related experimentation. In (ref. 29), there is a list of the completed and current projects in both programs. It is published periodically to advise research organizations, industry, and others of FHA's needs and interests.

## PARTICIPATING PERSONNEL AND ORGANIZATIONS

Many of the principal offices in the Federal Government involved with new housing have been noted in the preceding discussion of State-of-the-Art. Fortunately, the bulk of the Federal activity in urban housing is now concentrated within HUD. The Office of the Assistant Secretary for Research and Technology (pos. A, B) is perhaps most concerned with new concepts in materials and building technology (pos. C), supporting utilities and services (pos. E, F), and low-income housing (pos. D) -- as best witnessed by its definitive role in "Operation Breakthrough" and the "In-Cities" Program.

The Office of the Assistant Secretary for Mortgage Credit and Federal Housing Commissioner, emcompassing the former FHA, shares many of the interests of the Research and Technology Office (pos. H), but emphasizes the financial aspect in stimulating new housing developments. Considerable interest in new housing concepts exists within the Office of the Assistant Commissioner for Technical Standards, and its Architectural Division (pos. I, J) vigorously encourages and evaluates single family (pos. K) and multifamily (pos. L) demonstrations.

## CONTRIBUTING PROBLEM AREAS

An important consideration to keep in mind at all times is the necessary distinction between housing developments of single-family units and multifamily units and community development projects combining the two. Conceptually, new designs, materials, and construction techniques are needed for both new housing types. In realistic housing programs, an appropriate mix of both types, at all price levels, must be achieved. Lower cost and greater quantity - with upgraded quality - are the current watchwords. To realize these objectives requires that the constraints imposed by the following aspects of the housing problem be reduced or eliminated:

- land acquisition (ref. 67c, 67g, 67m, 67r)
- building codes (ref. 67, 67g, 67o, 67c)
- building materials (ref. 61)
- labor (ref. 61, 74, 91)
- management (ref. 41, 72, 91)
- public agencies
- local housing administrators
- supportive systems
- capital investment (ref. 67, 74)
- housing mortgage (ref. 67, 74)
- market fragmentation (ref. 67)
- housing development promotion
- seasonality of construction (ref. 91)
- public opinion (ref. 42, 67i)
- site location (ref. 56, 67e, 67l)

### New Low-Cost Housing

Design of low-cost housing units within a specified price range (ref. 26, 31):

(a) Exploit construction techniques and financing mechanisms used by mobile home manufacturers.

(b) Employ prefabrication concepts and design structurally independent core units for the building's supportive services.

(c) Test new materials for construction and fabrication purposes (ref. 79).

(d) Develop floor plan designs which maximize available space and speed-up housing unit assembly.

(e) Utilize "self-help" building techniques to reduce cost (ref. 62, 79, 84).

(f) Develop complete dwelling construction techniques using evolutionary subsystem housing components.

Evolutionary Design Concepts:

The incorporation of evolutionary concepts into new, low-cost housing units that do more than meet the basic needs of shelter, security, and safety (ref. 40, 70):

(a) Develop techniques for providing flexible, adjustable internal space within housing units; provide housing units which can grow along with increases in family size.

(b) Design minimal, initial housing units that can be easily upgraded as family income and aspirational levels increase; possible accessories would include: additional space, added facilities, and more furnishings.

(c) Explore the concept of inexpensive, short-term housing which could be replaced periodically with new models, large units, or more attractive designs; planned obsolescence, in the best traditions of Detroit.

(d) Develop housing concepts which provide high-density uses of urban land while allowing a maximum of individuality to the residential units -- for instance, an illusion of single-family living in multi-family projects.

## Supportive Systems and Services

Advances are required in the types of services afforded residents by new housing and in the manner in which these services are provided. Some of the more important services include:

- utilities - electricity, gas, water, sewage disposal
- solid waste collection and disposal
- adequate transportation
- recreational facilities
- community gathering areas
- privacy

(a) To develop methods whereby such services can be made available when not directly provided by the housing development itself.

(b) To ensure that residents are afforded equal access to such services; this enters directly into the planning function (ref. 56).

(c) To develop housing concepts in which many of these services are self-contained subsystems.

(d) To develop and evaluate multifamily, high-density projects which are self-sufficient; an internal community containing all necessary services for resident health and well-being.

## Industrial Construction

The design of on-site and portable factories and a determination of the innovative opportunities they would afford in new housing construction. Industrialization is treated more fully in the following Topic 3.

## Building Codes and Standards

Significant economics in construction could be achieved by modernizing and systemizing the myriads of building codes and standards existing throughout the Nation, including:

- building laws, regulations, and standards
- building ordinances
- state building codes
- building construction -- contracts and specifications
- building inspections
- building materials -- standards and specifications
- fire proofing and prevention
- heating requirements
- plumbing codes
- zoning legislation

In addition, unduly restrictive codes inhibit large-volume production for different areas and the use of truly evolutionary concepts, designs, and compounds. An extended analysis of all aspects of building codes is needed to determine (i) regulations which are outdated; (ii) regulations in need of modification; and (iii) a means of rapidly updating building codes to reflect and stimulate technological advances.

## Joint Development of Housing and Other Facilities

Joint land development proposals for housing communities and other non-residential urban facilities. Possible joint development projects include housing developments with:

- urban transportation systems (See Chapter III, Topic 9)
- major activity centers, such as shopping areas, parks, and recreational facilities
- necessary community service centers such as hospitals, fire departments, police stations, sanitation plants, schools, etc.

## 3. THE INDUSTRIALIZATION OF URBAN HOUSING

## THE PROBLEM

As stated in Section A of this chapter, the President's Committee on Urban Housing recommended that the Nation commit itself to producing 26 million new and rehabilitated housing units by 1978 (ref. 74). The dissection of this figure is roughly as follows:

    (a)  13.4 million housing units to satisfy the demand created by the formation of new households.

    (b)  The replacement of 3 million standard housing units that will be accidentally destroyed or purposefully demolished.

    (c)  1.6 million housing units to allow for enough vacancies for our increasingly mobile population.

    (d)  Replacement and rehabilitation of 8 million substandard housing units.

It should also be recalled that 6 to 8 million Federally subsidized dwellings were asked for in this recommendation. It should be further emphasized that this proposed national goal represents nearly a 40% increase in the current housing stock, better than a 10% increase in total housing production for the 20 years from 1940 to 1960, and 70% more than the total production for the decade of the 1950's.

To meet this recommended national housing goal, the housing industry must produce more than 2 million conventionally-financed housing units plus 0.6 million Federally subsidized units annually. But, in the last few years, the housing production rate has only been about 1.5 million starts per year, with current rates significantly lower due to tight money and high interest rates. It would, therefore, seem that the solution to the Nation's housing problem is to simply increase the housing production rate. But, because of the present structure of the construction and home building industries, this cannot easily be accomplished.

Past studies have confirmed that the construction and home building industries are highly fractionated and highly localized (ref. 74, p. 10). They are subject to constraints and vagaries of local markets, widely varying local building codes and zoning ordinances, and finally, are subject to local labor unions and labor practices. This fact can best be illustrated by noting that the largest on-site home builder produces less than 1% of the Nation's annual new housing starts. Also, the 50 largest producers of all types of housing (single and multi-family, site erected or factory built, including mobile homes) together account for less than 15% of the Nation's annual housing production.

It is also interesting to note that there are not only a large number of firms engaged in contract construction, but that most of these firms are very small and maintain less than ten employees. For example, in 1966, there were 322,781 firms with one or more employees engaged in contract construction; 54% of that total had one to three employees, and 10% had twenty or more employees. A 1964 survey by the National Association of Home Builders, which claims that its membership produces 75% of all single-family houses and 65% of all new housing, indicates that the vast majority of its member builders maintain relatively small operations, with an average production of 49 single-family units per year. About 27% of the membership constructed 11 to 25 units per year, both single and multi-family, while another 37% produced less than 10 units annually (ref. 67).

But despite the fact that the housing industry is a loose conglomeration of small participants who come together on a project-by-project basis, housing is considered the most important consumer good in the economy. In fact, Americans spend over $100 billion annually to buy, rent, operate, maintain, and furnish their places of residence. Most money spent in this sector of the economy goes to pay for the use of existing housing, but roughly 10% of the Gross National Product each year is devoted to new construction of all kinds, with residential buildings requiring about one-third of this amount.

The problem therefore seems to reduce to finding a way to use a large, but very fractionated and highly localized, industry to produce 26 million new or rehabilitated housing units before 1978, keeping in mind that all types of housing are needed: single-family detached, row, garden, low-rise, medium-rise, and high-rise. In addition to supplying these physical needs, housing manufacturers must consider such factors as climate, building sites, tradition, user preferences, building materials and available financing. Considerable flexibility and adaptability in housing are needed, but this does not preclude promoting a considerable degree of industrialization, standardization, and development of integrated systems (ref. 31, p. III-2). It is therefore hoped that some new industrialization concept could be found that involves a kind of superposition of mass production techniques over the existing construction industry, in such a manner that the advantages of mass production could be realized and existing talents applied without causing undue reorientation during the introduction process.

## STATE-OF-THE-ART

As indicated above, finding ways to increase the housing construction rate sufficiently to meet the future housing needs is a large enough problem in itself. But, to maintain the variety and quality necessary to make it acceptable to the public, while increasing the production rate, adds another dimension of complexity. There are currently about 85 companies experimenting in the building systems field in this country. Most of these companies are listed in the In-Cities Experimental Housing Research and Development Project, Volume III sponsored by the Department of Housing and Urban Development (HUD), (see Appendix A). The following outline of the state-of-the-art in industrialized housing is a condensation of a section of that volume. If further information is needed on any industrialized housing system outlined below, the appropriate manufacturer listed in Appendix A should be consulted.

The building systems described below are divided into two major groups: Prefabricated systems and in-place fabricated systems. In the first case, fabrication of building components takes place away from the final location of the components in the building, either elsewhere on the site or completely off-site in a factory. In the second case, fabrication of components occurs in-place in the building.

Prefabricated Systems

The major purpose of prefabrication is to reduce on-site construction time and, therefore, the cost of the structure. Also, by moving many of the construction steps to the factory, economies arise through better organization of work, improved materials handling, increased quality control, better working conditions, and cheaper labor. But, it is important to note that these savings are usually reduced by the cost of transportation, capital investment write-off, and the need for mechanical equipment for on-site assembly.

Prefabricated building systems can be divided into three major sections:

(a) Off-Site Prefabrication and Assembly. Since factory fabrication is generally cheaper than on-site fabrication, it is desirable to do as much factory fabrication and assembly of whole dwellings, the prime example of which is the mobile home construction process. The trend today is to use mobile homes in clusters and stacks to form

multi-family and single-family dwellings. Some of the

high-rise schemes require steel or concrete framing to

support the mobile homes components (ref. 2, 14, 69, 70).

One of the problems with mobile homes is that their linear

nature tends to create aesthetic and planning problems.

Units wider than 12 feet are expensive and difficult to

transport; therefore, by using smaller and shorter units,

or housing "segments", one can assemble a dwelling in a

variety of arrangements and still avoid the mobile home

tunnel effect. Segmented housing concepts have been con-

ceptualized in metal (ref. 14, 69, 71), wood (ref. 53, 71),

concrete (ref. 14, 19, 50, 73), and plastic (ref. 14, 19,

55). Another attempt to deviate from the linear nature of

mobile homes has been in the area of "expandable" units.

In this case, manufacturers offer units with wings which

are folded against a utility core during transport and are

unfolded on-site to provide additional floor area (ref. 2,

14, 69).

(b) Off-Site Prefabrication, On-Site Assembly. The on-site

savings in this form of prefabrication are not as great as

in off-site prefabrication and assembly because jointing

and finishing must be done in the field. However, the

parts are smaller and therefore easier to transport, resulting in a reduction in transportation costs. There are two general categories of off-site prefabrication, on-site assembly: bearing panel systems (ref. 55, 83, 87) and structural frame systems (ref. 73, 83, 87).

(c) <u>On-Site Prefabrication and Assembly</u>. As with the other prefabrication techniques, the purpose of this technique is to reduce on-site construction time, but the system goes one step farther by trying to eliminate the transportation restrictions. The fabrication of components, in this case, takes place on the building site but away from the final position of the component in the building. The unique disadvantage of this fabrication technique is that additional space must be available on the site for the prefabrication facilities. The systems currently being studied vary from on-site concrete molding to mobile prefabrication plants that are transported to the construction site and finally to generated plastic domes used to build detached, single-family dwellings.

<u>In-Place Fabricated Systems</u>

This method of construction is characterized by the fabrication of components in-place in the building. As with the prefabrication techniques, the purpose of innovations in this fabrication category is to reduce on-site construction time. But compared with prefabrication, in-place fabrication innovations, in most cases, reduce jointing problems and the project size needed to accommodate special equipment, eliminate restrictions imposed by transportation, and eliminate the need for space on-site for fabrication facilities. However, the main disadvantage is that high-cost skilled labor is needed.

Conventional construction today is in-place fabricated; there are, however, a number of innovations in this category which seem to offer potential savings in time and/or labor. Some of these current innovations include: in-place poured concrete bearing walls utilizing reusable forms; reinforced concrete dome structures fabricated with inflatable "balloon-forms"; reinforced concrete bearing walls constructed by wetting down steel reinforced "stacked sacks" of dry cement and aggregate; foamed in-place epoxy resin wall construction; and wall construction using metal lath and sprayed concrete. (See Appendix A for the list of manufacturers experimenting with these construction methods.)

## PARTICIPATING PERSONNEL AND ORGANIZATION

Although there is very little money available in the construction and homebuilding industries for research and development activities, some of the larger firms are intimately involved with innovations that have come about through Government-sponsored research. Therefore, some of the larger firms in the area of a housing systems study should be consulted.

In the Federal Government, the Department of Housing and Urban Development (HUD) is the agency most concerned with the industrialization of urban housing, with its Office of the Assistant Secretary for Research and Technology (pos. A) dealing specifically with new housing innovations. Under the latter, the Office of Building Technology (pos. C) and the Office for Research Planning and Coordination (pos. B) deserve additional emphasis.

Two other agencies in HUD are particularly involved in new housing innovations: namely, the Office of the Assistant Commissioner for Programs (pos. H) under the Assistant Secretary for Mortgage Credit and Federal Housing Commissioner, and the Architectural Division (pos. I) of the Office of the Assistant Commissioner for Technical Standards.

Other private organizations in the Washington, D. C., area that warrant consideration in the field of industrialized housing are the Urban Institute (pos. N) and the National Association of Homebuilders.

## CONTRIBUTING PROBLEM AREAS*

A building system may be defined as a set of interrelated building components and subsystems which are assembled according to a

---

* See Appendix A for the list of manufacturers involved with the innovations suggested in this section.

predetermined plan or procedure. Therefore, innovations in any of these subsystems or components would make a significant contribution to the industrialization of housing systems. The study areas listed below are not meant to be all-inclusive, but are areas that have been given considerable attention in the past few years and still require further innovation. A list of Federally-sponsored engineering studies related to building and heavy construction may also provide a nucleating point for additional, contributing study topics (ref. 5).

## Housing Subsystems and Components

The housing industry has long recognized how the time and cost of overall construction has been influenced by the special requirements of such subsystems as utility rooms, kitchens, bathrooms, heating, ventilating and cooling systems, electrical systems, and plumbing components. Any further innovations which reduce the cost and time associated with the installation of these subsystems can make a significant contribution to the industrialization of housing.

Current new concepts for utility rooms, kitchens, and bathrooms have been in the area of service walls, cores, and split cores. The service wall concept utilizes a factory-preassembled wall that contains plumbing trees, flues, and electrical services to which fixtures and appliances of the bathroom, kitchen, and utility areas are field-connected.

The core concept involves a single unit that is preassembled using factory methods, transported to the building site, and set into the dwelling at an appropriate time during construction as one package. The core contains all "utilities" functions (toilet-bath, kitchen, hot water, heating, and electrical distribution center), as well as the supporting structure. On the other hand, the split core concept divides the single core into separate functional units such as kitchen, bath, and utility cores, or some limited combination of such units like a joint bath-utility core.

Innovations in all types of heating-ventilating-cooling systems are needed to reduce cost and installation times.

Housing electrical system innovations are also needed. Several current developments that show promise are: ground fault circuit interrupts, surface mounted plastic strips with metallic conductors suitable for installation of snap-in-place receptacles, development of highly conductive elastomers to replace metallic electrical conductors, and baseboard electrical heaters with integral wireway assemblies.

The plumbing components of a single-family dwelling unit typically represent several hundred dollars of the initial material cost. Therefore, innovations in plumbing are critical to the construction of low-cost housing. Current technological trends are in the development of plastic pipes, bathroom components, and kitchen items. Plumbing trees, residential sewage collection and/or treatment systems, and high pressure water systems are also being studied.

## Building Materials

Although the construction and homebuilding industries have been experimenting with different building materials for many years, further investigations are certainly warranted. Such materials as cellular concrete and spray-on, moldable, and vacuum-formed plastic definitely deserve study.

## Market Aggregation

One of the major deterrents to the evolution of a sophisticated, residential, mass-production industry is the lack of assurance to the entrepreneur that he can claim a sufficiently large segment of the existing market to profitably amortize his initial capital investment in plant and equipment. Therefore, some new ways to aggregate the housing market and encourage the investment of private industry is a critical current need.

"Operation Breakthrough" is the most recent attempt by HUD to entice private industry into developing new housing concepts and to support such activity with a Federally-directed program of market aggregation (ref. 27).

## Housing Construction Management

Since the building industry is the most fragmented of the major industrial complexes in the country today, innovations in the management of existing building techniques could provide significant cost reductions. The application of certain industrial engineering techniques should be adopted, especially those applicable to procurement of materials and scheduling of process elements and labor.

## 4. THE REHABILITATION OF URBAN HOUSING

### THE PROBLEM

In the previous topic area, "The Industrialization of Urban Housing",
the need for an increased housing construction rate was established.
But new construction alone will not solve the Nation's housing problems.
To adequately meet future housing needs, the existing housing inventory
must be conserved; otherwise, the net effect of new construction will be
dissipated by the need to replace existing housing.

Using 1960 U.S. Census data, TEMPO estimated that in 1968, there
were 6.7 million occupied substandard dwellings - 4 million lacking indoor plumbing and 2.7 million in dilapidated condition. TEMPO also
estimated that only about two million of the six million vacant units are
in standard condition and available for occupancy (ref. 74, p. 8).
Finally, TEMPO projected that without public action, there will still be
4.3 million occupied substandard units in 1978, half of which will be
located in metropolitan areas (ref. 74, p. 100).

Faced with these predictions and the need to conserve our existing
housing stock, a program for continued maintenance of existing standard
dwellings coupled with the selective replacement or rehabilitation of
substandard dwellings is called for. The synthesis of such a program
could be a challenging topic for an interdisciplinary system design team,
since housing conservation through maintenance and rehabilitation

requires dealing with all the physical, economic, social, and political elements that comprise such substandard neighborhoods.

There are many complex problems involved in making simple, physical modifications to a substandard dwelling, but these may be loosely grouped into two categories. The first involves the ulitization of the so-called "rehabilitation industry", which is presently dominated by small firms, often one-man operations, which tend to specialize in remodeling work. In fact, merchant builders and general contractors, responsible for most new residential construction, are scarcely involved in rehabilitation. A 1964 survey by the National Association of Home Builders showed that responding members earned only about 2% of their gross sales income through remodeling contracts. The large building firms (over 76 new residential units per year), according to a survey by Practical Builder magazine, accounted for 59% of all new residential units but only 3% of the roughly 500,000 remodeling projects. 83% of these remodeling projects were carried out by building firms either not engaged in new residential projects or firms building no more than ten new residential units per year (ref. 74, p. 108).

The second category of problems associated with the physical rehabilitation of substandard dwellings encompasses the difficulties involved in actually making the dwelling modifications. For example, rehabilitation work is usually more complicated and more time-consuming than new construction. The physical modifications rarely lend themselves to highly sophisticated management techniques. Few jobs can be planned in advance and, in fact, decisions on what should be done will often depend on what is discovered when the walls are stripped. This uncertainty inherent in rehabilitation work means that the supply of materials and labor is difficult to schedule. The construction operations are likely to be slow and painstaking because many of the materials have to be custom-cut to fit the existing structure. Finally, this varied and highly specialized work requires skilled supervisors and craftsmen.

The economic problems associated with residential rehabilitation will probably be more difficult to solve than those associated with the physical improvement of the dwelling. For economical rehabilitation, it is desirable to handle a number of units at the same time. More importantly, rehabilitation must be done on a neighborhood-wide basis in order to obtain favorable financing, because a neighborhood of run-down houses will adversely affect the appraisal on a single improved dwelling. Some of the current lending policies and procedures must also be modified in order to obtain the necessary financial backing. Lenders commonly take neighborhood stability into account when reviewing mortgage loan applications. Since slum areas are not noted for their stable property values, many lenders tend to "blacklist" or "red-line" blighted areas and refuse to make loans on properties located within them under any circumstances.

The cost involved in the rehabilitation of a deteriorated building is generally less expensive than new construction in most downtown areas, but it is not insignificant. Considerable historical data collected on the cost of rehabilitation shows that the net cost to repair a structure may vary by a factor of two or more depending on the type, location of the unit, and the builder. For example, in Columbus, Ohio, it was profitable and feasible to acquire, rehabilitate, and sell a 1,400-square foot, four bedroom house for $12,000; while in other areas, the selling price had to be as high as $18,000 for a 900-square foot dwelling unit in a walk-up, multi-family arrangement (ref. 74, 31).

The most difficult problems to solve in residential rehabilitation are likely to be the social problems. Accompanying the physical deterioration and obsolescence of the homes, community facilities, and street pattern are such discouraging elements as overcrowding, increasing crime, excessive immigration of lower-income families, systematic exploitation of tenants by absentee landlords, and finally, a social alienation, hopelessness, and hostility toward the outside world. Therefore, the improvement of the physical environment alone is not enough and, in fact, may be less important than related actions which seek out the roots of social alienation and economic deprivation through the stimulation of hope, pride, skills, and opportunity (ref. 59).

Therefore, the difficult mission that faces an interdisciplinary design team is to develop an urban renewal program that not only improves the physical appearance of a deteriorated neighborhood through enforced maintenance and rehabilitation, but also one that eliminates the social and economic problems that underlie that deterioration.

## STATE OF THE ART

Rehabilitation is needed in almost every city in the United States; but, as mentioned above, it is also the most difficult to industrialize because of the extreme variation in problems from city to city and from building to building. It ranges from completely gutting the interiors, which leaves only the outside walls standing, to simply cleaning up (ref. 60).

The current innovation trends in rehabilitation take the form of new solutions to specific problems rather than generalized technological approach. For example, Westinghouse devised a rehabilitation procedure for multistory, walk-up buildings commonly called "row houses" or "tenements." Typically, these tenements are constructed with common masonry load-bearing walls on the property line, and floors spanning from side to side. The front and rear walls are nonload-bearing facades and are usually brick. Westinghouse's procedure involves the horizontal rehabilitation and combining of several of these tenement structures into one multi-family building with a central inexpensive elevator (ref. 31, p. U-2).

The need for new housing subsystems and components -- such as utility rooms, kitchens, bathrooms, heating, ventilating and cooling systems, electrical systems, and plumbing components -- is common to practically all rehabilitation projects (ref. 77). Therefore, rehabilitation projects provide an excellent opportunity for the installation of preassembled service walls, cores, and split cores. In fact, most of the innovations in revolutionizing the housing rehabilitation industry have taken place in the design and installation of these subsystems and are outlined in State-of-the-Art of the previous topic description. The list of manufacturers of housing subsystems and components in Appendix A should also be consulted.

Current attempts to solve the economic problems associated with housing rehabilitation programs are Federal mortgage insurance, low-interest loan and subsidy programs, Urban Renewal "write-downs" and local tax reforms (ref. 78).

The Federal Government has a number of programs to help finance rehabilitation. One of the earliest was the FHA, Title I, Home Improvement Loan program. Under this program, FHA insures unsecured loans of up to $5,000 per dwelling unit to finance repairs and improvements to property. This short-term, unsecured loan program has been supplemented with a number of FHA mortgage insurance programs, such as Sections 203, 207, 213, 220, and 221 of the Housing and Urban Development Act (ref. 74, 15, 47), which can be used to finance rehabilitation. By using these programs a housing owner can generally finance both a pre-existing high-interest rate, short-term mortgage and obtain funds to pay for the cost of rehabilitation by obtaining a single mortgage at a lower interest rate and for a longer term. Those who want to buy properties and rehabilitate them can obtain financing for both acquisition costs and rehabilitation costs under one mortgage. The low down-payment and long-term features of these loan programs have assisted many middle-income families in rehabilitating existing units.

The Federal Government has recently begun to offer assistance to local building code enforcement efforts. Since 1965, the Urban Renewal Law (ref. 15) has authorized the Federal Government to pay up to three-quarters of a local government's net cost in carrying out a concentrated code enforcement campaign in a specific area. Rehabilitation grants of up to $3,000 are available to low-income families (Sec. 115) and Section 312 offers a 3% loan in such areas to help finance the cost of rehabilitation.

If rehabilitation efforts through code enforcement are intended to help provide a decent home for the poor, housing subsidies are essential. Residents of low-income neighborhoods often find themselves in the anomalous situation of resenting their housing conditions, but at the same time resisting code enforcement. They know they will be unable to live in a neighborhood which is "up to code" unless they receive subsidies. All major Federal subsidy programs -- Public Housing, Rent Supplements, Section 221 (d) (3), 235 Homeownerships, and Section 236 -- can be used for rehabilitation as well as for new construction. There are a few subsidy programs specifically intended for rehabilitation. The Section 115 rehabilitation grants, and the Section 312 low interest rehabilitation loan programs of the Housing and Urban Development Act (ref. 15, 47, 74) can help provide the subsidies needed for rehabilitation in certain urban areas.

An additional subsidy and rehabilitation incentive can be provided through Urban Renewal "write-downs." Local renewal agencies can acquire a property for resale to a private owner, subject to an obligation to rehabilitate. Because the obligation to rehabilitate deflates the market value of the property, the difference between acquisition cost and selling price is charged to the renewal agency budget as a project expenditure (ref. 74, p. 102).

Local tax policy can play a significant role in impeding the rehabilitation of slum neighborhoods. Property taxes account for a large portion of a family's monthly housing costs. In the cases used in a McGraw-Hill Study (ref. 74, p. 99), property taxes represented 26% of monthly shelter costs in moderately-priced, single-family housing and 14% in elevator apartment units. Therefore, landlords cannot and will not upgrade their property unless the renters in the market they are serving can afford the increased rent necessary to pay for the increased property taxes. To decrease the retarding effect of property taxes on rehabilitation, many communities have secured legal authority to forego increasing local property taxes for a specified period of time if the renovated property is leased to a low or moderate-income family. Communities are also initiating measures to deny tax deductions to a property owner for depreciation on his property in any year in which he is convicted of a housing code violation with respect to that property.

There are very few, if any, current approaches to solving the social problems inherent in the rehabilitation of urban housing. The present trend is to concentrate on the education, orientation, and training of the residents of a deteriorated community. Reducing the inconveniences and anxieties caused by relocation through better coordination of construction timetables and helping the displaced residents to find temporary housing are two steps in the right direction (Ref. 43). Training residents in the skills needed to participate in the actual rehabilitation of their homes is another possible approach to help them develop hope and pride in their new neighborhood.

## PARTICIPATING PERSONNEL AND ORGANIZATIONS

Within the Department of Housing and Urban Development, there are three offices that are specifically involved with rehabilitation of urban housing. The first is the Office of the Assistant Commissioner for Programs (pos. H). The second is the Architectural Division of the Office of Assistant Commissioner for Technical Standards (pos. I), which has a Rehabilitation Housing Design Section (pos. M). The final office with particular interest in rehabilitation is the Office of the Assistant Secretary for Research and Technology (pos. A, B, C).

## CONTRIBUTING PROBLEM AREAS

Any innovations in the manufacture of housing cores and subsystems would greatly improve residential rehabilitation efficiency. Further development of materials and products in the following areas of rehabilitation would also have potential for reducing both cost and time expended (Ref. 31):

- Materials to cover badly deteriorated wall surfaces.

- Wiring harnesses to facilitate rewiring of units without damaging existing structures.

- Plastic moldings or extrusions to cover old trim.

- Prefabricated units to house utilities.

- One-step operation involving installation of new plumbing and heating ducts which includes housing and possible decoration.

- An inexpensive method of leveling existing floors and providing an acceptable finished floor surface.

- A method of recovering chipped or slightly irregular surfaces so that the finished surface does not show the underlying irregularities.

- Use of factory fabricated components.

- Electronic stud finders and marking devices.

- Wire and/or pipe finders.

- Small, portable harness terminating machines.

- Nondestructive devices for testing wood soundness, plaster and mortar integrity, and pipe integrity.

- Unitary, forced warm air system as an integral part of a prefabricated core.

- PVC pipe to supply hot water to perimeter hydronic heating system.

- Self-contained electric-hydronic baseboard heating units where electric rates permit.

- Unitary hot water systems utilizing boilers that are packaged with circulating pumps and expansion tanks. These boilers can be gas or electric.

- Valance cooling that can be combined with baseboard hydronic heating.

- Heat pumps in areas where additional resistance heating is not required.

- High temperature fluid systems for district heat on large complexes.

- Total energy systems where air conditioning is required and gas rates are reasonable.

- Electric, radiant, ceiling panels for self-help programs.

- Prefab fiberglass ducts for self-help programs.

- Unitary forced warm air units within the occupied space.

- Inexpensive stair, escalator, and elevator systems.

- Development and utilization of new security systems.

- New vermin control and extermination techniques.

# SECTION C

## AGENCIES AND OFFICIALS CONCERNED
## WITH URBAN HOUSING

## 1. DEPARTMENT OF HOUSING AND URBAN DEVELOPMENT (HUD)

451 - 7th Street, S. W.
Washington, D. C. 20410
Tel. (202) 655-4000

This Department was established in 1965 to administer the Federal Government's principal programs providing assistance for housing and for the development of the Nation's urban areas. Broadly speaking, the department has four areas of interest:

a. Demonstration Programs and intergovernmental Relations - Housing research; urban studies; slum clearance; defense planning and emergency preparedness; natural disaster relief; market analyses and trends affecting housing and capital market mortgage; housing and building codes; zoning and tax standards; open-space and urban beautification.

b. Mortgage Credit and Federal Housing - Private loan and mortgage insurance for property improvement; home mortgage insurance (especially for veterans' housing and disaster housing); cooperative and condominium mortgage insurance; urban renewal; low-income housing; housing for the elderly; nursing homes; housing for the military; disposition and liquidation of government property.

c. Metropolitan Development - Urban planning and evaluation; academic facilities; school construction; public works; public land; public facilities; natural disaster engineering; sanitation; urban transportation.

d.  Renewal and Housing Assistance - Urban Renewal and redevelopment; neighborhood renewal and rehabilitation; community renewal and social planning; code enforcement; demolition projects; open-space land and beautification; historic structures; land marketing; codes and building standards; engineering aspects of clearance, zoning, and land usage; college housing; technical aspects of low-rent housing for the elderly and handicapped; loan contracts; housing maintenance; legal aspects of housing assistance; equal housing opportunities; intergroup relations; land acquisition and appraisal.

The Department maintains a general information center in Washington, D.C., which answers inquiries, makes referrals, and provides advisory and consulting services:

Department of Housing and Urban Development
Information Center
451 - 7th Street, S. W.
Room 1202
Washington, D. C.  20410
Tel.  (202) 755-6420

Certain offices within HUD are particularly concerned with the topics outlined in Section B and with related areas which may be of interest to interdisciplinary systems studies or to individual researchers.

OFFICE OF THE ASSISTANT SECRETARY FOR
RESEARCH AND TECHNOLOGY

(A)  Harold B. Finger - Assistant Secretary
Rm. 4102
(HUD address as above)
Tel.  (202) 755-5600

(B)*  Albert Weinstein - Assistant Director of
Research Planning and Coordination
Rm. 4102
(HUD address as above)
Tel.  (202) 755-5604

Note:  * Denote interviewees

-176-

(C)*      James R. Simpson - Director
        Office of Building Technology
        Rm. 4206
        (HUD address as above)
        Tel. (202) 755-5606

(D)*      James R. Simpson - Acting Director
        Low-Income Demonstration Project
        Rm. 4206
        (HUD address as above)
        Tel. (202) 755-5606

(E)      Alan R. Siegel - Director
        Utilities Technology
        Rm. 4204
        (HUD address as above)
        Tel. (202) 755-5610

(F)*      Arthur J. Ziezel
        Utilities Technology
        Rm. 4204
        (HUD address as above)
        Tel. (202) 755-5610
          (Urban hydrology and utility services)

## OFFICE OF THE ASSISTANT SECRETARY FOR MORTGAGE CREDIT AND FEDERAL HOUSING COMMISSIONER

### Office of the Assistant Commissioner for Programs

(G)      M. Carter McFarland - Assistant Commissioner
        Rm. 6128
        (HUD address as above)
        Tel. (202) 755-6497

(H)*      R. Harold Denton - Deputy Assistant Commissioner
        Rm. 6130
        (HUD address as above)
        Tel. (202) 755-6495

### Office of the Assistant Commissioner for Technical Standards

(I)*      S. Porter Driscoll - Director
        Architectural Division
        Rm. 5224
        (HUD address as above)
        Tel. (202) 755-6210

(J)* James McCullough - Deputy Director
     Architectural Division
     Rm. 5224
     (HUD address as above)
     Tel. (202) 755-6210

(K)* Duane E. Keplinger
     Architectural Division
     Single Family Housing Design Section
     Rm. 5220
     (HUD address as above)
     Tel. (202) 755-6207

(L) Orville G. Lee
     Architectural Division
     Multifamily Housing Design Section
     Rm. 5228
     (HUD address as above)
     Tel. (202) 755-6206

(M) Roswell H. Graves
     Architectural Division
     Rehabilitation Housing Design Section
     Rm. 5218
     (HUD address as above)
     Tel. (202) 755-6215

## HUD REGIONAL OFFICES

In addition to the central headquarters in Washington, D. C., the Department also maintains seven regional offices which will furnish information concerning HUD programs.

Region I    (Conn., Me., Mass., N.H., N.Y., R.I., Vt.)

          26 Federal Plaza
          New York, N.Y. 10007
          Tel. (202) 264-8068

Region II    (Del., D.C., Md., N.J., Pa., Va., W.Va.)

          Widener Building
          1339 Chestnut Street
          Philadelphia, Pa. 19107
          Tel. (215) 597-2560

Region III    (Ala., Fla., Ga., Ky., Miss., N.C., S.C., Tenn.)

      Peachtree - 7th Building
      Atlanta, Ga.  30323
      Tel.  (404) 562-5585

Region IV    (Ill., Ind., Iowa, Mich., Minn., Neb., N.D., Ohio,
     S.D., Wis.)

      360 North Michigan Ave.
      Chicago, Ill.  60601
      Tel.  (302) 353-5680

Region V    (Ark., Colo., Kan., La., Mo., N.M., Okla., Tex.)

      Federal Office Building
      819 Taylor Street
      Fort Worth, Texas  76102
      Tel.  (817) 334-2867

Region VI    (Ariz., Calif., Guam, Hawaii, Nev., Idaho, Utah,
     Wyo., Alaska, Mont., Ore., Wash.)

      450 Golden Gate Ave.
      P. O. Box 36003
      San Francisco, Calif.  94102
      Tel.  (415) 556-4752

Region VII    (P. R.)

      P. O. Box 3869 GPO
      San Juan, P. R.  00936

## 2.  THE URBAN INSTITUTE

      1900 L Street, N. W.
      Washington, D. C.  20036
      Tel.  (202) 223-1950

The Urban Institute is a private, non-profit research corporation devoted to study of urban problems.  Formed in April 1968, the Institute engages in a broad program of research, experimentation, and evaluation.

Institute personnel include specialists in such fields as housing, transportation, employment, public administration, education, community organization and finance, city planning, systems analysis and communication. Work is currently underway on:

a. Housing - The Institute will study changes that could expand housing choices for low-income families and upgrade housing services for urban residents. This will include investigation of the demand for housing, the cause of changes in the quality and amount of tax deterrents and incentives in housing, the relationship of housing to employment opportunities, and factors preventing free entry into the housing market.

b. Fiscal Studies - Studies of the potential for -- and obstacles to -- increasing prices of cities' utility-type operations; providing effective tax incentive for improving the urban environment; and increasing Federal or state financial support for cities.

The Urban Institute intends to become a center for knowledge on urban research. It will accumulate information about research activities on a systematic and continuing basis and will channel it to researchers and policymakers concerned with urban problems. It also plans to establish a variety of Fellowships to meet the needs and draw on the resources of recognized scholars, predoctoral students, and action-oriented minority group leaders.

General information may be obtained from the Institute at the above address. Members of the Urban Institute with an expressed interest in topics presented in Section B include:

(N)* Mort Isler
c/o above address
(Directing much of the Institute's activity
in Urban Housing)

(O)*        Joseph H. Lewis
                c/o above address

(P)*        Duncan Macrae
                c/o above address
                    (Economic aspects of the Urban
                        environment)

## 3.  BUILDING RESEARCH ADVISORY BOARD

                        Division of Engineering
                        National Research Council
                        NAS/NAE
                        2101 Constitution Ave., N. W.
                        Washington, D. C. 20418
                        Tel. (202) 961-1348

The Building Research Advisory Board (BRAB), part of the Division of Engineering, is the principal unit of the National Academy of Sciences/National Academy of Engineering/National Research Council concerned with activities and services related to building science and technology -- specifically to housing, building and construction, environmental and community design, and related technologies. BRAB's mission is to foster continuous and progressive development of national building sciences and to assess and advise on the status of new sciences and technology. BRAB also provides unique, unbiased advisory services to government and industry and provides for appropriate dissemination of information whenever doing so is in the interest of the public.

BRAB also brings together leaders in building technology in two councils -- the Federal Construction Council, in which nine major construction agencies of the Federal Government and the National Bureau of

Standards participate; and the Building Industry Manufacturers Research Council, in which twenty private companies participate.

BRAB also sponsors the BRAB Building Research Institute, a national, interdisciplinary organization dedicated to the science and technology of building. The Institute publishes a journal, entitled: Building Research, four to six times per year.

> (Q)*        Robert Dillon - Executive Director
> Rm. 203
> 2100 Pa. Ave., N.W.
> Washington, D.C. 20037
> Tel. (202) 961-1348

## 4. NATIONAL ASSOCIATION OF HOME BUILDERS

> 1625 L Street, N.W.
> Washington, D.C.
> Tel. (202) 737-7435

The National Association of Home Builders will respond to inquiries in all areas of housing and housing construction. They may be directed to the above address and, if related to a specific area, should be marked appropriately.

## 5. NATIONAL ASSOCIATION OF HOUSING AND REDEVELOPMENT OFFICIALS

> 2600 Virginia Ave., N.W.
> Washington, D.C. 20007
> Tel. (202) 333-2020

General inquiries may be made to NAHRO and should be directed to Sandra Blake (at the above address).

1.  American Socity of Planning Officials, <u>Threshold of Planning Information Systems</u>, Chicago, Ill., April 1967.

    This document contains 13 selected papers presented at the ADP Workshops conducted at the ASPO National Planning Conference. Topics include State of the Art, Exploration in Municipal Information Systems Research, Geographic Implications of Urban Information Systems, and Data Processing for Planning.

2.  Batelle Memorial Institute, <u>The State of the Art of Prefabrication in the Construction Industry</u>, Final report to the Building and Construction Trades Department, AFL-CIO 29 September 1967.

    A well organized study of the history, the current state and the future of prefabrication. The section on current prefabrication techniques in the United States describes the accomplishments of the Mobile Home Manufacturer, the Sectionalized Home Manufacturers, the Home Manufacturer, Traditional Builders using preassembled components, on-site fabricators, component manufacturers and other participants. Prefabrication in Europe is studies under the headings of Industrialized Building, Background Information, Systems Building, Degree of Factory Prefabrication and Finishing, and Non-Building. The future state of the art of prefabrication has chapters on the construction environment, technological advances, constraints to the future growth of prefabrication and the estimated state of the art by 1975. A final section forecasts the impact of the future state of the art of prefabrication upon the union effication. The report forecasts that progress in the application of prefabrication techniques in the building industry in the United States by the Year 1975 will be mild and describes architects as inimical to such progress.

3.  Beyer, Glenn H., <u>Housing and Society</u>, MacMillan, New York, 1965.

    A review of the housing literature providing a quick way of familiarizing oneself with the problem in its many aspects. Of particular interest are chapters on housing production, housing design, future needs, and housing research.

4.  "Building the American City", <u>Urban Land</u>, Vol. 28, No. 23, Urban Land Institute, Washington, D.C., March 1969.

    This is a commentary on some of the issues raised by the National Commission on Urban Problems report <u>Building the American City</u>, published in its entirety on 5 March 1969. The article concentrates on those aspects of the report having direct impact on land use.

5.  Building Research Advisory Board, <u>Engineering Studies and Investigations Relevant to Building and Heavy Construction by Federal Agencies</u>, Survey of Practice Report No. 6, National Academy of Sciences - National Research Council, Washington, D.C., 1965.

    This is a list of engineering investigations that are completed, in process, or authorized by Federal construction agencies. 35 Federal agencies were surveyed in the preparation of this listing.

6.  Building Research Advisory Board, "Research and Experimental Strategy for Community and Urban Excellence", National Academy of Sciences, Washington, D.C., April 1967.

    This report comprises a preliminary outline of considerations and relationships essential to establishing a strategy for application of research and technology to the problems of urban building and rebuilding. Constraints, priorities, sequential questions are all presented in outline form.

7.  Bureau of the Budget, <u>Statistical Services of the U.S. Government</u>, Office of Statistical Standards, Bureau of the Budget, Executive Office of the President, U.S. Gov. Printing Office, Washington, D.C. 20402, Revised 1968.

    Describes the organization and operation of the statistical system of the Federal Government, various forms of presentation, and the meaning of certain indicators. Principal statistical programs are outlined, and significant publications by each of the Federal agencies are listed and described.

8.  Bureau of the Census, <u>Bureau of the Census Catalog</u>, U.S. Gov. Printing Office, Washington, D.C. 20402, Quarterly.

    The Publications Section of the catalog lists available Bureau of the Census publications, while statistics stored on punched cards and magnetic tape are listed in the Unpublished Materials Section. The catalog is published quarterly with annual compilations.

9.  Bureau of the Census, Construction Statistics Division, <u>Housing Construction Statistics: 1889 to 1964</u>, U.S. Gov. Printing Office, Washington, D.C. 20402, 1966.

    This document is organized in two sections, presenting data on New Housing Units Started and New Housing Units Authorized in Permit - Issuing Places.

10. Bureau of the Census, <u>Current Population Reports</u>, U.S. Gov. Printing Office, Washington, D.C., Monthly

    Results of surveys conducted under the Current Population Survey, special censuses, and estimates: Series P-20, Population Characteristics of a sample of 52,500 households in 449 areas; Series P-25, Population Estimated of the population in the largest SMSA's; in particular:
    1) P-25, No. 360, "Projections of the Number of Households and Families 1967 to 1985", 3 October 1967.
    2) P-25, No. 375, "Revised Projections of the Population of States, 1970-1985", 3 October 1967.

11. Bureau of the Census, "Metropolitan Area Statistics", a reprint from <u>Statistical Abstracts of the United States, 1968</u>, U.S. Gov. Printing Office, Washington, D.C. 20402, September 1968.

    Statistics from various Federal Government and private sources are presented here for areas officially defined as Standard Metropolitan Statistical Areas (SMSA's). Table 1 presents 166 items of information for the 110 SMSA's of 250,000 inhabitants or more in 1960; Table 2 includes 83 items for the remaining SMSA's. Such topics as population, housing, income, employment, business, etc. are documented.

12. Bureau of Labor Statistics, <u>Employment and Earnings and Monthly Report on the Labor Force</u>, U.S. Gov. Printing Office, Washington, D.C., Monthly

    Survey covers the week including the 12th of each month and, with National data, includes periodic tabulation and analysis of labor force statistics for 20 largest metropolitan areas and 14 central cities and for the poverty and other urban neighborhoods of the 100 largest metropolitan areas.

13. Carp, Frances Merchant, <u>A Future for the Aged: Victoria Plaza and its Residents</u>, University of Texas Press, Austin, Texas, 1966.

    An extensive study of housing for the aged at Victoria Plaza, outlining many of the important socio-psychological considerations in such special-purpose developments.

14. Carreiro, Joseph, et. al., <u>The New Building Block: A report on the Factory-Produced Dwelling Module</u>, Research Report No. 8, Center for Housing & Environmental Studies Cornell University, Ithaca, N.Y., 1968.

    This report is essentially a review of what is happening in the field of modular construction with a brief commentary on individual efforts and their possible significance for the future of housing. This report is one of the most complete collections of modular construction alternatives available.

15. Committee on Banking and Currency, <u>Basic Laws and Authorities on Housing and Urban Development</u>, Revised through 15 January 1968, House, 90th Congress, 2nd Session, U.S. Gov. Printing Office, Washington, D.C. 20402, 1968 ($2.50).

    A comprehensive collection of all relevant legislation in housing, Urban Development, and related functions.

# HOUSING

16. "Computers and Information Systems in Planning and Related Governmental Functions", Exchange Bibliography No. 42, Council of Planning Librarians, Post Office Box 229, Monticello, Ill. 61856, February 1968

17. Conklin, Groff, The Weather Conditioned House, Reinhold Publishing, New York, 1958.

    A textbook discussion of environmental considerations in housing construction: principles of thermal control, principles of moisture control, heating and cooling systems, principles of sound control, and prevention of deterioration.

18. "Data Bank on Information Systems Publications - with Emphasis on Land Use", Exchange Bibliography No. 59, Council of Planning Librarians, Post Office Box 229, Monticello, Ill. 61856, July 1968.

    An extensive bibliography of references related to the planning and maintenance of information systems in land use planning.

19. Davies, R. M., Plastics in Building Construction, Blackie & Son, Ltd., London, 1965.

    Properties of plastics, sandwich panels, industrialized building, structural applications, thermal insulation, plastic piping, economics of use of plastics in building.

20. Deeson, A. F. L. (ed), The Comprehensive Industrialized Building Annual (Systems and Components), House Publications, Ltd., London, 1966.

    Illustrations and information on the 260 systems being used in England.

21. Department of Housing and Urban Development, "Austin Oaks '68", Washington, D.C., 1968.

    This brochure contains the separate architectural site plans of ten private contractors who each designed and built one single-family dwelling unit for HUD's Austin Oaks Project in Texas. Also included are the contracting firms' addresses. This brochure comes strongly recommended since it reflects the state of the art in low-cost, single family dwelling units.

22. Department of Housing and Urban Development, Equal Opportunity: A Bibliography of Research on Equal Opportunity in Housing, Compiled by HUD Library, U.S. Gov. Printing Office, Washington, D.C. 20402, April 1969. ($0.30).

    A bibliograph of 166 entries grouped under seven topic areas: Background, settlement patterns, economic aspects, sociological studies, community action process, research needs and methodology, and other sources.

23. Department of Housing and Urban Development, FHA Annual Statistical Summary, U.S. Gov. Printing Office, Washington, D.C. 20402, Annually.

    Summaries of volume and characteristics of operations under individual mortgage and loan insurance programs during and through proceeding calendar year.

24. Department of Housing and Urban Development, Fredella Village, Vicksburg, Miss., F/TS-27, Federal Housing Administration, U.S. Gov. Printing Office, Washington, D.C. 20402, December 1968.

    A case study of an experimental effort to reduce the cost of housing for low-income families. One of many projects involving FHA insurance on properties which include technologies not yet recognized by most as standard. The project involves 28 two-story low-cost multifamily townhouses; modular construction with industrialized techniques.

25. Department of Housing and Urban Development, Housing and Planning References, U.S. Gov. Printing Office, Washington, D.C., Monthly.

    A monthly publication which lists writings and articles received by the library of Department of Housing and Urban Development Over 500 documents are classified as to subject -- from acoustics to finance to zoning. Department Publications and HUD sponsored reports are cross-referenced and a geographic index is included.

26. Department of Housing and Urban Development, Housing Sales, Sales of New One-Family Homes, Census-HUD Series C-25, U.S. Gov. Printing Office, Washington, D.C. 20402, Monthly.

    Data derived from a survey of one-family homes for which building permits have been issued in permit issuing plans and of homes started in nonpermit areas.

27. Department of Housing and Urban Development, "HUD News", Washington, D.C. 20410, 10 July 1969.

    An updated report on material issued 11 June 1969 on HUD's "OPERATION BREAKTHROUGH", including a Fact Sheet about the program itself, and official statements by Secretary George Romney, Under Secretary Richard Van Dusen, and Assistant Secretary Harold Finger.

28. Department of Housing and Urban Development, Industrialized Building, A Comparative Analysis of European Experience, Washington, D.C., April 1968.

29. Department of Housing and Urban Development, List of Technical Studies and Experimental Housing Projects, FT/TS-1, Federal Housing Administration, Washington, D.C., Revised 1 September 1967.

    This publication lists current and completed projects in both the Technical Studies and Experimental Housing programs. It is published periodically to advise research organizations, industry and others of FHA's needs and interests, to stimulate research and experimentation, and avoid duplication of research efforts.

30. Department of Housing and Urban Development, The Model Cities Program, U.S. Gov. Printing Office, Washington, D.C. 20402, May 1969.

    A history and analysis of the Model Cities planning process in three cities -- Atlanta, Ga., Seattle, Wn., and Dayton, Ohio.

31. Department of Housing and Urban Development, Phase I, Composite Report: In-Cities Experimental Housing Research and Development Project, Washington, D.C., March 1969.

    A four volume report which outlines constraints inhibiting the introduction of innovations in housing production for low-income families.
    Volume I, User Needs: A discussion of the needs of low-cost housing, potential occupants, and the nearby community.
    Volume II, Constraints: Outlines factors which inhibit the development of innovations which could reduce the cost of housing, improve its rate of production, or increase its availability or acceptability.
    Volume III, Technology: Technological innovations in housing construction, their classification, and a preliminary assessment of their utility.
    Volume IV, City Data: Data on 56 cities selected to act as hosts for specific subexperiments.

32. Department of Housing and Urban Development, Request for Proposal No. H-55-69, Office of the Assistant Secretary for Administration, Washington, D.C., June 1969.

    A request to industry for proposals for projects related to "OPERATION BREAKTHROUGH" -- Application of Improved Housing Systems Concepts for Large Volume Production" from W. J. Prime, Director of Contracts and Agreements Division, HUD. Nine attachments describe the program plan and contract details.

# HOUSING

33. Department of Housing and Urban Development, Science and The City, U.S. Gov. Printing Office, Washington, D.C. 20402, 1967. ($0.45).

An informational document based on discussions and recommendations of the 1966 Summer Study on Science and Urban Development held at Woods Hole, Mass., and sponsored by Dept. of Housing and Urban Development and the Office of Science and Technology in the Executive Office of the President. It is intended to give perspective as to how science and technology can be brought to the service of the city rather than specific and immediate solutions.

34. Department of Housing and Urban Development, Survey of Occupants of New Housing Units, U.S. Gov. Printing Office, Washington, D.C. 20402, Biannually.

Statistics on households that move into newly constructed housing units, including information on the new units and units occupied previously.

35. Department of Housing and Urban Development, Urban and Regional Information Systems: Support for Planning in Metropolitan Areas, U.S. Gov. Printing Office, Washington, D.C. 20402, 1968. ($3.25).

This report explores the problem of how the availability and accessibility of information can be improved through the application of automatic data processing. Establishing data base requirements, Data Base Management, the Data Processing System, and existing software are discussed in detail. An extensive bibliography is included, along with case studies of nine major agencies and their experiences in the area.

36. Department of Housing and Urban Development/Federal Housing Administration, "Very Low-Cost Housing - Ashburn, Georgia", Office of Technical Standards, Washington, D.C. 1968.

This booklet presents a series of original and revised architectual site plans with explanations for revision, a detailed cost breakdown, and timetables for the Ashburn, Georgia housing project. The project is one of a series of experiments to determine whether low-cost housing can be produced using various industrialized methods.

37. Duhl, Leonard J., (ed), The Urban Condition: People and Policy in the Metropolis, Basic Books, New York, 1963.

An excellent collection of papers, many of which have direct relevance to low-cost or low-income housing.

38. The Economically and Socially Disadvantaged and the City, Metropolitan Housing and Planning Council, 53 West Jackson Blvd., Chicago, Ill. 60604, June 1967.

Proceedings and Working Papers of a national conference held at Wingspread, Racine, Wisconsin. Topics include questions submitted by HUD, Human Renewal, Needed Reforms in Housing Tax Policies, and Rehabilitation.

39. Foote, Nelson, et. al., Housing Choices and Housing Constraints, McGraw-Hill, New York, 1960.

A comprehensive study of the demand aspects of housing, what factors influence user choice, and factors which inhibit these choices.

40. Fuller, R. Buckminster, Fifty Years of the Design Science Revolution and the World Game, World Resources Inventory, Southern Illinois University, Carbondale, Ill.

An attempt to present the fifty-year public discussion of Fuller's "design science revolution" which includes the following topics:
1. The 4D Fuller House and the World Town Plan
2. The Fuller Dymaxion bathroom
3. An inventory of the world's resources
4. The Dymaxion Dwelling Machine
5. The Geodesic Dome and its acceptance

41. Gill, Paul G., Systems Management Techniques for Builders and Contractors, McGraw-Hill, New York, 1968.

A guide to the systems management approach for builders and contractors in which all operations are coordinated under one management system. Systems management techniques are employed to structure, manage, control, and develop construction plans and schedules. A 50 semi-custom home construction program is used as a case study from planning stages through the entire cycle of construction management.

42. Glazer, Nathan, "Housing Problems and Housing Policies", The Public Interest, Vol. 4, Spring 1967.

An excellent overviews of the U.S. situation with particular emphasis on the sociological aspects in Public Housing, Housing preferences, etc.

43. Groberg, Robert P., Centralized Relocation, National Association of Housing and Redevelopment Officials, 2600 Virginia Avenue, N.W., Washington, D.C. 20037, April 1969.

This report surveys the experience of 11 cities that have established centralized relocation services for people forced to move by public land acquisition and code enforcement. The book develops standards for relocation assistance and a theory of centralized relocation assistance.

44. Highway Research Board, Urban Development Models, Special Report 97, Washington, D.C., 1968

A record of the HRB Conference on Urban Development models held at Dartmouth College. Topics include: Planning, Decision-Making and the Urban Development Process, Design and Construction of Models, use of Models.

45. Holleb, Doris B., Social and Economic Information for Urban Planning, The Center for Urban Studies, University of Chicago, Chicago, Ill., 1969.

This book attempts to trace ways for planners and public officials to extract the information most relevant to urban problems from the growing corpus of urban statistics. The major factors in developing a metropolitan information system oriented towards probing complex issues are analyzed. Included are available Urban Statistics sources, Computers and Sophisticated Analytical Techniques, and a review of data sources.

46. Hooper, William L., "A Summary of Presentations Made by Manufacturers of Mobile Homes", New Housing Systems Concepts, Office of Science and Technology, Executive Office of the President, Washington, D.C., 14 February 1967.

Leaders of the mobile home manufacturing industry present their views on the potential of the mobile home concept, i.e., factory constructed, sectionalized living units -- as a solution to the shortage of satisfactory housing faced by low and middle-income residents of urban areas. Includes "Design Presentations and Observations" prepared by the Mobile Homes Manufacturers Association.

47. Housing and Urban Development Act of 1968, House Report No. 1785, 90th Congress, 2nd Session, U.S. Gov. Printing Office, Washington, D.C. 20402, 23 July 1968.

48. "Housing Renewal and Development Bibliography", Exchange Bibliography No. 46, Council of Planning Librarians, Post Office Box 229, Monticello, Ill. 61865, 1968.

49. Human Needs in Housing, United States Savings and Loan League, Chicago, Ill., 1964.

A report on a round table conference sponsored by the Menninger Foundation/U.S. Savings and Loan League. Discussions include themes and issues, social trends, the House, the community, the market, special problems -- the elderly, and new solutions.

50. Illinois Institute of Technology Research Institute, Application of Component Construction to Multi-story, Low-Income Housing, for Department of HUD, HUD Project No. Ill. LIHD-3 Contract No. H-747, Washington, D.C. 20410, January 1968.

An extensive survey of industrialized building methods now in use throughout the world which resulted in their adoption of the open-top box module as the system best conforming to the present posture of the U.S. construction industry. IIT's objective was to discover means of lowering multi-story housing costs for low-income families in response to the current need for six million of such housing units. Excellent annotated bibliographies in the areas of precast concrete building systems and modeling were compiled in the process.

51. International Labour Organization (Building Committee), Report II, Social Aspects of Prefabrication In The Construction Industry, Geneva, 1968.

Large-scale, guaranteed market is necessary to induce manufacturers to invest in prefab machinery. On-site labor has been reduced 10% up to 30% elsewhere. Social problems of displaced workers offset any economies of production. Rents have not been lowered. A very negative view of prefabs.

52. Johnson-Marshall, Percy, Rebuilding Cities, Aldine Publishing, Chicago, Ill., 1966.

An extensive presentation of the "total design" concept in urban development. New concepts in design and planning are set against a background of traditional techniques and practices. Comprehensive planning in London, Coventry, and Rotterdam used as examples.

53. Jones, Rudard A., Sectionalized Houses, Research Report 62-2, University of Illinois, Small Homes Council - Building Research Council, Urbana, Ill., October 1962.

A report of a study on the feasibility of a sectionalized house operation in connection with a retail lumber yard. This study was conducted by the University ot Illinois in cooperation with the Lumber Dealers Research Council.

54. Kaiser Engineers, Information On and Evaluations of Innovations in Housing Design and Construction Techniques as Applied to Low-Cost Housing, Berkely, Calif., March 1969. (Revised April 1969)

A collateral literature survey in connection with Phase II of HUD's In-Cities Demonstration Project. Kaiser Engines contracted with Professors Alonso, Hassid, and Smith of the University of California at Berkeley to compile this report on published materials relating to cost-reducing innovations in the production of housing. The report includes a history of the social aspects and design in housing, current production technology, a review of business aspects in housing innovations, and suggested research methods and objectives. The report is referenced with a detailed, annotated bibliography of over 1,000 entries. A section is also included listing HUD Low-Income Housing Demonstration Staff Reports.

55. Kaltman, Larry, and Uri Sofer, The Cellular System - Low-Cost Quality Housing for Urban Areas, Oakland Redevelopment Agency, Oakland, Calif., 1967.

Use of sandwich panels with foamed plastic cores, used structurally, floor and roof framing eliminated.

56. Katz, Robert, Design of the Housing Site: A Critique of American Practice, University of Illinois, Small Homes Council - Building Research Council, Urbana, Ill., 1965.

Investigates - (1) Development factors and physical characteristics influencing the quality of site planning of multi-family housing projects; (2) Ways of increasing single-family housing intensity without sacrificing livability. Identified factors, both technical and procedural, essential to high quality, residential site planning; documents current practices throughout U.S.; and recommend ways of improving site planning. Also focuses on housing design and its relation to livability.

57. Kelly, Burnham, The Prefabrication of Houses, MIT Press and John Wiley and Sons, New York, 1951.

A classic work on prefabrication. Has a very complete history of prefabrication industry and deals with such topics as Management, Design, Procurement, Production, and Marketing.

58. Lee, Douglass B., Jr., Analysis and Description of Residential Segregation, Center for Housing and Environmental Studies, Cornell University, Ithaca, N.Y., February 1966.

A thesis presented in partial fulfillment of requirements for Master of Regional Planning which attempts to apply certain quantitative techniques in the analysis of residential segregation.

59. McFarland, M. Carter, "Residential Rehabilitation: The State of the Art and Its Potential", Department of Housing and Urban Development, Washington, D.C., 1 April 1966.

A forty-page paper prepared for HUD. The paper describes the housing problem in urban areas including the social, political, and economic aspects. Mr. McFarland seeks to show the advantages of residential rehabilitation from a broad point of view. There is little, if any, discussion on the technical aspects of rehabilitation.

60. McFarland, M. Carter and Walter K. Vivrett, (ed.), Residential Rehabilitation, University of Minnesota, Minneapolis, Minnesota, 1966.

A compilation of papers presented at the Training in Residential Rehabilitation, University of Minnesota, July 19-30, 1965. The compilation is divided in three parts: (1) Elements of Urban Renewal Rehabilitation; (2) Case studies in Urban Renewal Rehabilitation; and (3) Novel Approaches to Rehabilitation.

61. McGraw-Hill Information Systems Company, 1969 Dodge Construction Pricing and Scheduling Manual, McGraw-Hill, 330 West 42nd Street, New York, N.Y., 1969.

Information and prices on present day labor and construction, compiled from reliable sources which reflect current price and cost situations. Cost adjustment index charts are included to provide a basis for adjusting most of the labor and material units to suit current costs in 21 major metropolitan areas which accounted for over 60% of the National volume of construction in 1969.

62. Margolis, Richard J., Something to Build On, International Self-Help Housing Associates and the American Friends Service Committee, 1346 Conn. Ave., N.W., Washington, D.C. 20036, July 1967.

This book is an attempt to interpret the complexities of self-help housing -- its history, its current uses and non-uses. Included is a partial list of self-help housing projects in the U.S.

63. Mayer, Albert, The Urgent Future, McGraw-Hill, New York, 1967.

This book calls for a new approach to Housing and Urban development which recognizes the "underlying dynamics" of communities. In dealing with the full spectrum of Urban Life, the author discusses the dynamics of social and physical development, public housing, new towns, the city center, and total metropolitan planning.

64. Metropolitan Washington Council of Governments, Interim Report: Metropolitan Planning Data from Local Governments, Washington, D.C., July 1967.

This study seeks to demonstrate whether comprehensive planning data can be made available through local governments. Subject areas include -- defining data needs, analysis of land use concepts, recommended data items and codes.

# HOUSING

65. "Model Cities", Exchange Bibliography No. 48, Council of Planning Librarians, Post Office Box 229, Monticello, Ill. 61856, May 1968.

An extensive bibliography of publications related to all aspects of the Model Cities Program.

66. National Association of Housing and Redevelopment Officials, Critical Urban Housing Issues: 1967, Washington, D.C. December 1967.

A solution of paper presented at NAHRO's Housing Policy Forum. Four critical issues are discussed: Housing Assistance Programs & Techniques; Social Dimensions in Housing; Changing Concepts of the Tenant Management Relationship; Housing Organization.

67. The National Commission on Urban Problems, Building the American City, U.S. Gov. Printing Office, Washington, D.C., 1969. ($4.50).

This is the final report of the Douglas Commission. It recommends federal, state, and local action on production of low-income housing, reducing housing costs, cooperative housing, economic and racial segregation, building code reform, modern building methods, housing codes, revenue sharing, income tax and property tax changes, restrictive building practices, and land use management. Organized in six parts: 1. Population, Poverty and Race; 2. Housing Programs; 3. Codes and Standards; 4. Government Structure, Finance and Taxation; 5. Reducing Housing Costs; 6. Improvement of the Environment.

Following are source documents which provided background studies for the final report of the National Commission on Urban Problems:

(a) National Commission on Urban Problems, Hearings Before the National Commission on Urban Problems, U.S. Gov. Printing Office, Washington, D.C., May 1968. (Five Volumes).

Record of hearings held in 18 cities in all parts of the country by the Douglas Commission. Five volumes have been published: Vol. I - Baltimore, New Haven, Boston, and Pittsburgh, May 12 to June 10, 1967; Vol. II - Los Angeles and San Francisco, June 30 to July 7, 1967; Vol. III - Denver, Atlanta, Houston, Fort Worth, Dallas, Arlington, and Miami, June 10 to August 26, 1967; Vol. IV - New York City and Philadelphia, September 1967; Vol. V - Detroit, St. Louis, East St. Louis, and Washington, D.C., October 11 to 28, 1967.

(b) Netzer, Dick, Impact of the Property Tax, NCUP Research Report No. 1, U.S. Gov. Printing Office, Washington, D.C., 1969. ($1.00).

(c) American Society of Planning Officials, Problems of Zoning and Land-Use Regulations, NCUP Research Report No. 2, Communication Service Corp., 1333 Conn. Ave., Washington, D.C., 1969. ($2.50).

(d) Hodge, Patricia Leavey and Hauser, Philip M., The Challeng of America's Metropolitan Population Outlook - 1960 to 1985, NCUP Research Report No. 3, U.S. Gov. Printing Office, Washington, D.C., 1969. ($1.00).

(e) Smart, Walter, Walter Rybeck and H.E. Shuman, The Large Poor Family - A Housing Gap, NCUP Research Report No. 4, Communications Service Corp., 1333 Conn. Ave., Washington, D.C., 1969. ($1.00).

(f) Slitor, Richard E., The Federal Income Tax in Relation to Housing, NCUP Research Report No. 5, U.S. Gov. Printing Office, Washington, D.C. 20402. 1969 ($1.25).

(g) Manvel, Allen D., Local Land and Building Regulation, NCUP Research Report No. 6, U.S. Gov. Printing Office, Washington, D.C. 20402, 1969 ($0.55).

A survey of agencies, personnel, salaries, building code restrictions, etc.

(h) Keith, Nathaniel, Housing America's Low- and Moderate-Income Families, NCUP Research Report No. 7, U.S. Gov. Printing Office, Washington, D.C. 20402, 1969 ($0.40).

(i) George Schermer Associates, More than Shelter, NCUP Research Report No. 8, U.S. Gov. Printing Office, Washington, D.C., 1969 ($1.75).

Study of Social Needs and Programs in Public Housing

(j) Manvel, Allen D., Housing Conditions in Urban Poverty Areas, NCUP Research Report No. 9, U.S. Gov. Printing Office, Washington, D.C. 20402, 1969 ($0.35).

A survey based on Census Statistics

(k) Kristof, Frank S., Urban Housing Needs Through the 1980's: Analysis and Projection, NCUP Research Report No. 10, U.S. Gov. Printing Office, Washington, D.C. 20402, 1969 ($1.00).

(l) Raymond and May Associates, Zoning Controversies in the Suburbs: Three Case Studies, NCUP Research Report No. 11, U.S. Gov. Printing Office, Washington, D.C. 20402, 1969 ($0.75).

Examines disputes over increased density, residential versus industrial, and unconventional development.

(m) Three Land Research Studies, NCUP Research Report No. 12, U.S. Gov. Printing Office, Washington, D.C. 20402, 1969 ($0.70).

Contains "Trends in the Value of Real Estate and Land, 1956 to 1966", by Allen D. Manvel; "Land Use in 106 Large Cities", by Manvel; and "Estimating California Land Values from Independent Statistical Indicators", by R.H. Gustafson and R.B. Welch.

(n) Milgram, Grace, U.S. Land Prices - Directions and Dynamics, NCUP Research Report No. 13, U.S. Gov. Printing Office, Washington, D.C. 20402, 1969.

(o) Grad, Frank P., Legal Remedies for Housing Code Violations, NCUP Research Report No. 14, U.S. Gov. Printing Office, Washington, D.C. 20402, 1969.

(p) Bosselman, Fred P., Alternatives to Urban Sprawl: Legal Guidelines for Governmental Action, NCUP Research Report No. 15, U.S. Gov. Printing Office, Washington, D.C. 20402, 1969 ($0.70).

(q) Eaves, Elsie, How the Many Costs of Housing Fit Together, NCUP Research Report No. 16, U.S. Gov. Printing Office, Washington, D.C. 20402, 1969.

(r) Slavel, Joseph S., and Melvin R. Levin, New Approaches to Housing Code Administration, NCUP Research Report No. 17, U.S. Gov. Printing Office, Washington, D.C. 20402, 1969.

(s) Coke, James G., and John J. Gargan, Fragmentation in Land-Use Planning and Control, NCUP Research Report No. 18, U.S. Gov. Printing Office, Washington, D.C. 20402, 1969.

68. National Committee on Urban Growth Policy, The New City, published for Urban America , Frederick A. Praeger, New York, N.Y., 1969

A report co-sponsored by the National League of Cities, National Association of Counties, U.S. Conference of Mayors and Urban Americas, Inc., calling for (1) New Cities within Existing Cities, (2) Accelerated growth of centers using existing small communities, and (3) the creation of entirely new communities. Also stresses the need for the development of a national urban growth policy.

69. "New Concepts in Low-Cost Residential Housing", Jones & Laughlin Steel Corporation, 3 Gateway Center, Pittsburgh, Penn. 15230, 1967.

Jones & Laughlin Steel Corp is a supplier of structural steels for mobile homes and other types of light construction , and therefore, assigned the development of concepts for low-cost manufactured space for residential housing to Dalton-Dalton Assoc., Inc. (Cleveland based firm, specializing in planning, architecture, and engineering projects). This brochure is the product of that assignment and presents 7 different sectionalized housing designs.

70. New Housing Systems Concepts, Mobile Homes Manufacturers Association, 20 North Wacker Drive, Chicago, Ill. 60606, February 1967.

This booklet is divided into two main parts: (1) A Summary of Presentations Made by Manufacturers of Mobile Homes by William L. Hooper ( Tech. Asst. to the Director of Office of Science & Technology, Executive Office of President, Washington, D.C.) (2) Design Presentations and Observations. The possible application of mobile home size units to low, medium, and high population density areas is discussed.

71. Owen, C. L., Design and the Industrialized House, Institute of Design Press, Chicago, Ill., 1965.

A history of prefabrication. A survey of U.S. firms' activities in prefab. Design of an integrated system module.

72. Pilcher, Roy, Principles of Construction Management, McGraw-Hill, London, England, 1966.

An elaboration of basic construction management techniques , based upon current practices, and expanded upon, where necessary, by theoretical argument. Includes fundamentals of network analysis for planning construction work, the possible application of the new science of Operations Research, and a treatment of the Critical Path Method.

73. Prefabricated Concrete Components for Low-Cost Housing Construction, Ideas and Methods Exchange No. 59, Housing and Home Finance Agency, Office of International Housing, Washington, D.C. 20410, October 1963.

This report discusses many of the principal features of Prefabricated Concrete Homes, illustrating the design process, prefabrication operations, transportation to site, and assembly. Specific two and four-room building designs are used as examples.

74. The President's Committee on Urban Housing, A Decent Home, U.S. Gov. Printing Office, Washington, D.C. 20402 , December 1968. ($2.00).

This is the Committee's final report. The Committee, headed by Chairman Edgar F. Kaiser, was charged by the president to find a way to "provide the basic necessities of a decent home and health surroundings for every American family". Included is the main Committee Report, "The Shape of the Nation's Housing Problem" and several support ing staff studies: "The Shape of the Problem"; "Federal Housing Programs" currently in existence; "Making Better Use of The Housing We Have"; "Housing Markets and Rehabilitation; and "Building Houses". Also included is a summary of commission and staff recommendations.

75. The President's Committee on Urban Housing, Technical Studies, U.S. Gov. Printing Office, Washington, D.C. 20402, 1968 (Two Volumes).

The series of technical studies prepared for the Kaiser Committee. Volume I includes studies of housing needs and Federal housing programs. Volume II selections concern housing costs, production efficiency, finance, manpower, and land.

76. Reach, Barbara, Social Aspects of Cooperative and Non-Profit Housing: New and Rehabilitated, Department of Public Affairs, Community Service Society of New York, 105 East 22 Street, New York, N.Y. 10010, May 1968.

A report prepared for HUD for the National Comm. on Urban Problems. Discusses the value and limitations of non-profit rental and cooperative housing in meeting the needs of low and moderate-income families. It discusses construction, operation and social benefits and includes cases on six cities and legal restrictions.

77. Rehabilitation Guide for Residential Properties, U.S. Dept. of Housing and Urban Development, U.S. Gov. Printing Office, Washington, D.C. 20402, January 1968 ( $0.40).

A compilation of physical guidelines for the rehabilitation of existing residential properties to provide minimum design and construction criteria on a national basis. The guidelines cover the following areas: Acceptability criteria, site, building planning, fire protection, materials, construction, exterior and interior finishes, and mechanical equipment.

78. Rothenberg, Jerome, Economic Evaluation of Urban Renewal, The Brookings Institution, 1775 Mass. Avenue, N.W., Washington, D.C., September 1967.

This study concentrates on the redevelopment aspects of urban renewal and formulates a procedure by which a benefit-cost analysis of the programs can be carried out. Part I deals with scope and structure of urban renewal; Part II measures the benefits; and Part III discusses issues of public policy.

79. Schmidt, Lewis, and Olin, Construction Lending Guide: A Handbook of Homebuilding Design and Construction, American Savings and Loan Institute and McGraw-Hill, Chicago, Ill. 60601, July 1966.

A first edition text, intended primarily for student's use, which provides practical, working details on the following aspects of homebuilding: Land Planning, Design, Appraising, Construction, Construction Loan Procedures. Each of the five sections contains a main text, which develops the subject matter, and a working file, which summarizes important information and serves as a reference source.

80. Schorr, Alvin L., Slums and Social Insecurity, U.S. Gov. Printing Office, Washington, D.C., 1963.

An excellent survey of literature on housing preferences and housing welfare. Considerable attention is given to the needs of poor and working class residents. A bibliography of 271 items is included.

81. Sears, Roebuck and Co., Urban Renewal Division, A.B. Citizens in Urban Renewal, Chicago, Ill., 1969.

This book deals with ways to stimulate constructive citizen support for revitalizing neglected neighborhoods through the Urban Renewal process. Seven points of citizen involvement are discussed in detail.

82. Seymour-Walker, K.J., Developments in Production of Concrete Panels, Building Research Current Paper 14/68, Building Research Station, Bucknalls Lane, Garston, Watford, Herts., England, February 1968.

The first part of the Paper describes a number of the more sophisticated production techniques at present in use for making concrete panels for industrialized building. In the second part, techniques developed at the research station are described. Illustrations of the process and 25 references on prefab. concrete technology.

# HOUSING

83. Seymour-Walker, K. J., Vertically Cast L-Shaped Panels, Building Research Current Paper 16/68, Building Research Station, Bucknalls Lane, Garston, Watford, Herts., England, February 1968.

The manufacturing technique is briefly discussed and a comparison is made between the cost of these panels and other systems of building. Plans of several low-rise house constructions are given showing how the L-shaped concrete bearing wall panels are most effectively used.

84. Shenkel, William M., The Unfinished But Habitable Home, Prepared for the Housing and Home Finance Agency, U. S. Gov. Printing Office, Washington, D. C., May 1965.

A discussion of unfinished homes, the construction of which can be completed by the purchasers and which have enabled many families of limited incomes to become homeowners.

85. Sternlieb, George, The Tenament Landlord, Urban Studies Center, Rutger's University, New Brunswick, N. J., 1966.

A penetrating discussion of slums and substandard housing, with emphasis on housing law enforcement, rental housing, and minority group housing. A significant bibliography is included.

86. Study Group on Housing and Neighborhood Improvement, "Let There Be Commitment": A Housing, Planning and Development Program for New York City, Institute of Public Administration, New York, N.Y. 10036, Sept. 1966.

A report to the Mayor of New York proposing a comprehensive and urgent attack on the problems of the ghettoes and a drastic reorganization of the city government to make this possible. Suggested programs consider low-income housing, rehabilitation, and relocation for the Harlem-East Harlem, South Bronx, and Central Brooklyn areas. A complete renewal strategy with maps.

87. Technologies Study: The Application of Technological Innovation in the Development of a New Community. A report prepared by David A. Crane, Architect, and Keyes, Lethbridge, and Condon, Architects, Associated Architects and Planners for Fort Lincoln New Town, for Edward J. Logue, D. C. Redevelopment Land Agency, National Capital Planning Commission, D. C. Government, Washington, D. C., December 1968.

This report is an exploration of the applicability of technological innovation at Fort Lincoln New Town (FLNT) which promise to improve both the individual dwelling unit and the entire living and working environment. It examines the practical application of technological innovation, both specifically in the construction industry, and generally, in the development process itself. It assumes that FLNT will be a demonstration community in both the physical and social sense. This report has a very good sections on technological innovations in industrialized building systems and mechanical and service systems.

88. United Nations, Department of Economic and Social Affairs, Methods for Establishing Targets and Standards for Housing and Environmental Development, United Nations Publication No. E. 68. IV. 5, New York, 1968.

Discussion of Housing and environmental development on the national and international scale. The study is particularly concerned with large-scale planning and setting guidelines and objectives appropriately. Housing standards and community development are treated in detail.

89. Walkley, Rosabelle Price, et. al., Retirement Housing in California, Diablo Press, Berkeley, California, 1966.

A study of California's retirement housing conducted for UCLA School of Public Health. The first phase contains a statewide survey of special group housing facilities for elderly persons and is presented in this volume. Other phases will follow. Various structures are discussed, along with related social and economic characteristics.

90. Wheaton, William L. C., (ed.), Urban Housing, The Free Press, New York, 1966.

The first volume in a series on urban planning and development. More than 50 readings organized in eight major sections: Historical and conceptual background, the neighborhood, the housing market and demand economics, the needs of special groups, the housing industry, finance, housing standards, and the residential aspects of urban renewal. An extensive bibliography is also attached.

91. Willrock, Jan, Reducing Seasonal Unemployment in the Construction Industry, Organization for Economic Cooperation and Development, Paris, 1967.

The fourth in an OECO series entitled, "Developing Job Opportunities. An analysis of all aspects of seasonality in construction and recommendations for reducing these fluctuations. The construction industries in 15 nations are described and compared.

92. Wilson, James Q. (ed.), Urban Renewal: The Record and the Controversy, The MIT Press, Cambridge, Mass. 1966

A collection of papers intended to describe Urban Renewal in depth. Topics include: The Economics of Cities and Renewal, Backgrounds and Goals, Case Studies, Planning and Design, Government and Citizen Participation, and the future of Urban Renewal.

93. Wolkstein, Harry W., Accounting Methods and Controls for the Construction Industry, Prentice Hall, Englewood Cliffs, N. J., 1967.

This book is designed to give accountants an up-to-date sourcebook for understanding the peculiarities of the construction contractor's accounting system and contract cost system, as well as usual fiscal activities.

94. Wood, Elizabeth, Social Planning: A Primer for Urbanists, Community Education Program, Planning Department, Pratt Institute, Brooklyn, N. Y., 1965.

This document stresses the relevance of "social planning" to the complete urban planning process. Chapters concentrate on: The goal of social planning, upward mobility, making the natural process work better, social and welfare services and social planning, urban renewal and social planning. A case study on the impacts of relocation is included.

ELEMENTS OF THE URBAN ENVIRONMENTAL PROBLEM

## ENVIRONMENTAL QUALITY

The question of environmental quality presents a disarming paradox to urban planners.  Man has traditionally taken steps to extend and improve the livability of his immediate environment by developing transportation systems, building better housing, and providing various utility services.  At the same time, however, he is rapidly making that environment less habitable due to the contaminating by-products of a growing technology.  Well-meaning actions to counteract specific forms of environmental pollution can yield net-reductions in overall environmental quality.  Incineration of refuse releases contaminants to the atmosphere; disposal of solid waste in sanitary land fills can pollute underground water supplies; and sewage disposal facilities often overburden downstream water purification systems.  The interrelationships between various elements of the urban environment inevitably make  the isolated solution to one problem a complicating factor in the satisfactory resolution of others, particularly when the elements are dealt with exclusively by competing interest groups.

Two of the  most basic considerations in maintaining a livable environment are the level of quality which people actually desire and the willingness of society to pay the price necessary to achieve it. Standards and criteria for future programs dealing with environmental quality will necessarily involve unequivocal decisions between alternative uses for water, land, air, and dollars. Solutions to the problems of pollution must weight the productive purposes for which we use our environment against the corresponding social and economic costs of resource depletion, discomfort, health hazards, and "clean-up". An overall balancing of these factors serves to avoid the establishment of overly restrictive environmental quality standards and the possible denial of reasonable public use of the environment's resources.

To use the words of the Environmental Studies Board, the most pressing need is to " ... combine a factual study of existing and contemplated levels of contamination, their consequent effect on both human health and the rest of the environment, and engineering, economic, and social data which will clearly establish the feasibility and cost of achieving any desired level of control or reduction of contamination" (ref. 8, p. 8).

## HISTORY - THE FEDERAL EFFORT

Federal interest in the quality of the environment has expanded overwhelmingly within the last decade. The formation of the Subcommittee on Science, Research, and Development in 1963 under the House Committee on Science and Astronautics was the first in a series of major steps to achieve Congress' national goal of adequate environmental quality " ... The maintenance of the natural environment in a status

which combines esthetic values with productivity in all the myriad ways

man uses his physical surroundings " (ref. 13, p. 1). In 1965, the

President's Science Advisory Committee produced an extensive assess-

ment of the state of the Nation's environment, complete with recom-

mended actions for overcoming the deficiencies which had been pin-

pointed (ref. 6). Beginning shortly thereafter, the House Subcommittee

gathered facts and informed opinions on the role of science and tech-

nology in environmental management, and published two excellent

source documents, (ref. 3) in July of 1966 and (ref. 12) in October of

the same year.

In June of 1967, the National Academy of Sciences produced an in-

formative report (ref. 6) calling for a " ... broader and more intensive

National effort on the integrity and sufficiency of the environment";

and the Secretary of Health, Education, and Welfare (HEW) received a

final report (ref. 14) from his special Task Force on Environmental

Health and Related problems, which recommended action goals,

priorities, and a Departmental strategy in the areas of air quality,

water quality, solid waste disposal, etc.

The following month, the Chairman of the Subcommittee on Science,

Research, and Development published a statement which elaborated on

the need for an increased Congressional capability to deal with ramifi-

cations of technological development. It was reasoned therein that the legislative function is where scientific information can best be integrated with informed opinion on how and when to apply technological efforts to the social and natural environment. Joint House-Senate efforts during the following year culminated in a position paper and policy formulation on Federal involvement in environment quality standards and control (ref. 11). The ultimate conclusion called for a long-range strategy as necessary for active management of the natural environment.

In the summer of 1969, the problem of environmental quality and control was considered by the Nixon administration to be a sufficiently serious national issue to warrant the formation of a new Cabinet-level group, the Council on Environmental Quality, composed of the heads of many Federal Departments and led by the President's Science Advisor, Dr. Lee DuBridge. With the creation of this special committee, the Federal Government has become the effective locus for discussion and policy-making on large-scale environmental problems by transcending the responsibility and authority of other Federal agencies. Forthcoming policy statements on the environment will now come from the highest Executive level, and program directives will invariably receive widespread national publicity, the support of Federal funding, and immediate-action plans for implementation.

# TOWARD A LIVABLE URBAN ENVIRONMENT

The compilation of specific environmental topics presented in this chapter is not an attempt to canvass the full range of remaining urban problems.  It is rather an effort to suggest approaches and stimulate research in five areas which are crucial to a livable urban environment:

1. Air Pollution Abatement
2. Water Pollution Control
3. Solid Waste Management
4. Noise Abatement
5. Comprehensive Urban Health
   Care Systems

The first four topics suggest the need to stop degrading the natural environment; the fifth involves a positive application of man's technological capability to create an urban environment which better serves him.  Taken individually, each problem appears to be self-contained; but, as has already been pointed out, the various environmental problems are closely interrelated and intimately involved with considerations raised in the two preceding chapters.  As the Congressional Hearings on the Nation's Environment strongly state (ref. 3, 12 ), a constant awareness of these interdependencies and of the way in which environmental problems relate to problems in urban housing and transportation will lead to more meaningful conclusions in any interdisciplinary urban design project.

# SECTION B

## INTERDISCIPLINARY RESEARCH TOPICS FROM THE URBAN ENVIRONMENT

1. Air Pollution Abatement

2. Water Pollution Control

3. Abatement of Urban Noise

4. Solid Waste Management

5. Comprehensive Urban Health Care Systems

# 1. AIR POLLUTION ABATEMENT

## THE PROBLEM

Few major urban areas in the Nation are unacquainted with the peril and cost of air pollution. The rapid growth of industrial societies, with expanding per capita demands for technology, energy, and transportation, is increasing the threat of a contaminated atmosphere. Growing urbanization and rising use of motor vehicles are exposing larger populations to the adverse effects of the dangerous air pollution levels now experienced primarily in choked central cities.

In 1966, the Department of Health, Education, and Welfare (HEW) estimated a total of 142 million tons of contaminants being released to the Nation's atmosphere annually from all sources (ref. 30, p. 11). The most recent estimates by the Department's National Air Pollution Control Administration (NAPCA) revise the annual-figure to approximately 173 million tons. In Figure B-1 on the following page, the total is divided among five pollutant types and between the two source classifications.

By weight, motor vehicles account for some 77% of the more than 87 million tons of carbon monoxide emitted annually. Vehicular sources are also responsible for more than half of the nationwide hydrocarbon emissions and nearly half of the nitrogen oxides. Particulates and sulfur oxides result mostly from non-vehicular sources and are especially heavy in northeastern areas where coal and residual fuel oil are primary power sources, although the automobile is the chief source of atmospheric lead particulate.

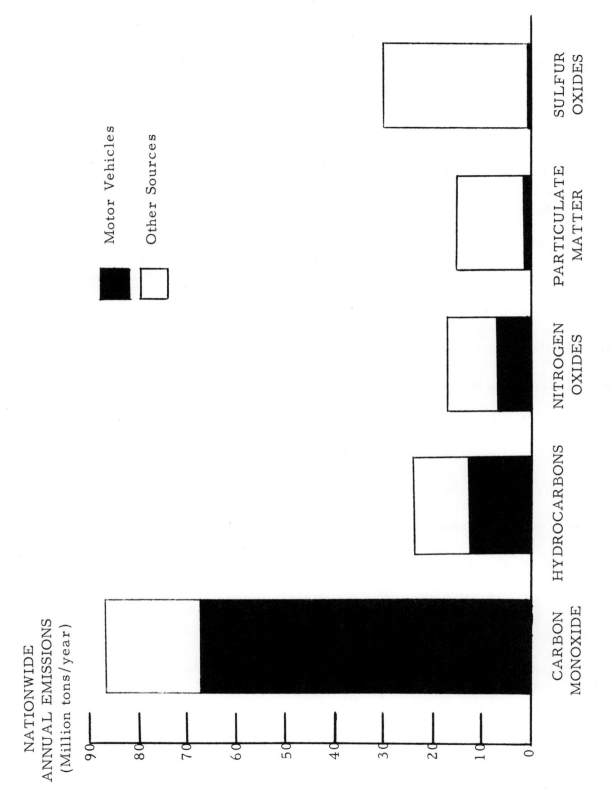

Figure B-1. The motor vehicle's nationwide contribution to five major air contaminants.

These figures do not, of course, reflect the local differences in pollution levels which may occur because of varying concentrations of vehicles and industry or local geographical and meteorological differences. Contributions from vehicular sources in urban areas are significantly higher than the nationwide proportions, typically producing more than 90% of the carbon monoxide and up to 75% of the hydrocarbon emissions.

Generally, atmospheric pollution shortens life, destroys vegetation, damages property, and endangers basic meteorological processes. The types and levels of air pollution which are common in many American communities are strongly associated with such chronic diseases as asthma, bronchitis, emphysema, and lung cancer. Carbon monoxide is known to have a strong affinity for hemoglobin and can dramatically impair the ability of the blood to transport oxygen. Certain hydrocarbons are suspected of having carcinogenic effects on lung tissues. Oxidents such as ozone and peroxyacyl nitrates are irritating to eyes and impair respiration. Residual accumulation of lead is directly toxic to man (ref. 30, 31, 19, 29).

Beyond the problems of chronic discomfort and disability, unchecked air pollution looms as a potential mass killer. London, in December of 1952, experienced protracted pollution of great intensity which resulted in an estimated 3500 to 4000 deaths. Similar episodes of concentrated air pollution occurred in the Meuse Valley of Belgium in 1930 and in Danora,

Pennsylvania in 1948, taking 60 and 20 lives respectively and sickening thousands. New York City has experienced several periods of severe atmospheric contamination, attributing a total of 405 deaths to air pollution in 1963 (ref. 30).

Air pollution is also becoming increasingly evident as a cause of widespread damage to plants and property. Though the cost and severity of such destruction is not completely understood, some national estimates assess damage as high as $12 billion per year. Particular estimates in 1967 assessed crop loss in California due to ozone and organic oxidents alone on the order of $6 to $10 million (ref. 30, p. 15).

Furthermore, air pollution may pose a significant threat to the atmosphere and meteorological processes in general. Large scale increases of atmospheric carbon dioxide is thought to adversely affect heat dissipation rates, and projections to the year 2000 suggest a 25% increase in the atmospheric carbon monoxide residual.

The air pollution problem is a combination of varied elements. Different contributing sources require different control methodologies and hardware. Though most acute in the urban areas, air pollution is unaware of municipal boundaries and is often unassailable through a provincial approach. The dimensions of the problem itself are not adequately understood for all afflicted areas. Many of these elements are outlined in Contributing Problem Areas and can suitably serve as the focus for various systems efforts to reduce the air pollution problem or as areas in which concentrated research is still warranted.

A general introduction to the topic of environmental pollution may be obtained from (ref. 1, 9, 14), and extensive discussions of overall air pollution causes, effects, trends, and alternatives are contained in (ref. 23, 24, 31). Air Pollution Publications by the Department of Health, Education and Welfare contains an extensive compilation of references on all aspects of the problem (ref. 22).

## STATE-OF-THE-ART

Perhaps the most current and complete summary of national progress in combatting air pollution can be found in the annual Reports to Congress by the Secretary of Health, Education, and Welfare, as required by the Air Quality Act of 1967 (ref. 18, 19, 20). To date, public action to abate air pollution has relied primarily on tracing damage and discomfort to particular pollutants and sources and setting stringent emission standards. The Secretary's Reports document extensive health effects research and meteorological research (ref. 20) and the development of effective air quality criteria (ref. 19). Additional information on air quality and the rationale for standards is set forth in (ref. 3).

Air pollution abatement has been ordered in terms of contributing sources -- vehicular and stationary. The literature is extensive with respect to vehicular pollution; one of the most comprehensive studies to date was sponsored by the Department of Commerce Technical Advisory

Board (ref. 30). The primary effort against pollution from motor vehicles has been through a program of Federal standards that limit the emission of harmful pollutants (ref. 20, p. 38). The State of California has been a motivating force in this campaign and has instituted its own set of stringent limits on vehicular emissions (ref. 20).

Exhaust emissions are the principal components of vehicular air pollution and have received the greatest attention from abatement agencies. Control technologies which are relatively well-developed include altering the mixture of air and fuel, timing adjustments, injection of air into hot exhaust gases, and advancements in engine design (ref. 20, 30). Anticipated emission control technologies include large manifold reactors near the engine in which hot gases react with injected air, direct flame after-burners, and catalytic converters.

However, there is less than universal agreement that emission controls will be sufficient to meet 1970 and 1972 standards, or, if these standards are met, that any real gains against urban air pollution will result. The delay in the replacement of old vehicles with new ones, combined with increasing dependence on motor vehicles and anticipated increases in traffic, may completely negate the overall effects of meeting Federal standards (ref. 33). In addition, hardware to meet 1970 standards is expected to cost a total of one-half billion dollars, adding $48 to the cost of each new auto.

A more direct attack against vehicular air pollution is also underway in the form of Federal efforts to stimulate the development of alternative energy, power, and propulsion systems. At present, about $8 to $10 million is being spent annually on electrical vehicle research, half by private industry and half by government (ref. 33). Extensive studies have recently been completed for NAPCA by Arthur D. Little and Battelle Memorial Institute on electric and other nonconventional power systems (ref. 16, 26). Additional references on electrical vehicles are (ref. 25, 30). The steam engine is also being investigated under NAPCA auspices as an alternative low-pollution power source. Five firms have submitted proposals in competition for a contract to design and build a practical passenger car steam power plant: Planning Research Corp. STP Corp., Battelle Memorial Institute, Continental Motors Corp., Vought Aeronautical Division of Ling-Temco-Vought, and Thermo Electron Corp. Two others, Lear Motor Corp. and Thermodynamics Systems, Inc., have been selected by the California Highway Patrol to install steam engines in patrol cars for year-long tests. Also, see Chapter III, Topic 11, for a more complete discussion of evolutionary vehicle design.

The control of stationary sources of air pollution, though typically a regional or local concern, is now being supported by a $14 million Federal program in 1969. The principal Federal emphasis to date has been a series of studies instituted to provide a better definition of research and development needed to cope with any segment of the stationary source problem: industrywide surveys of basic industries; device-oriented studies to achieve wide applicability of control equipment; and pollutant-oriented studies to provide a better definition of problems associated with particular contaminants and identify more effective control technologies (ref. 20). Several studies are also currently being conducted under NAPCA contract to investigate contributions to air pollution from solid waste disposal facilities and appropriate control methods (ref. 19, p. 50).

Perhaps the characteristic element of the national approach to air pollution is its regional accent. The Air Quality Act of 1967 provided the blueprints for a systematic effort to deal with air pollution on an intermetropolitan basis (ref. 15). Within the Department of HEW, NAPCA is charged with defining broad "atmospheric areas" of the Nation and directed to designate specific air quality control regions. As soon as air quality criteria and data on control technologies are made available by NAPCA, regions are then expected to begin developing specific air quality standards and an "implementation plan" to achieve those standards. Aspects of this regional approach and details on the implementation plan are contained in (ref. 19, 21). Examples of a regional approach to air pollution can be found in (ref. 27).

Significant research is also underway in improving current methods of forecasting and monitoring air pollution. The basic goal of NAPCA's study program of meteorological effects on air pollution is to provide pollution control agencies with a logical -- and defensible -- basis for initiating control measures to achieve the desired quality in specific locations or industries. Since 1960, NAPCA has been developing mathematical models for urban areas that relate pollutant sources and atmospheric concentrations by simulating meteorological processes. Such tools can be used for predicting future air pollution levels with respect to growth patterns, for evaluating the impact of various urban configurations, and for assessing various control measures. An extensive study by TRW, Inc. is expected to yield a comprehensive and sophisticated model of regional air pollution aspects for use by the air quality regions in assessing their particular pollution problems. Specific modeling techniques, forecasting programs, and areas of research are outlined in (ref. 19, 20), and other techniques for forecasting are presented in (ref. 28, 29, 32).

The air pollution monitoring and data acquisition activities of the NAPCA have two primary objectives: (1) Provide an adequate nationwide baseline of air quality and emission data so as to define the present population exposures by levels of risk; and (2) Provide adequate ongoing means for appraisal of the effectiveness of nationwide control of air pollution.

NAPCA maintains an extensive surveillance system of both continuous and intermittent samplers. The continuous air monitoring program (CAMP) uses sampler-analyzers to produce numerical and/or graphic information automatically. The implementation of such equipment by state and local agencies had increased to over 600 stations in 1968. Manual systems which collect samples of either gaseous or particulate pollutants for subsequent laboratory analysis are being expanded into a network of over 1,000 stations to serve all major metropolitan areas of more than 25,000 in population (ref. 19, 20).

Emission inventories of carbon monoxide, oxides of nitrogen, oxides of sulfur, hydrocarbons, and particulates have been collected for nearly 100 standard metropolitan statistical areas of the United States as a prelude to designating national air pollution control regions (ref. 20). The data are also to be used in long-term research on such problems as source-receptor relationships, testing of meteorological models, and zoning and transportation planning.

NAPCA also maintains a centralized air quality data bank SAROAD, the "storage and retrieval of air data" system. This facility presently contains air quality information from more than 760 stations, representing approximately 410 urban and 55 nonurban areas and 60 fringe sites.

Until recently, the economic effects of air pollution and the costs of its control were largely unexplored areas. To meet the need for reliable, useful, economic information, NAPCA is conducting studies to: (1) Secure basic data on the damage air pollution causes to vegetation, livestock, and materials; (2) Determine the cost of controlling air pollution emissions; and (3) Analyze the overall economic impact of air pollution control (ref. 20). A general discussion of pollution economics is found in (ref. 5).

## PARTICIPATING PERSONNEL AND ORGANIZATIONS

The bulk of Federal activity concerned with most aspects of air pollution is concentrated in NAPCA within the Department of HEW's Public Health Service. NAPCA operates with about 1,000 employees and on an annual budget of about $74 million as of 1969. Total Federal authorizations for air pollution control in the 1968-1970 time frame amount to $428 million. NAPCA headquarters are in Washington, D. C., with major centers in Durham, N. C., and Cincinnati, Ohio. The Administration conducts a comprehensive program of research and training, financial and technical assistance to State and local agencies, and abatement and control activities. In 1969, contracts with private institutions for research and development totaled more than $16.8 million.

The addresses of the National Air Pollution Control Administration and of Agency officials are as follows:

NAPCA
Ballston Center Tower 2
801 N. Randolph St.
Arlington, Va. 22203

Dr. John T. Middleton - Commissioner
Rm. 905
(NAPCA address as above)
Tel. (703) 557-0234

Jack C. Oppenheimer - Assistant to the Commissioner
Rm. 904
(NAPCA address as above)
Tel. (703) 557-1691

Raymond Smith - Assistant to the Commissioner
for Program Development, Rm. 808
(NAPCA address as above)
Tel. (703) 557-0224

Some work in air pollution is also being conducted elsewhere in the Federal Government, although under NAPCA auspices. Studies on meteorological effects and atmospheric diffusion models are being undertaken within the Environmental Science Services Administration (ESSA), and the Bureau of Mines is studying the pollution problems associated with solid waste disposal.

At the present time, nine Air Pollution Control Regions have been designated. They are listed with addresses and telephone numbers of their directors in (ref. 21).

Various State agencies, particularly California's State Department of Public Health and its State Air Resources Board, are familiar with large urban area problems in air pollution. Metropolitan authorities such as the Los Angeles Motor Vehicle Pollution Control Board and the New York City Department of Air Pollution Control are additional sources of data, specific abatement plans and policies, and technical information.

## CONTRIBUTING PROBLEM AREAS

Most of the major study areas outlined below are sufficiently broad that relatively large systems studies could be easily accommodated. The successful completion of such efforts would mark significant advances in combatting atmospheric pollution. The various subtopics are particularly appropriate for more intensive research and development efforts.

## Vehicular Air Pollution Sources

Contaminants from motor vehicles must be significantly lessened -- or completely eliminated -- if the urban atmosphere is to be salvaged (ref. 30, 19, 20, 25, 33):

(a) Develop improved emission control devices which may be easily installed on the Nation's fleet of conventional automobiles and which would permit the achievement of national emission standards.

(b) Develop an efficient and economical low emission alternative to the internal combustion power plant (see Chapter III, Topic 11). Development of an unconventional vehicle should also consider implementation plans.

(c) Evaluate quantitatively the possible reductions in pollutant levels which might be obtained by introducing various forms of mass transit into the urban area (see Chapter III, Topic 6)

(d) Incorporate pollution considerations into highway planning and urban design; assess the pollution aspects of various roadway configurations and traffic control schemes (see Chapter III, Topics 3 and 4).

## Stationary Air Pollution Sources

A good deal of control technology presently exists for stationary sources; effective application, however, is not always the case.

(a) Develop more efficient and cost effective methods and equipment for reducing air pollution from industrial and power-generating sources.

(b) Develop methods of adequately controlling pollution from the thermal destruction of solid wastes -- both incinerator and non-incinerator burning (see Topic 4 of this Chapter).

(c) Achieve a more complete understanding of dispersion phenomena with respect to stationary sources. Perfected diffusion models are required, particularly for groups of many centrally-located sources.

## Meteorological Research

It is necessary to satisfactorily relate meteorological conditions to pollution effects.

(a) Better understand atmospheric transport, diffusion, and disposition processes in order to assess potential pollution levels and composition of effluents.

(b) Gain a more complete profile of the atmosphere over urban areas, including boundary layer dynamics; the urban heat island effects on temperature gradients and wind structure must be adequately described to permit pollution forecasting.

## Economic Aspects

Identify the types and costs of air pollution damage to various food crops and forms of vegetation, textiles, and other materials.

(a) Identify social and economic effects of changes in air quality.

(b) Assess the costs and benefits to government, various industries, and consumers of meeting National emission standards.

## Air Pollution Monitoring and Data Acquisition

A properly designed monitoring system should be capable of measuring both gaseous and particulate pollutants and of providing data to show trends in pollution levels with time, seasonal variations and meteorological changes, as well as the influence of topography, population density, fuel use, industrial activity, etc. Such information is essential for intelligent planning and in determining the relationship between source emissions and air quality levels.

(a) Design an economically effective continuous automatic regional monitoring system capable of sampling and analyzing particulate and gaseous pollutants in many locations and telemetering data to a regional receiving and processing center.

(b) Develop a multifunctional emission detector capable of tracing carbon monoxide, nitric oxide, and sulfur dioxide from vehicular or stationary sources.

(c) Investigate new sensors and detection technologies for remote evaluation of automobile emissions and stack effluents.

(d) Develop inexpensive in-stack instruments for monitoring stationary sources.

(e) Develop long-path air quality surveillance systems for assessing air quality and pollution characteristics over whole regions; techniques of satellite surveillance of air pollution should be investigated (ref. 7, 8).

## 2. WATER POLLUTION CONTROL

### THE PROBLEM

The problems of water pollution and adequate water supply are becoming progressively more acute in the Nation's urban areas. Not only are metropolitan growth rates outstripping existing supply systems, but cities themselves compound the crisis by contaminating their own water resources and polluting water bodies used by other urban areas. Water pollution is both a lamentable product of urban living and a major threat to the health and aesthetics of the urban environment.

It is impossible to assign an absolute percentage of our Nation's waters to a "polluted" category, since most water bodies lie somewhere between the extremes of naturally clean and obviously contaminated. Waterways are more meaningfully characterized by states of temporary or functional pollution. For instance, rivers are more likely to be polluted at certain times during the year, or lakes might be suitable for industrial uses but not for recreational purposes.

Complex problems are associated not only with preventing water pollution at its various sources but also with cleaning up already contaminated waters. Living organisms, such as bacteria and viruses, oxygen-demanding organics, oxygen-consuming chemical reactants, sediments, soluble and nutrient minerals, heat -- even the life forms proper to water -- all may be considered pollutants when one or a combination of several occurs in excess. Although percentages of water quality degradation caused by municipal, industrial, and non-point waste sources of the above-mentioned pollutants are unknown, the relative magnitudes of the major pollutants dumped into waterways have been categorically tabulated according to discharge source and are listed below[1].

### Sewered Municipal Wastes

(a)  Significant source of decomposable organic solids and bacteria; daily production by the Nation's sewered population:

    .  22.6  Million pounds of biochemical oxygen-demanding material.

    .  27.1  Million pounds of solids.

(b)  Strengths of final waste discharges have been estimated on the basis of average waste treatment efficiencies and are presented below:

Domestic Waste Discharges
(Million pounds per day)

| Type of Treatment | Millions of People | Biochemical Oxygen Demand | Solids |
|---|---|---|---|
| None | 10.3 | 1.7 | 2.1 |
| Primary | 45.2 | 5.0 | 3.6 |
| Secondary | 80.5 | 2.6 | 4.8 |
| Total | 136.0 | 9.3 | 10.5 |

---

1  The facts and figures found in the following six subsections are taken from a letter by FWPCA's Assistant Commissioner for Operations to the National Wildlife Federation's Managing Editor, dated 8 July 1969.

## Industrial Waste Discharges

(a)   Two general classes of material:

  .   Suspended solids and precipitates.

  .   Oxygen-demanding organic material.

(b)   An incomplete listing has indicated a total of at least 51 agents being introduced into the Nation's waters as a result of industrial processes:

Discharge to Waterways (Est. )
(Million pounds per day)

|  | Biochemical Oxygen Demand | Solids |
|---|---|---|
| Wasteload (Est. ) | 60. 3 | 54. 3 |
| 19% Treatment by public agencies | (6. 6) | (6. 0) |
| 57% Treatment by industries | (19. 7) | (17. 9) |
| Total | 34. 0 | 30. 9 |

(c)   Major water-using industries discharge approximately three times the weight of each class of waste compared to that of all sewered persons in the United States.

## Thermal Power Generation

(a)   Approximately 150 billion gallons per day of water heated to an average of $13^{\circ}$F above ambient temperature are discharged from thermal, electric power-generation plants.

(b)   The advent of nuclear power-generation plants has proven even more disrupting to the temperature regimen of waterways' aquatic ecosystems.

(c)   Acceleration of chemical reaction rates, both desirable and undesirable, and increased solubility of materials in water are the consequences.

## Salinity of Waters

(a)   Principal man-caused source is irrigated agriculture.

(b) Methods of producing saline waterways:

. Flushing of soil salts from root zones of plant life.

. Evapotranspiration processes that fail to reduce the volume of minerals in solution in the residual water supply.

## Mining

(a) Significant source of sediment, dissolved minerals, and acidity.

(b) Chemical reaction of water against exposed mineral seams in man-made mines is reportedly responsible for the introduction of four million tons of sulphuric acid equivalents into waterways each year.

## Natural Runoff

(a) Largest single source of material transport to waterways:

. Weight of sediments from runoff is at least ten times greater than that of all municipal and industrial waste discharges.

. Most runoff materials are inert and settleable.

. Erosion is increased by a factor of four to nine on agricultural land and by as much a 100 in construction areas.

(b) Paving and drainage systems facilitate flushing of urban areas, but --

. Urban runoff is strong in organics and bacteria.

. Urban runoff is roughly twice as concentrated as raw municipal sewage in the initial phases of a rainfall.

The problem, therefore, is to develop new and evolutionary methods for eradicating existing water pollution in urban areas and preventing further contamination of urban water supplies.

## STATE-OF-THE-ART

In 1956, Congress passed the first permanent Federal Water
Pollution Control Act (ref. 46), which inititated a program of Federal
grants for municipalities to assist them in building and improving sewage treatment works. The construction grants program, which began
one year later, provided for and supported the building and expansion
of more than 8,000 treatment facilities during the next decade, costing
a total of $4.5 billion, of which more than $1.0 billion was in Federal
funds.

The Water Quality Act of 1965 (ref. 47) marked the beginning of a
major offensive against water pollution with the establishment of the
Federal Water Pollution Control Administration (FWPCA) within the
Department of Health, Education, and Welfare. This public law also
required all states to establish water quality standards for their interstate and coastal waters. The passage of this legislation initiated blue-
print action on guides to future planning, waste treatment works construction, manpower training, technical assistance, and a program for
pollution surveillance. Furthermore, means for enforcement action
through Federal intervention which had been clearly defined in previous
legislation (ref. 35), were restated for cases where States failed to
adopt appropriate water quality standards -- with particular emphasis
on situations in which polluted waters from sources in one locality or
State affected people living in another.

In 1966, the Clean Water Restoration Act (ref. 34) transferred the FWPCA to the Department of the Interior and greatly increased authorizations for grants to help build sewage treatment plants, for research, and for grants to State water pollution control programs.

For planning purposes, the Nation has been divided into twenty major river basins, and immediate pollution clean-up needs and long-range preventive measures have been charted. The Federal contribution is to work with the State Waterway Planning Commissions and other local agencies in formulating up-to-date, overall pollution control plans for each basin, which outline the possible and feasible technical solutions, indicate how the costs are to be shared (ref. 40), and recommend the necessary institutions for effective implementation. Acting upon the above-mentioned legislation, coordination of an effective pollution control program has been undertaken by the FWPCA, whose efforts include the review of basin planning activities and an evaluation of current State clean-up activities (ref. 37). The development of comprehensive water quality control and abatement plans for basins is currently receiving considerable aid in the form of Federal grants, technical programs, and authorized funds for RD&D projects (ref. 38, 41).

The FWPCA's research efforts now run the gamut of scientific investigation and technological development -- from basic research through applied research, pilot plants, field evaluation, and demonstrations. Research activities are carried on either through work in its own laboratories or indirectly through grants to colleges, universities, and other public and private institutions. The state-of-the-art for on-going research in all phases of water pollution control is adequately summarized in its yearly listing of RD&D projects (ref. 38, 41) in which a complete record of grants and contracts awarded for that particular fiscal year is provided. Many such projects, which are currently underway, have as goals the demonstration of wastewater purification and reuse, acid mine-drainage control, improved industrial waste processes, and control or treatment of combined sanitary and storm sewer overflow. Advanced waste treatment means and methods are presently in greatly needed to assist in the development of effective, safe, and economical wastewater systems.

Sections 5 and 6 of Public Law 660 (ref. 46) authorize the award of grants and contracts for research, development, and demonstration projects. Five types of grants and contracts exist, all of which may be awarded to individuals and educational institutions and which are more fully described in (ref. 36). The following lists the five types of available funds:

1. Demonstration Grants and Contracts
2. Storm and Combined Sewer Grants and Contracts
3. Advanced Waste Treatment Grants and Contracts
4. Industrial Waste Treatment Grants and Contracts
5. Research Grants and Contracts

Details concerning these awards and applications are available from:

Project Coordination
Office of Research and Development
FWPCA
U.S. Department of the Interior
Washington, D.C. 20242

Public Law 660 also authorizes Training Grants and Research Fellowships designed to encourage cooperation with appropriate agencies, institutions, and individuals in the conduct of training related to study of the causes, control and prevention of water pollution. Further details may be obtained from:

Division of Manpower and Training
Office of Operations
Training Grants Branch
FWPCA
U.S. Department of the Interior
Washington, D.C. 20242

Each year, the FWPCA issues a report entitled "The Cost of Clean Water" (ref. 39), which notes the advances made in pollution control systems and effectively presents the changing state-of-the-art.

## PARTICIPATING PERSONNEL AND ORGANIZATIONS

### Federal Water Pollution Control Administration

Independence Building, Crystal Mall
1921 Jefferson Davis Highway
Arlington, Virginia 22202
Tel (703) 557-1221

This Federal organization oversees the national water pollution-control program, much of which was outlined in the previous subsection. The FWPCA's responsibilities are clearly defined in the Federal Water Pollution Control Act and its subsequent amendments (ref. 35, 46, 47). Representatives from the different divisions are available for presentations at universities, provided sufficient lead time is allowed for the formulation of travel plans. Valuable initial assistance and background information in the field of water pollution control is provided by FWPCA's Office of Public Information. Helpful publications are available through this Office for any proposed project (ref. 38, 39, 41). A listing of current water research publications can be found in (ref. 45). The FWPCA's "Clean Water Fact Sheets", also obtained through the Public Information Office, afford the public a simple overview of on-going programs and indicate by what methods individuals, communities, cities, and states can become involved in the water pollution control program.

State Water Pollution Control Agencies and Interstate Commissions

The title and address for each state water pollution control agency and the eight interstate commissions are listed on the following page (reprinted from FWPCA "fact sheet"). Information about water pollution in each locality is perhaps more directly available through these agencies and commissions. It is important to remember that all water pollution control projects and programs are generally initiated at the State and interstate level. At present, the FWPCA is attempting to coordinate the various state policies and organize them into a national set of optimal standards for water quality, the problems of which are outlined in (ref. 42).

# State Water Pollution Control Agencies

INFORMATION about water pollution activities in your locality is available from the offices listed below:

**ALABAMA**
Water Improvement Commission
State Office Building
Montgomery, Alabama 36104

**ALASKA**
Alaska Dept. of Health & Welfare
Alaska Office Building
Juneau, Alaska 99801

**ARIZONA**
Environmental Health Service
Department of Health
Hayden Plaza West
4019 North 33rd Avenue
Phoenix, Arizona 85017

**ARKANSAS**
Arkansas Pollution Control Comm.
1100 Harrington Avenue
Little Rock, Arkansas 72202

**CALIFORNIA**
State Water Resources Control Board
1416-9th St
Sacramento, California 95814

**COLORADO**
Department of Public Health
4210 East 11th Avenue
Denver, Colorado 80220

**CONNECTICUT**
State Water Resources Commission
Room 223, State Office Building
650 Main Street
Hartford, Connecticut 06115

**DELAWARE**
Delaware Air and Water Resources
Commission
Loockerman Street and Legislative
Avenue
Dover, Delaware 19901

**DISTRICT OF COLUMBIA**
District of Columbia Department of
Public Health
300 Indiana Avenue, N.W.
Washington, D. C. 20001

**FLORIDA**
Air & Water Pollution Control Comm.
306 W Jefferson
Tallahassee, Florida 32301

**GEORGIA**
State Water Quality Control Board
47 Trinity Avenue, S. W.
Atlanta, Georgia 30334

**GUAM**
Public Health and Social Services
Government of Guam
P.O. Box 2816
Agana, Guam 96910

**HAWAII**
Environmental Health Division
Hawaii Dept. of Health
P. O. Box 3378
Honolulu, Hawaii 96801

**IDAHO**
Engineering & Sanitation Div.
State Department of Health
P. O. Box 640
Boise, Idaho 83701

**ILLINOIS**
State Sanitary Water Board
State Office Building
400 South Spring Street
Springfield, Illinois 62706

**INDIANA**
Stream Pollution Control Board
1330 West Michigan Street
Indianapolis, Indiana 46207

**IOWA**
Water Pollution Division
State Department of Health
Lucas State Office Building
Des Moines, Iowa 50319

**KANSAS**
Environmental Health Services
State Department of Health
Topeka Avenue at Tenth
Topeka, Kansas 66612

**KENTUCKY**
Kentucky Water Pollution Control
Comm.
275 East Main Street
Frankfort, Kentucky 40601

**LOUISIANA**
Louisiana Stream Control Commission
P. O. Drawer FC, University Station
Baton Rouge, Louisiana 70803

**MAINE**
Water and Air Environmental Improve-
ment Commission
State House
Augusta, Maine 04330

**MARYLAND**
Environmental Health Services
State Department of Health
2305 N. Charles Street
Baltimore, Maryland 21218
and
State Dept. of Water Resources
State Office Building
Annapolis, Maryland 21401

**MASSACHUSETTS**
Division of Water Pollution Control
Department of Natural Resources
100 Cambridge Street
Boston, Massachusetts 02202

**MICHIGAN**
Water Resources Commission
Station A, Steven T. Mason Bldg.
Lansing, Michigan 48913

**MINNESOTA**
Minnesota Pollution Control Agency
717 Delaware St., S.E.
Minneapolis, Minnesota 55440

**MISSISSIPPI**
Mississippi Air and Water
Pollution Control Commission
P. O. Box 827
Jackson, Mississippi 39205

**MISSOURI**
Missouri Water Pollution Board
P. O. Box 154
Jefferson City, Missouri 65101

**MONTANA**
Montana Water Pollution Council
State Department of Health
Laboratory Building
Helena, Montana 59601

**NEBRASKA**
Environmental Health Services
State Department of Health
Box 94757, State House Station
Lincoln, Nebraska 68509

**NEVADA**
Bureau of Environmental Health
Dept. of Health, Welfare & Rehabilitation
Nye Building
201 South Fall Street
Carson City, Nevada 89701

**NEW HAMPSHIRE**
Water Supply and Pollution Control
Commission
61 South Spring Street
Concord, New Hampshire 03301

**NEW JERSEY**
Div. of Air and Clean Water
State Department of Health
P. O. Box 1540
Trenton, New Jersey 08625

**NEW MEXICO**
New Mexico Water Quality Control Comm.
Department of Health & Social
Service
P. O. Box 2348
Santa Fe, New Mexico 87501

**NEW YORK**
Division of Pure Waters
State Department of Health
84 Holland Avenue
Albany, New York 12208

**NORTH CAROLINA**
State Dept. of Water and Air
Resources
P. O. Box 9392
Raleigh, North Carolina 27603

**NORTH DAKOTA**
Environmental Health & Engineering
Services
State Department of Health
Bismarck, North Dakota 58501

**OHIO**
Water Pollution Control Board
State Department of Health
P. O. Box 118
Columbus, Ohio 43216

**OKLAHOMA**
Environmental Health Service
State Department of Health
3400 North Eastern
Oklahoma City, Oklahoma 73111

**OREGON**
Oregon State Sanitary Authority
P. O. Box 231
Portland, Oregon 97207

**PENNSYLVANIA**
Bureau of Sanitary Engineering
State Department of Health
P. O. Box 90
Harrisburg, Pennsylvania 17120

**PUERTO RICO**
Puerto Rico Dept. of Health
Ponce de Leon Avenue
San Juan, Puerto Rico 00908

**RHODE ISLAND**
Div. of Water Pollution Control
Rhode Island Dept. of Health
335 State Office Building
Providence, Rhode Island 02903

**SOUTH CAROLINA**
S. C. Water Pollution Control Authority
J. Marion Sims Building
Columbia, South Carolina 29201

**SOUTH DAKOTA**
Division of Sanitary Engineering
State Department of Health
Pierre, South Dakota 57501

**TENNESSEE**
Tenn. Stream Pollution Control Board
Cordell Hull Building
Sixth Avenue, North
Nashville, Tennessee 37219

**TEXAS**
Texas Water Quality Board
1108 Lavaca Street
Austin, Texas 78701

**UTAH**
State Water Pollution Control
Committee
44 Medical Drive
Salt Lake City, Utah 84113

**VERMONT**
Vermont Department of Water
Resources
State Office Building
Montpelier, Vermont 05602

**VIRGINIA**
State Water Control Board
P. O. Box 11143
Richmond, Virginia 23230

**VIRGIN ISLANDS**
Virgin Islands Dept. of Health
Charlotte Amalie
St. Thomas, Virgin Islands 00802

**WASHINGTON**
Washington Water Pollution Control
Commission
P. O. Box 829
Olympia, Washington 98501

**WEST VIRGINIA**
Division of Water Resources
Department of Natural Resources
1201 Greenbrier St., East
Charleston, West Virginia 25311

**WISCONSIN**
Division of Environmental Protection
Department of Natural Resources
P.O. Box 450
Madison, Wisconsin 53701

**WYOMING**
Division of Sanitary Engineering
State Department of Public Health
State Office Building
Cheyenne, Wyoming 82001

# Interstate Commissions

Bi-State Development Agency
Suite 619 Paul Brown Bldg.
St. Louis, Missouri 63101
Illinois
Missouri

Interstate Sanitation Commission
10 Columbus Circle
New York, New York 10019
Connecticut
New Jersey
New York

Ohio River Valley Water Sanitation
Commission
414 Walnut Street
Cincinnati, Ohio 45202
Illinois          Ohio
Indiana          Pennsylvania
Kentucky         Virginia
New York         West Virginia

Delaware River Basin Commission
25 Scotch Road, P.O. Box 360
Trenton, New Jersey 08603
Delaware
New Jersey
New York
Pennsylvania

Klamath River Compact Commission
P. O. Box 388
Sacramento, California 95802
California
Oregon

Tennessee River Basin Water
Pollution Control Commission
Central Services Building
Nashville, Tennessee 37219
Kentucky
Mississippi
Tennessee

Interstate Commission on the
Potomac River Basin
Transportation Building
815-17th Street, N.W.
Washington, D. C. 20006
District of Columbia
Maryland
Pennsylvania
Virginia
West Virginia

New England Interstate Water
Pollution Control Commission
73 Tremont Street
Boston, Massachusetts 02108
Connecticut          New York
Maine                Rhode Island
Massachusetts        Vermont
New Hampshire

U. S. DEPARTMENT OF THE INTERIOR
Federal Water Pollution Control Administration
Office of Public Information
Washington, D.C. 20242

## Water Resources Council (WRC)

> 1025 Vermont Avenue, N. W.
> Suite 900
> Washington, D.C.  20005
> Tel  (202) 382-6104

Since 1936, Federal interest has existed in economic models and optimal planning for water resources, which includes dealing with the economic impact of preserving scenic rivers.  To achieve these ends, the Water Resources Planning Act of 1965 (ref. 52) established the Water Resources Council  along with four river basin river commissions.

1. The Pacific Northwest
2. The Great Lakes
3. The Souris-Red-Rainy, and
4. The New England

The Secretaries of the various Executive Departments comprise the WRC's membership, which now makes a Cabinet-level agency responsible for the development of unified plans and policies on current and future water-resource problems.  Activities of the WRC to date are summarized in detail in (ref. 50, 51).  The Council's concern for urban water problems centers principally upon municipal water supplies and flood plans; the WRC's major emphasis, however, is on the river basin concept of water-resource analysis and planning.  WRC's purpose, the nature of its policies, and its reviewing procedure for reports are outlined in (ref. 48).  The Council's most recent report on proposed procedures for evaluating water and related land resources projects is (ref. 49).

Available information on any aspect of the WRC's history or on-

going activity can be obtained from its Executive Director at the

above address.

## CONTRIBUTING PROBLEM AREAS

The following areas represent only a few of the critical elements

in water pollution problems. At best, they ask a number of the more

important questions which are, perhaps, most pertinent to specific

urban areas.

### Public Perception of Water Pollution

(a)  What criteria do people employ in determining whether a
     waterway is polluted:

  - Appearance
  - Taste
  - Knowledge of the waterway's uses
  - Availability for public use

(b)  What standards define acceptable levels of water pollution.

(c)  To what extent does the public wish to participate in defining
     these standards.

(d)  In what ways does the public feel it can participate in
     combatting the water pollution problem.

### Community Groups Involved in Water Pollution Clean-Up

A study on the evolution of community groups, responsible

for the initiation of river basin programs and other waterway

projects, should be made to determine (ref. 44):

(a) Whether sufficient authority is invested in the initial constituents of such groups.

(b) To what extent they have been successful:

- Formulating problem definitions
- Creating public awareness
- Actual fund-raising and program implementation

(c) What recognizable constraints or barriers exist to prevent the origin and operation of concerned community organizations.

## Basic Design Programs

(a) Adequately formulate a water pollution control project for a given locale which outlines in particular:

- A definition of necessary water standards based upon local consumption purposes.
- Alternative proposals which can effectively attain and maintain these standards.
- Associated costs for each alternative proposal.
- A statement on unavoidable political constraints and expected community interference to the implementation of the different action-plans.
- A final recommendation.

(b) The compilation of available Federal, State, and local assistance for the benefit of concerned community organizations.

(c) A formal study on the implementation aspects of a basic design proposal, ranging from necessary interaction with the local community to supporting Federal policy and possible assistance; deserving special emphasis should be the political constraints.

## A Definition of Water Pollution

Based upon order-of-magnitude estimates for waste products dumped into waterways, determine:

(a) Relative percentages of the different waste materials currently in local area waterways.

(b) Levels of concentration for each waste material which would constitute a polluted situation (i. e. , a violation of existing health standards).

(c) Each pollutant's effect on the waterway's ecology and what limitation it imposes upon human uses.

## Industrial Pollutants

(a) Establish cost profiles (ref. 39, vol. 4) for:

- The harmful effects which individual waste products have upon waterways.
- The reduction of these pollutants to acceptable levels.

(b) A catalog outlining on-going, industrially-sponsored water pollution control programs.

(c) A study on how the public perceives industrial pollution and a summary of community-action programs undertaken to combat the dumping of industrial pollutants into local waters.

(d) Proposals for methods to reduce industrial pollutants, specifying:

- Who should direct such a program.
- Where the financial responsibility must be assumed, taking into account all sources of available funds.
- Recent technological developments which aid in the reduction of pollutants.

## Public Benefits

A statement on what the public stands to gain from a clean-up of polluted waterways, supported by a cost-benefit analysis which assigns relative values to the different benefits:

(a) Can community-action programs to clean up waterways afford related benefits to economically disadvantaged areas.

(b) Can such proposals win support through a redistribution of Federal and Municipal funds currently used to pipe fresh water from outlying reservoirs.

## Waste Treatment Plants

(a) What size plant is feasible and economically justified.

- Regional (macro-level) plant which requires significant piping and trenching.
- Neighborhood treatment plants for individual communities.
- Water treatment plant at the family level to purify and eliminate certain wastes.

(b) Large-scale studies are needed to assess the impact on the overall community water pollution program of various plant locations, sizes, and combinations.

(c) Evaluate current waste removal techniques; propose evolutionary methods for handling waste waters.

## Mathematical Modeling

(a) State-of-the-art: FWPCA has developed a 200 by 2000 array matrix which incorporates linear and non-linear programming to define a dynamic flow model for urban waste waters.

(b) Additional needs:

- Identification of modeling constraints.
- How to make initial assumptions which bring the program closer to reality.
- Reduction of idealization without increasing matrix complexity.

(c) Further application:

- Employment of gaming techniques to simulate political reaction to water treatment and control programs.
- Establishment of data storage and retrieval systems containing levels of waterway pollutants and information preventive pollution control programs.

(a) Develop flow simulation models for storm waters channeling through urban areas:

.   Define sub-basins within the metropolitan area.
.   Determine volume-time paths.
.   Determine the locations for necessary water
    control valves.

(b) Design efficient storm water control valves for operation
    during emergency conditions:

.   Storage areas where storm waters can be held
    until they can be handled by treatment plants during
    off-peak hours (e. g. , underground tank in Chicago).
.   Means of increasing volume flow rates (e. g. , addition
    of certain polymers to pipe water in Dallas has been
    shown to reduce internal friction and thus speed up
    the flow).

# 3. ABATEMENT OF URBAN NOISE

## THE PROBLEM

Aircraft at municipal airports, intensive construction in downtown areas, and motor vehicles have combined with innumerable other noise sources to produce unparalleled levels of disturbance in every city throughout the Nation (ref. 62). Surely, efforts to promote a more attractive urban environment cannot be fully successful if the increased distraction and annoyance of unwanted noise remain unchecked. The Science Adviser's Committee on Environmental Quality called noise "sound without value" (ref. 56), yet even this definition does not adequately underscore its physiological hazards and economic costs. New and louder sources of noise have appeared in the urban area as the inevitable by-product of a modernized society. In fact, recent studies have revealed that people often equate noise production with useful power (ref. 56). Consequently, noise has, in many cases, become the publicly-accepted accompaniment to progress -- a misconception which frequently stifles any inclination to initiate abatement programs.

The medical world has become increasingly concerned about prolonged public exposure to high noise levels, frequently citing the various adverse effects to sensory and other physiological functions (ref. 54, 58, 53). Surprisingly, intense noise is found not only in heavy industrial or aircraft operations, but in commercial and business areas as well. In fact, findings have concluded that possible noise levels in dwellings, particularly in kitchen areas, are beginning to approach those experienced in factories (ref. 56). The psychological and social stresses to which society is subjected are partly traceable to irritation provoked by undesirable noise sources. In addition, noise has been found to be a disruptive influence at all times of the day, capable of interfering with both job performance (ref. 55) and relaxation (ref. 58).

Although the sonic boom created by jet aircraft has received widespread public attention (ref. 61, 59), numerous other sources of excessive noise within buildings, as well as in the outdoor environment, have not yet been adequately analyzed. The solution lies not only in improving our scientific capability to meet the problem, but also in establishing public conviction that a less noisy urban environment is a reasonable and attainable objective (ref. 57). Unwanted sound must be eliminated through joint technological and economic planning. This will involve certain costs, of course, but the willingness of society to meet them depends upon its unwillingness to tolerate valueless sound.

## STATE-OF-THE-ART

The most comprehensive on-going study on all aspects of the noise problem is currently being compiled by the Commerce Technical Advisory Board (CTAB) within the Department of Commerce. The CTAB plans to publish a report of its findings in early 1970 which will discuss extensively the physics of noise, different sources and causes, and resulting structural damage and deleterious effects to human health and the environment. Generic mechanisms for abating noise are being investigated in connection with many of the typical problems which noise creates. The economics of providing desirable public benefits through a noise abatement effort are also being studied, along with the legal aspects of the problem. It is hoped that the forthcoming document will also provide a concluding, definitive statement on the possible roles for citizens, industry, and the Government.

Various approaches to the study of noise have been constructively assimilated by the Federal Government, thus delineating specific topic areas which are ideal for detailed investigation. In the category of "outdoor noise" there are the two major contributors: aircraft and surface transportation. Within the Department of Transportation, the Federal Aviation Administration is directly concerned with the former, while the Office of Noise Abatement has dealt specifically with the latter (see Chapter III for further details). Other primary noise sources in the urban environment are building construction, heavy industry, and commercial delivery operations. As of yet, these sources have received considerably less attention from Federal authorities.

Federal interest in "indoor noise" problems has resulted in an expanded program for applied experimental research in architectural acoustics under the direction of the National Bureau of Standards. The Federal Housing Administration has sponsored research work along similar lines and has fostered studies on noise control in both urban and suburban apartments. Studies conducted by FHA on the insulation of dwellings against aircraft noise have provided building contractors with a comprehensive guide to solving the intricacies of the architectural acoustics problem. The Public Health Service has sponsored research projects on noise control in hospitals over the past seven years. In the industrial sector, relatively little effort or funding has been devoted to basic or applied research and the development of improved testing techniques in the areas of architectural acoustics and noise control. Relevant university research has generally been limited to short-term studies due to lack of program continuity and adequate laboratory facilities.

Under the category of "occupational noise", studies have determined that the numbers of workers who experience conditions unsafe to hearing is estimated to be in excess of 6 million and may be as high as 16 million (ref. 56, p. 32). Recognition of the harmful role noise plays in hearing loss has prompted research aimed at defining noise-exposure criteria for safeguarding hearing; existing data permits only tentative judgments for certain types of occupation exposures. Federal activities concerned with occupational noise problems and their control can be classified into research, training, and regulatory areas ---- an excellent, overall account of which is given in (ref. 56, pp. 36-38).

Widespread recognition of the need to institute noise abatement programs has occurred only within the last decade. Consequently, the state-of-the-art in controlling urban noise has not progressed much beyond the indentification of specific problem areas. Today's project proposals for attacking the noise problem in urban areas will constitute the basic groundwork for all future efforts in the field.

## PARTICIPATING PERSONNEL AND ORGANIZATIONS

With the exception of well-publicized civic efforts to combat the sonic boom problem created by jet aircraft and air traffic noise at municipal airports, there have been relatively few coordinated attacks against urban noise or adamant public complaints about its resulting health hazards. Increased sensitivity to the situation on the part of the Federal Government, however, has resulted in the establishment of several committees whose responsibility is to define the scope of the existing noise problem and its future significance.

The Federal Council for Science and Technology's Committee on Environmental Quality represents one element within the Government that has reviewed the noise problem (ref. 54) with the explicit purpose of proposing a more adequate Federal program directed toward ident-fying the effects of noise on man and his environment and developing effective means for abatement.

The Commerce Technical Advisory Board (CTAB) within the
Department of Commerce (DOC) is scheduled to wind up its comprehensive study of the noise problem by late 1969. To date, the Committee's
efforts represent the most intensive Federal attempt to confront the
"noise" issue on a nationwide scale. Further information on the status
of the CTAB report can be obtained from:

> \* Daniel R. Flynn - Executive Secretary
> Room 5088
> CTAB Panel on Noise Abatement
> Office of Assistant Secretary for Science and
> Technology
> Department of Commerce
> Washington, D.C. 20230
> Tel. (202) 967-4595

The Secretary of Commerce is the chairman of the Subcommittee
on Noise Pollution of the recently formed Environmental Quality
Council. Other members of this Executive level group include the
Secretaries from the Departments of Transportation, Housing and Urban
Development, and Health, Education, and Welfare. It was under this
Subcommittee's direction that the CTAB was formed.

The DOC has also maintained a specific concern in the noise
problem through its National Bureau of Standards which is responsible
for measuring noise levels, providing calibration techniques, and
presenting the state-of-the-art in architectural acoustics.

Both the Department of Transportation (DOT) and NASA have

---

\* Denotes Interviewee

allocated substantial funds for further investigation of aircraft noise.

Directing the noise abatement effort in the areas of air traffic and surface transportation within DOT's Office of the Secretary is:

Charles R. Foster - Director
Office of Noise Abatement
Department of Transportation
Room 801
800 Independence Ave., S. W.
Washington, D. C.  20590
Tel.  (202)  962-5503

The Environmental Science Services Administration is conducting significant research work in its Air resources Lab with particular interest having been expressed in the propagation of both the sonic boom and infra-sonic noise.

The Department of Housing and Urban Development is in the process of initiating housing projects which will have minimal noise generation in the construction process and will exhibit model insulation techniques.

## CONTRIBUTING PROBLEM AREAS

### Noise Control and Acoustical Considerations for Indoors

(a) Correlate human response with physical measurements of acoustical performance for different wall designs -- specifically:

. Light frame construction
. Hollow core doors
. Holes and cracks as possible noise leaks
. Points of entry for pipes

(b) Establish the applicability of lab tests on wall and floor models to predict the acoustical behavior of large wall and floor constructions.

(c) Determine the noise level outputs of essential home service systems such as plumbing, heating, and kitchen appliances.

(d) Propose methods for determining how adaptable man has become to specific noise sources commonly found in today's households and whether adapatability is related to evolved hearing defects.

## Noise Radiating from Surface Transportation in the Urban Area

(a) Determine the generation source and intensity of traffic noise for the different types of urban environment, such as:

- downtown traffic intersections
- office building sectors
- localities where construction is underway
- commercial business districts
- residential areas

(b) Establish means for effectively controlling traffic noise:

- Adoption and enforcement of anti-noise ordinances
- Improved design, construction, and location.
- of expressways and traffic arteries.
- Reduction of the noise levels and elimination of the noise sources on the various metropolitan vehicles.

(c) Conduct cost studies on adverse effects resulting from traffic noise:

- Value depreciation of property along noisy arteries.
- Providing sufficient sound-proofing for homes, apartments, schools, etc.

## Occupational Hazards of Noise

(a) Develop techniques for rating noise hazards, and classify them according to degree of potential harm.

(b) Distinguish between the types of noise workers are subject to and the harmful effects caused by each:

- Impact noise
- Narrow-band noise
- Intermittent noise
- Ultra-and infra-sonic noise.

# 4. SOLID WASTE MANAGEMENT

## THE PROBLEM

Continuing technological progress and improvements in methods of manufacturing, packaging, and marketing have resulted in new conveniences for the consumer and a rapid choking of the urban environment. With the appearance of aluminum containers, plastic wrappings, "no return" glass bottles, and metal foil, the material discarded by purchasers has increased drastically in bulk and been altered dramatically in its characteristics.

Whereas, the average American was responsible for 2.7 lbs. of trash per day in 1920, per capita solid waste accumulation is now more than 5 lbs. per day. Excluding solids and dissolved materials in domestic sewage, solid wastes from residential, commercial, and industrial sources presently exceed 200 million tons per year, and are increasing at a compound annual rate of 3% (ref. 76, 77, 19). Agricultural, forestry, and animal wastes push the overall annual total up to about 350 million tons. Solid waste from urban areas alone is estimated to be near 185 million tons per year. This represents a 60% increase in the Nation's tonnage of solid waste since 1950, twice as great as the percentage population growth for the same period. Furthermore, the annual tonnage is expected to increase by another 50% in the next decade.

The rising concentration of population in expanding metropolitan and other urban areas has presented these communities with serious financial, management, intergovernmental, and technical problems. San Francisco, for example, had disposed of its solid wastes in the lowlands of San Francisco Bay for decades; but, continued pollution of the Bay was prohibited, and the city has been unable to get the go-ahead on incinerators from the air pollution control authorities. The only alternative remaining for disposal of the city's 1800 daily tons of refuse is to transport it -- either 375 miles by rail north to barren areas in Lassen County or to the nearby community of Mountain View to reclaim waste land for a future park -- or to develop new disposal technologies.

Other cities are similarly feeling the pinch of diminishing dumping grounds and increasing solid waste accumulation. Philadelphia is investigating the possibility of burying garbage in worked-out anthracite mines 100 miles away. Chicago and Milwaukee are also considering rail-haul solutions to the solid waste crisis. The potential magnitude of the problem is dramatically underscored by the 1968 "garbage strike" in New York City.

Inefficient and improper methods of disposal of solid wastes result in scenic blights and create hazards to public health -- including pollution of air, water, and land resources, accident hazards, and increases in rodent and vector disease. Accumulations of waste also have an adverse effect on land values and create public nuisances. There is an urgent need to stimulate evolutionary concepts and techniques in solid waste management or face the alternative of urban areas being inundated with refuse. Innovations are required in the collection, disposal, and salvage of waste materials and in planning waste management systems. A perceptive discussion of future facilities needs is presented in (ref. 64).

## STATE-OF-THE-ART

There are three basic methods of solid waste disposal presently in wide use: open dumping, incineration, and sanitary landfill. Rough estimates suggest that about 75% of the Nation's trash by tonnage still ends up in open-air dumping grounds, 15% is burned in incinerators, and 5% is used in the sanitary landfill processes (ref. 63, 71, 73).

Because the volume of solid waste is increasing so rapidly and excess land suitable for dumping is decreasing, this simple disposal method is rarely considered in future solid waste management plans for urban areas. Where presently unusable land is available, sanitary landfill is popular and economically competitive. A year's rubbish from 10,000 persons will cover an acre to a depth of seven feet.

Incineration is the most common alternative to raw dumping being utilized by metropolitan areas. Burning of solid waste can reduce the volume to approximately 10% of the original, and waste heat generated can be utilized for power generation. The Mayson Plant in Atlanta and the Southwest Plant in Chicago are examples of this productive use of waste. Montreal is building an $8.5 million incinerator facility which will consume 1,200 tons per day and produce marketable steam which will reduce waste disposal costs to less than $5.50 per ton. In addition, it has made use of the latest technology for eliminating air pollution effects (ref. 63, 71, 73).

The possibility of turning waste material into a productive resource is perhaps the most attractive alternative to traditional disposal methods and is receiving considerable attention on the Federal level. The Solid Waste Disposal Act of 1965 notes that "... the failure or inability to salvage and reuse such materials economically results in unnecessary waste and depletion of our natural resources..." (ref. 76).

A significant program is being conducted within the Department of Interior's Bureau of Mines to recover the mineral content of the Nation's wastes (ref. 66, 68). Of the 50 million or so tons of solid waste which is collected annually in a systematic manner, there are about 30 million tons of paper, 4 million tons of plastics, 48 billion cans, 26 billion glass containers, and 100 million worn-out tires. When municipal wastes are incinerated, minerals and glass account for about 75% of the residue. It is estimated that the residues discharged by incinerators annually contain 3 million tons of ferrous metals and 250,000 tons of mixed, non-ferrous metals including aluminum, zinc, copper, lead, and tin (ref. 70 ).

In the Bureau of Mines College Park Program, a pilot project has been set up to investigate the feasibility of recovering such minerals from incinerator residues. Another research activity is seeking ways to recover glass from refuse, which may total 15 million tons annually. The Bureau is also attempting to ascertain new uses for recovered materials and to make recycled wastes competitive costwise with natural resources (ref. 70).

Another candidate for reuse is the junked automobile. Each year, millions of autos are abandoned across the Nation, 50,000 on the streets of New York City alone. Moreover, the national car discard rate is expected to reach 8 million per year by 1975. The Bureau of Mines has been involved in finding new uses for these autos, as scrap steel, sources of non-ferrous metals, and catalysts in steel production (ref. 67).

The possibility also exists of building with refuse. A Japanese developer, Tezuka Kosan Co., Ltd., has publicized a method of compacting solid waste into building blocks. Chicago and Detroit are investigating compacting methods -- either to produce building and fill material from waste or simply as a means of reducing its volume.

Composting, popular in European countries, is virtually unexplored in the United States as a means of productively utilizing solid waste. A bibliography on the subject is (ref. 79).

The collection and transportation of solid waste still accounts for 75% to 85% of the cost of disposal in urban areas. Present methods and future concepts are described in (ref. 63, 64). An analytical study of planning for such collection is presented in (ref. 75).

Under the Solid Waste Disposal Act, the Department of Health, Education, and Welfare (HEW) is empowered to encourage, where practicable, interstate, interlocal, and regional solid waste disposal programs and make grants to states and interstate agencies for conducting surveys of practices and problems of developing solid waste disposal plans for such areas. Examples of regional studies and plans of this type are (ref. 65, 69, 74, 78).

## PARTICIPATING PERSONNEL AND ORGANIZATIONS

Federal interest in solid waste management is concentrated primarily in two agencies: The Bureau of Solid Waste Management in HEW's Public Health Service, and the Bureau of Mines Solid Waste Research Program in the Department of the Interior.

HEW is responsible for the bulk of the activity in collecting, transporting, and disposing of solid waste. The Solid Waste Disposal Act allocated $20 million to the Department for this purpose in Fiscal Year 1969, and authorized the Secretary to make grants-in-aid to public or private agencies and institutions and to individuals for research, training, surveys, and demonstrations.

The address of the Bureau of Solid Waste Management and Agency officials are as follows:

Bureau of Solid Waste Management
Environmental Control Administration
Twinbrook Bldgs.
12720 Twinbrook Parkway
Rockville, Md. 20852

Richard Vaugh - Director
Rm. 309
(address as above)
Tel. (301) 496-8441

Andrew W. Breidenbach - Director of Research
Rm. 317                           and Development
(address as above)
Tel. (301) 496-8441

The Department of the Interior is responsible for waste management associated with mining and for investigating the recovery and reuse of mineral resources from municipal solid waste. In 1969, Research and Development activities received $480,000.

The Department's Solid Waste Management Program is under the direction of:

* Frank J. Cservenyak - Manager
Solid Waste Management Program
Bureau of Mines
Rm. 4633
18th and C Sts., N.W.
Washington, D.C. 20240
Tel. (202) 343-4743

According to the Solid Waste Disposal Act, the collection and disposal of solid wastes should continue to be primarily the function of State, regional, and local agencies. Federal action through financial and technical assistance and leadership in the development, demonstration, and application of new and improved methods and processes to reduce the amount of waste and unsalvageable materials and to provide for proper and economical waste disposal practices.

---

* Denotes Interviewees.

CONTRIBUTING PROBLEM AREAS

The collection, disposal, and reuse of solid waste materials are all appropriate areas for introducing evolutionary concepts and methods. A possible interdisciplinary systems design project could combine all three considerations in developing a solid waste management system for a particular urban area. Topics for in-depth research in solids waste management include:

## Waste Disposal and Urban Housing

There is a need to incorporate a plan for adequate waste disposal facilities into housing design and to consider the housing unit as a component in the overall municipal system.

(a) Assess the concept of in-house reduction units (grinders, compactors, etc.) as opposed to centralized facilities; design evolutionary mechanisms to function as shredders at the household level.

(b) Develop performance standards for solid waste disposal in new housing.

(c) Develop innovative solid waste handling facilities for multi-family dwellings, e.g., drop-shafts, central penumatic tube systems, hydraulic and vacuum methods.

## Collection and Handling of Solid Waste

As the largest cost component in solid waste disposal programs, collection and transportation would seem particularly appropriate for evolutionary technology.

(a) Develop an evolutionary means of collecting and transporting municipal solid waste.

(b) Determine optimum collection schemes with conventional equipment -- decentralized feeder stations; a centralized waste processing facility, etc.

## Conventional Disposal Methods

Most solid waste will be managed by conventional methods for several decades. These must be made more efficient and economical.

(a) Design more effective means of thermally destroying waste, which will minimize air pollution and maximize usable by-products.

(b) Design volume reducing methods and other techniques which facilitate conventional disposal.

(c) Investigate composting as an alternative to disposal.

## Reuse of Solid Waste Components

Reuse can simultaneously reduce disposal burden and increase the supply of useful resources.

(a) Develop new uses for solid waste and processes for recovery of useful elements.

(b) Improve techniques for separating useful minerals from useless residue.

(c) Develop economical uses and processes for using abandoned automobiles; an automobile "disassembly" process might be investigated.

## Planning to Reduce Solid Waste

Investigate legal and economic means of changing packaging techniques and promoting reuse and recovery programs.

# 5.  COMPREHENSIVE HEALTH CARE SYSTEMS

## THE PROBLEM

In 1965, in his health message to Congress, President Johnson said that,

> "Our first concern must be to assure that the advance
> of medical knowledge leaves none behind.  We can --
> and we must -- strive now to assure the availability
> of and accessibility to, the best health care by all
> Americans, regardless of age or geography or economic
> status. " (ref. 94, p. 11).

This message seems to underscore a growing trend in the United States -- to regard proper health care as a basic human right rather than a privilege.  The enactment of Medicare and Medicaid legislation by the 1965 Congress also adds practical emphasis to this concept.

However, any social programs designed to guarantee all people proper medical care are certain to increase pressure on the already strained national force of health manpower.  The lack of physicians is one aspect of this strain (ref. 88).  In 1965, there were about 305,000 physicians in the United States, but 8,000 of them were retired from active practice.  This means that there was an average of 147 "active" physicians for every 100,000 people; however, even a great many of these "active" M. D.'s were heavily engaged in research, teaching, and administration and were therefore not available for patient care.

Each year, about 8,000 doctors graduate from the 91 schools of medicine and five schools of osteopathy in the United States.  Within the next few years, an additional 1,000 M. D.'s per year are expected

from new medical schools being planned and under construction. Current

projections are for the total number of physicians to increase at a faster

rate than the population and to reach 362,000 by 1975. But, even though this

increase will result in relatively more physicians by 1975, there is ex-

pected to be a greater shortage of "family physician services" (ref. 94).

The ratio of physicians in private practice whose primary role is

"family care" (i. e., general practitioners, internists, and pediatricians)

has sharply declined in the past few years, even though the physician-

population ratio has remained fairly constant. In 1950, there were ap-

proximately 82 physicians primarily involved in family care out of every

100,000 physicians in private practice; by 1965, there were only 55 per

100,000. And today, with less than 2% of the medical graduates going

into general practice, this figure should be significantly lower (ref. 94, 111).

Therefore, if increasing specialization continues to reduce family

health services, a greater number of physicians will be required to

guarantee everyone's right to proper health care. The U. S. Department

of Labor estimates that, during the period 1966-1975, there will be a

need for 145,000 additional physicians: 95,000 to meet new demands

of a growing population and 50,000 to replace physicians leaving practice.

At this rate, even with a continued reliance on foreign-trained doctors

(in 1965 about 1,700, almost 19% of the newly licensed physicians in the

U. S., were foreign-trained), the country's medical schools will have to

immediately increase their output by 6,600 per year to meet the pro-

jected demand (ref. 94, p. 8; 6 ).

Health care is a labor-intensive industry at all levels, and there-fore, the physician shortage is not the only strain on health manpower. One out of every 20 individuals in the national labor force is employed in the medical field (ref. 96). There are more than 200 types of trained medical assistants, and, although estimates vary greatly, between 11 to 13 health workers are required for each physician. The American Hospital Association predicts that by 1970, this ratio of health workers to physi-cians will increase to 17 to 1 (ref. 94, p. 7).

There is an immediate need to increase the available force of health manpower, but the current "health crisis" involves an entire "system" of health services. This fact was aptly expressed by the National Advisory Commission on Health Manpower (ref. 111, p. 2):

> "There is a crisis in American health care. The intuition of the average citizen has foundation in fact. He senses the contradiction of increasing employment of health manpower and decreasing personal attention to patients. The crisis, how-ever, is not one of numbers. It is true that sub-stantially increased numbers of health manpower will be needed over time. But if additional per-sonnel are employed in the present manner and within the present patterns and "systems" of care, they will not avert, or even perhaps alleviate, the crisis. Unless we improve the system through which health care is provided, care will continue to become less satisfactory, even though there are massive increases in cost and in numbers of health personnel."

New and more efficient ways of using present health professionals and facilities are urgently needed, and the rewards for improvement are very high. For example, a 4% increase in physician efficiency would be equivalent to adding 11,000 more physicians to the active list (ref. 94, p. 7). Also, if the average cost in general hospitals could be reduced by only 10%, the current savings would amount to about $1 billion per year and, by 1975, would total $3 billion annually (ref. 111, p. 55).

Despite the fact that the incentives to increase efficiency in hospitals are significant, there is a very wide economic variation among hospitals with essentially equivalent facilities and staffs. For example, among 22 voluntary short-term teaching hospitals in New York City, the average per diem costs in 1965 ranged from a low of about $50 to a high of $87. In 42 voluntary community hospitals in New York City, the corresponding range was $34 to $61, and an even wider range existed among 51 voluntary hospitals just outside the city (ref. 111, p. 55).

These cost variations in similar hospitals are not surprising when one considers the current methods of providing and paying for health care. Insurance coverage is directed primarily at expenses incurred by persons while they are in the hospital, thus encouraging patients and their doctors to choose hospitalization when less costly outpatient facilities or services would be equally satisfactory. Health professionals are generally paid in proportion to the amount of service they render and, therefore, have no economic incentive to avoid providing unnecessary care. And finally, since the utilization of the facilities of a hospital is essentially controlled by the individual physicians associated with that hospital, it is extremely difficult to exercise any coordinated and effective control over hospital costs (ref. 111).

Regardless of the economic advantages of increasing a health system's efficiency, one must always be cognizant of the effect which increased efficiency will have on the quality of the health care. It is relatively easy to reduce cost by reducing the quality or scope of the health service, but this approach is hardly acceptable.

Even with a highly efficient system for supplying health services and a greatly expanded supply of health manpower, the "health crisis" would not be completely resolved. There would still be unnecessary duplication of facilities and services, uneconomically small hospitals, gaps in geographical coverage and in scope of services provided, and other failures to achieve optimum distribution of health facilities and services at minimum cost. During the 1940's, the Commission on Hospital Care summarized the problem:

> "We frequently refer to our splendid system of hospitals, whereas actually there is none. Governmental units, church bodies, philanthropists, industries, and individuals have participated in the construction of hospital facilities. The diversity of background and objectives of the sponsoring interests has resulted in widely disparate patterns of organization, administration, and control of hospitals. There is very little coordination. In some instances, there even may be competition. Because of the rapid development and the nature of hospital service and the independence of the sponsoring agencies, we find disorganized, unrelated, and oftentimes overlapping patterns of hospital care. Critics describe them as uneconomic and ineffective. Patrons admit there is room for improvement." (ref. 93, p. 20).

The random and uncoordinated growth that characterizes the construction of American hospitals is perhaps indicative of the free enterprise system. High value is placed on individual initiative and private, independent action. However, the waste and inefficiency resulting from a patchwork pattern of health facilities and services has produced the growing opinion that some freedom of individual action should be sacrificed to promote a more uniform and extensive national health care system.

The aspect of the problem most easily grasped and most often mentioned is unnecessary duplication of facilities and equipment. For example, a 1961 survey disclosed that 77% of all hospitals equipped for open-heart surgery performed fewer than 50 operations per year. The initial capital expenditures for open-heart and other medical facilities are large enough in themselves, but the financing necessary to maintain these facilities is much larger. Each dollar invested in facilities commits a hospital to an estimated 15 to 20 dollars for services during the useful life of the facilities. In other words -- waste begets waste (ref. 93, p. 22).

There is little disagreement with the idea that some kind of planning or coordination is needed, but there is considerable controversy over how this planning should be implemented. One approach is to use government money to control and direct the distribution of health facilities and services. Another is to form private voluntary planning organizations that attempt to influence planning through persuasion. And finally, the traditional approach concludes that hospitals should be allowed to develop their own voluntary patterns of cooperation and self-restriction.

Regardless of which approach is taken, there are some inherent dangers in community or regional planning that must be recognized. These hazards are expressed in the 1966 Annual Report of the Kaiser Foundation Medical Care Program:

> "... any attempt to impose some order on existing, somewhat chaotic patterns, will have a strong tendency to perpetuate these patterns. Planning, although it offers the hope of coherent development and optimum distribution of health services, also poses a very real threat of antagonism and resistance to innovation and to development of alternative means of organizing and distributing health care services. People who operate health facilities which function in a traditional fashion naturally tend to prefer and support traditional approaches and to view alternatives with skepticism."
> (ref. 93, p. 24).

By recognizing proper health care as a basic human right, the United States is faced with a "health crisis". This crisis is the result of the need to rapidly expand our current health services while keeping the quality up and the cost down. The shortage of health manpower is but one symptom of this crisis; increasing medical costs is another. University interdisciplinary systems engineering teams may be able to devise some new ways of modifying current national health systems to help alleviate this crisis. However, if tactfully approached, local health services and facilities will probably provide the most opportune study topics. Students could then conceivably identify local health problems, talk with the people directly affected, attempt solutions, and possibly implement their recommendations (ref. 91).

## STATE-OF-THE-ART

To adequately outline the state-of-the-art in health care systems is a difficult task, particularly if one attempts to include all the relevant areas of medical science, equipment design, procedures, administration, and economics. Therefore, this section will be basically limited to a discussion of the following important problem areas: Community Planning, Design, Construction, and Equipment; Organization and Administration; and Services.

### Community Planning

Planning of health facilities and services has long been an integral part of the Hospital Survey and Construction Act (Hill-Burton Act) since its inception in 1946. Briefly, the purposes of the Hill-Burton program are:

> "... to assist the several States to inventory their existing hospitals, to survey the need for construction of hospitals, and to develop programs for construction of such public and other nonprofit hospitals as will, in conjunction with existing facilities, afford the necessary physical facilities for furnishing adequate hospital, clinic, and similar services to all their people ..."
> (ref. 101, p. 1).

Between 1946 and March 1964, Hill-Burton construction projects represented a total investment of $6,523,000,866 of which $2,070,574,730 was the Federal share. The 7,118 projects have added a total of 302,656 beds and 2,003 public health units (ref. 101, 105, 106, 107).

The Kaiser Foundation Medical Care Program is a private, nonprofit, prepayment program that serves more than 1,300,000 subscribers in the Pacific Coast States and Hawaii. It began by serving the medical needs of workmen on remote construction projects during the 1930's. The program adopted community-wide coverage in 1945 (ref. 92).

In the past few years, there have been many studies, conferences, books, and reports on comprehensive planning of health systems. Most of these are products of the Public Health Service of the Department of Health, Education, and Welfare (ref. 83, 84, 86, 102); but various National commissions and individuals have also made important contributions (ref. 96, 89, 97, 81, 99).

Design, Construction, and Equipment

This is the area of health care in which applied technology can perhaps have the greatest impact. Technology can be applied to utilize health manpower more efficiently and to improve patient care. In fact, the $50 billion a year health care industry is now making great strides in applying new and innovative technology to its health care procedures.

A variety of automated patient monitoring devices are now in general use (ref. 104, 108), and computers are beginning to take over much of the paper work that now restricts doctors, nurses, and hospital administrators. In fact, computers may soon be used to store information on patients, drugs, and treatments for instant retrieval and visual display before a physician in his office. Computers are also being used widely to automate clinical laboratories.

Many more current activities could be listed from hospital utilization studies, to studies for the planning of a surgical suite, to the study of the fire and explosion hazards of static sparks in oxygen tents; but, these and other projects are more adequately described in various research listings (ref. 101).

## Organization and Administration

There are limits as to how much more productive the individual doctor can become solely by working harder or faster, or relying on machines. Only through better organization can health resources be allocated rationally.

Although there is much general research being conducted on the organization and administration of health care (ref. 101, 80, 95), most of the current studies are concerned with economics, costs, and financing (ref. 112, 113, 98, 85, 114, 87).

In addition, the political problems for administering health policy and coordinating services are also being studied (ref. 82).

## Services

The studies covered in this category concern such special

medical services as: emergency (ref. 109), outpatient (ref. 110),

dietary, pharmaceutical, laundry, record, and laboratory.

One new innovation being developed and implemented at

the U. S. Public Health Service Hospital in Baltimore, Md., is

a Multiphasic Health Screening Clinic (ref. 90). Its purpose

is to identify unrecognized diseases or defects using a battery

of rapid, inexpensive tests.

## PARTICIPATING PERSONNEL AND ORGANIZATIONS

The Branch of the Department of Health, Education, and Welfare

that is concerned with health is the U. S. Public Health Service. The

major functions of the Public Health Service are to conduct and support

research and training in the medical and related sciences, and in public

health methods and administration; provide medical and hospital services

for persons authorized to receive care from the Service; aid in developing

the country's hospital and related facilities and prevent introduction of

communicable diseases; assist the State and local governments in ap-

plying new knowledge to the prevention and control of diseases; furnish

technical aid to other nations, through the Department of State and inter-

national health organizations; and compile and publish health statistics.

Major components of the Public Health Service which serve as

sources of scientific and technical information include the Office of the

Surgeon General, the National Library of Medicine, the National Institutes

of Health, the Bureau of State Services, and the Bureau of Medical Services.

The Office of Information and Publications, Office of the Surgeon

General, serves as the primary source of information on all of the

programs of the Public Health Service.

> Office of Information and Publications
> Public Health Service
> Fourth & Independence Ave., S. W.
> Washington, D. C. 20201
> Tel. (202) 963-6227

Information which may be obtained includes health statistics;

data on water supply and control, including industrial wastes, air

pollution, food, air, and water protection; accident incidence and

prevention; poisons and their control; radiological health data; occu-

pational health hazards and their control; communicable diseases;

chronic illnesses, such as heart disease, cancer, mental illness;

dental health; neurological diseases and blindness; arthritis and the

metabolic diseases; child health and human development; data on

nursing and hospitals; the health status and problems of the American

Indian and Alaskan natives; information on world health problems and

international health organizations; biomedical research and its progress

here and abroad; hospital and health center construction; mental retard-

ation; health education; and other health information.

Another useful information source of the U. S. Public Health

Service is the National Library of Medicine:

> 8600 Wisconsin Ave.
> Bethesda, Md. 20014
> Tel (212) 656-4084

This Library has holdings in excess of a million books, journals, theses, pamphlets, prints, and microfilms. Material is collected on every aspect of medicine, including dentistry, pharmacy, nursing, and related disciplines in the basic biomedical sciences. In 1963, the Library established a computer-based system known as MEDLARS (Medical Literature Analysis and Retrieval System) to support its bibliographical services. Only libraries may borrow from the collections and are expected to utilize local resources before directing requests to the National Library of Medicine. Individuals may borrow through their local libraries or use the Library's materials on the premises.

Within the Public Health Service, the following agencies made significant contributions to this topic description and are sources of additional information.

National Center for Health Services Research
    and Development

        National Institutes of Health   Bldg. 31
        8120 Woodmont Ave.
        Bethesda, Md.   20852

The Center serves as the Federal focus for health services research and development. It supports, conducts, and fosters a national program of research, development, demonstration, and training projects addressed to major problems in the availability, organization, distribution, utilization, quality, and financing of health services, facilities, and technical equipment.

The Center's programs are directed to developing new methods or improving existing methods of organizing, delivering and financing health services. The ultimate goal is to assist physicians, hospitals and clinics, professional health schools, governmental and voluntary health agencies, and health insurance firms to improve the distribution and quality of services and to make more efficient use of manpower, funds, and facilities.

The officials that were particularly helpful are:

*Dr. Paul J. Sanazaro - Director
    Rm. 2A52
    (address as above)
    Tel. (301) 495-6201

*Dr. Gilbert R. Barnhart - Assistant Director
    Rm. 2A25                    for Program Planning
    (Address as above)      and Evaluation
    Tel. (301) 495-6281

*Sherman R. Williams - Director of Health Care
    Rm. 203                      Institutions Program
    Ballston Center Tower 1
    800 N. Quincy St.
    Arlington, Va.  22203
    Tel. (703) 557-6697

Office of Equipment Consultation in the Health Facilities
    Planning and Construction Service

7915 Eastern Ave.
Silver Spring, Md.  20910

Although the interests of the Office of Equipment Consultation range over the entire health services field, it is primarily involved in five areas:

---

*    Denote interviewees

1. Administers a program for determining equipment resources needed and disseminates specified technical data through educational and training programs for hospitals.

2. Participates in the formulation of policy relating to adequate and proper equipment for hospitals.

3. Develops and conducts a program for obtaining and presenting data on comparable items of equipment, for reviewing and analyzing equipment item comparability, and for distributing such information to health facilities throughout the country, and to members of the public concerned with the hospital and health facility equipment area.

4. Promotes development of high standards.

5. Provides technical direction, leadership, consultation, and guidance to regional office staff, state agencies, individual hospitals, and other representatives of the hospital community.

The two officials in the Office of Equipment Consultation are:

> Sheldon A. Miller - Director
> (address as above)
> Tel. (301) 495-5300

> *Howard E. Fagin
> (address as above)
> Tel. (301) 495-5300

## Health Services Research

> Health Services Research Branch
> U. S. Public Health Service Hospital
> 3100 Wyman Park Drive
> Baltimore, Md. 21211

The Health Services Research Branch is actively engaged in applying scientific methods, tools, and techniques to the physical layout and design, organization, and administrative policies of hospitals. The staff consists of a highly organized team of physicians, industrial engineers, computer programmers, a nurse, pharmacist, and architect. The current areas of investigation by the multi-disciplinary group emphasizes the exploitation of modern technology in the health services systems. Recent projects include the development of a multiphasic health screening clinic, scientific measurement studies, the application of computers in various areas of health services, and studies information storage and retrieval.

Health Services Research Branch officials that were particularly helpful are:

> Dr. Richard K. C. Hsieh - Chief
> (address as above)
> Tel. (301) 338-1100

> *Andrew T. Sumner
> (address as above)
> Tel. (301) 338-1100, Ext. 551

## CONTRIBUTING PROBLEM AREAS

The following list contains selected examples of areas in which further exploration might prove useful to the hospital and related health care systems. It is not intended to be comprehensive or restrictive, but rather as a means to stimulate the formation of broader ideas, interests, and renewed efforts in research studies, and demonstrations. This subsection is organized in the same manner as State-Of-The-Art, and most of the suggested research topics were taken from (ref. 101).

## Community Planning

- Planning of services, hospitals, and related facilities for suburban areas due to rapid population growth.

- Methods of meeting population requirements for general, chronic, tuberculosis, and mental disease hospital services and methods of providing these services.

- Outpatient needs, services, utilization, and trends.

- Regional planning for personnel recruitment, training, and educational programs and resources.

- State and local programs for hospital services including payment for indigent care.

- Related mental health needs, facilities, and resources in the light of the dynamic changes in community attitudes and programs of care for the mentally ill.

- The need for rehabilitation centers and resources for treating certain types of physical and mental disabilities.

- The role of the hospitals in Civil Defense, including emergency expansion of facilities.

- Relationship of diagnostic clinics to hospitals.

- The effect of home care and community nursing on hospital needs and activities.

- The patterns and trends of group practice.

- Hospital-patient relationships, including attitudes, and the physical, social, psychological, and economic impact on the patient and family.

- The interrelationships between the services provided by hospitals, related health facilities, and community health agencies.

- Need for regional, area, and local planning groups.

- Methodology for coordinated health facility planning.

- The most effective role of the chronic disease unit of a general hospital as contrasted with services in a nursing home.

- Effect on general hospital utilization of variations in availability of long-term care facilities.

- The problem of small hospitals in a large city.

- Utilization rates under varying patterns of medical care.

- Length of stay, by condition or diagnosis of the patient, in relation to the specialty and training of physician.

- Methods of remuneration of the physician, and their possible effect on utilization policies, particularly prior to hospitalization.

- Medical evaluation of hospitalized patients at a given time.

- Systematic collection of basic data from many hospitals, so that individual hospitals could measure their own performance against the statistics of others.

- Medical criteria for hospital admission.

- Planning and utilization of facilities providing care in day and night hospitals, halfway houses, outpatient departments, and other such facilities for mental health.

- Planning and utilization of Group Practice facilities and the development of the group practice of medicine and dentistry and of comprehensive prepaid medical and dental care plans.

- Measures for determining need for various types of health facilities.

- Means of achieving balanced urban hospital resources and minimizing duplication of facilities within communities.

## Design, Construction, and Equipment

- Evaluation and development of planning guides for the construction of physical facilities, and for equipment and supplies, all essential to safe and economical operation of hospital departments, such as anesthesiology, radiology, pathology, laboratory, pharmacy, dietary, medical records, patient units, emergency, maternity and outpatient services.

- How equipment needs can best be met to eliminate inefficiency and waste and reduce overall cost; problems of maintenance, particularly of expensive complicated modern equipment.

- Modernization and replacement needed to adapt obsolete facilities to changing functions and to modern practice.

- The need for better design and construction of facilities for short- and long-term general, tuberculosis, and mental hospital services in the community.

- Design and construction of day hospitals, facilities for mentally retarded, halfway houses, outpatient departments, and other such facilities for mental health.

- Special design considerations for facilities in fast-growing suburbs, in certain sections of metropolitan areas occupied principally by minority groups, and in many rural areas.

- Design features of public health centers and other outpatient facilities which provide preventive and ambulatory care.

- Development of an integrated program for all types of facilities and services within an urban area, according to a community plan.

- Guides for constructing long-term care facilities and renovating obsolete institutions.

- The need for improved functional design of structures for maximum efficiency and to permit easy adaptation to techniques developed from application of new knowledge.

- Equipment and supply needs for rendering dental services in the hospital.

- The need for change in hospital design as a result of automation process in various departments.

- Demonstration construction projects for various hospital services, e.g., laboratory, surgery, pharmacy, central supply.

- Methods to reduce infection through design of most efficient housekeeping equipment for hospital use.

- Space requirements, including floor plans and traffic flow, for various services in the hospital.

- Food refrigeration and methods of food storage.

- Equipment standards and specifications for laundry, housekeeping, and medical services in the hospital.

- Considerations relating to age, type of structure, fire-proofing of hospitals.

- Environmental engineering, to determine, evaluate, and solve major problems characteristic of the hospital surroundings, including heating, lighting, ventilation, fire safety, plumbing, and acoustics.

## Organization and Administration

- More effective hospital organizational patterns.

- Standards for evaluation of organization and adminstration, including board of trustees.

- Facets of hospital operations where there may be a potential savings, and application of results to development of more efficient methods of administration.

- Characteristics of medical staff organization.

- Legal and professional aspects, requirements, and responsibilities in the field of medical and surgical services.

- Introduction and use of social science approaches, methods, and instruments in hospital administrative research.

- Development of internal controls in business management functions of hospitals.

- Admitting practices and procedures.

- Guides and methods for uniform reporting, financial and statistical, for hospitals and related facilities.

- Legal aspects of hospital administration, taxation, licensure, contractual agreements, and obligations.

- Criteria by which administrative department performance may be evaluated.

- Centralized administration in rural hospitals.

- Hospital services with regard to: organizational structure to determine most efficient methods to achieve goals of patient care; and efficiency of operation.

- Methods of administrative research, including: proper statistical procedures, data processing, compatibility, and information retrieval and utilization of material.

- Barriers to effective communication findings, such as cultural, social, and psychological resistance to various types of communication, and to certain sources and channels of information.

- Volume and cost of hospital inpatient and outpatient care to indigent patients.

- Medical and nursing teaching costs and their relation to total hospital economy.

- Problems of financing hospital and related services.

- Hospital income sources.

- Utilization of automation in all departments of the hospital and its potential usefulness in possibly decreasing hospital costs while increasing efficiency.

- The uses of electronic equipment in hospitals, its limitations, dangers, and pitfalls as well as values.

## Services

- Methods used in appraising medical care and nursing care service.

- The role and effectiveness of local hospital associations and the impact on coordination of hospital services.

- Patient needs in medical-surgical field to develop standards of safer and more beneficial patient care.

- Legal and professional guides to requirements and responsibilities in the field of medical-surgical services.

- Hospital responsibility in group practice.

- Determination of optimum size of clinical departments and services.

- Criteria by which clinical departments may be evaluated.

- Hospital dental services in relation to needs and clinical, technical, and administrative problems.

- The role of the health educator in the hospital.

- Policies, procedures, techniques, and equipment standards such as those covering public health laboratories.

- Plans, equipment, personnel requirements, and administrative procedures for organizing and maintaining blood banks.

- Types of medical record systems now in use. Medical record guides should be developed especially for small hospitals, health centers, clinics, and outpatient departments.

- A uniform and simplified method for keeping medical records.

- Use of automation and computers in medical records.

- Availability, utilization, and costs of outpatient services and how they can be improved.

- Various aspects of hospital pharmacies including standard levels of service, operations, drug costs, personnel, equipment; and space required. A selected group should be studied to determine the minimum size and type of hospital which can do mass compounding and efficiently manufacture

parenteral solutions. Studies are also needed
to determine effective measures for reducing
the medication cost to the patient. Criteria
for establishing an active pharmacy committee,
simplified formulary, purchasing, storage,
inventory, and control of drugs.

- The organization of the physical medicine department in hospitals and health centers.

- Utilization of physical therapy and occupational
therapy departments.

- Examinations and treatments by number, type,
and professional qualifications of personnel
administering them in general and specialized
hospitals of varying sizes.

- Methodology for evaluating work load in radiology
department. Development of schematic plans,
equipment, personnel requirements and administrative procedures for radioactive isotope services.

# SECTION C

## AGENCIES AND OFFICIALS CONCERNED WITH THE URBAN ENVIRONMENT

The following is a listing of agencies whose scope spans the total field of environmental problems; for the most part, they are concerned with the general question of "environmental quality", although many have extended their interests to specific problem areas. This list is not intended to be all-inclusive, but rather presents those agencies whose activities with respect to environmental problems were found to be more broadly directed than organizations listed specifically within each of the topic areas in Section B.

1.   OFFICE OF SCIENCE AND TECHNOLOGY (OST)

> Executive Office Building
> 17th Street and Penn. Ave., N. W.
> Washington, D. C.  20506
> Tel.  (202)  395-3544

This Executive Office, headed by the President's Science Adviser, Dr. Lee DuBridge, is the parent organization of the Federal Council on Science and Technology (FCST), under which the Committee on Environmental Quality (CEQ) functions. Appointed members from each of the Federal Departments comprise the CEQ which concerns itself with the management of the Nation's resources and finding preventive measures to combat the acceleration of environmental pollution.

A Presidential Directive, issued in the summer of 1969, created the Environmental Quality Council (EQC) with Dr. DuBridge as its Executive Secretary. This new organization is comprised of Cabinet-level officers and other key figures within the Executive Branch. Greater detail on this new committee is provided in Section A of this Chapter. Further information on national policies, plans and programs for the environment, plus inter-agency planning, administration, and coordination of Federal research and development programs, can be obtained by writing to the above address.

## 2. ENVIRONMENTAL STUDIES BOARD (ESB)

National Academy of Sciences
National Academy of Engineering
2101 Constitution Ave., N. W.
Washington, D. C. 20418

The ESB was created in March of 1967 for the purposes of coordinating all NAS-NAE activities in the area of environmental studies, working directly with the Legislative and Executive Branches of the Government in attacking related problems, and initiating broad new studies when necessary. A major consideration behind its formation was to provide a national focus for widespread interdisciplinary efforts toward controlling pollution and reducing other environmental problems. The responsibilities given to the ESB by the Councils of the NAS and

NAE are outlined in the minutes of its first meeting and presented in synopsized form in (ref. 4) which also defines the ESB's initial operating grant, its relationship to the National Research Council, and the structure and procedures whereby it coordinates the activities of these three bodies.

Primarily, the ESB has concentrated on handling requests for assistance on existing environmental problems with strong technological or engineering content. Recently, the Board has turned to dealing with problems of a long-range, interdisciplinary character.

Principal officers of the ESB are:

(A)   Dr. Harold Gershinowitz - Chairman
      25 Sutton Place, South
      New York, N.Y.   10022

(B)   Charles K. Reed - Executive Secretary
      Rm. 306
      2100 Penn. Ave., N.W.
      Washington, D.C.   20037
      Tel.  (202) 961-1706

(C)*  B. J. Driscoll - Consultant
      (address and telephone as above)

## ESB COMMITTEES ON ENVIRONMENTAL POLLUTION

In addition to its concern with overall environmental quality, the ESB is addressing particular environmental problems in detail through four ad hoc, engineering-oriented committees: Committee on Solid Waste Management; Committee on Air Quality Management; Committee on Waste Quality Management; and Committee on Noise. All of these

---

\* Denotes Interviewees

organizations are currently engaged in joint research with certain

agencies in the Executive Branch of the Federal Government, in addi-

tion to acting as reviewing bodies with respect to outside research in

their fields of interest.

Reports will be published periodically under the auspices of the

NAS-NAE National Research Council. There is a central coordinating

and information office for all the committees under the direction of:

    (D)  R. W. Crozier - Executive Secretary
          Rm. 320
          2100 Penn. Ave., N. W.
          Washington, D. C.  20037
          Tel.  (202)  961-1701

## 3.  ENVIRONMENTAL SCIENCE SERVICES ADMINISTRATION (ESSA)

The creation of ESSA within the Department of Commerce in July

of 1965 brought together the functions of the Weather Bureau and Coast

and Geodetic Survey. Three new divisions were established within

ESSA soon thereafter: namely, the Environmental Data Service, the

National Environmental Satellite Center, and the Institutes for Environ-

mental Research, which later became known as the ESSA Research

Laboratories.

Of particlar relevance to urban-related environmental problems

are surveys and projects conducted by the Weather Bureau and the En-

vironmental Data Service within ESSA's Division of Environmental

Science Services. The Environmental Data Service provides a single source of readily-available environmental information through data collection and processing centers for geodetic, geomagnetic, seismological, climatological, and other geophysical information. This Service is also active in the development of advanced data storage and retrieval methods and computer applications.

Information on ESSA-related activities is readily available from its Office of Public Information:

> (E)   Stanley Eames
>        Rm. 810 - Bldg. 5
>        Executive Boulevard
>        Rockville, Md.  20852
>        Tel.  (201)  496-8177

Particular interest in pollution problems exists at the ESSA Air Resources Laboratories in Washington, D. C., and at its major field offices in Cincinnati, Oak Ridge, and Las Vegas; and also at the Geophysical Fluid Dynamics Laboratory located in Washington, D. C.

Supervising activities of the Air Resources Laboratory is:

> (F)   Lester Machta - Director
>        Grammax Building
>        8060 - 13th Street
>        Silver Spring, Md.  20910
>        Tel.  (301)  495-2252

## 4.   UNITED STATES CONGRESS

Efforts at the Congressional level to tackle the environmental pollution problem are being spearheaded by two groups in particular. Within the House of Representatives, the Subcommittee on Science, Research, and Development, under the Committee on Science and

Astronautics, has initiated significant legislation over the past five

years based upon extensive reports dealing with environmental

management and quality. Copies of past reports and legislation are

available through the office of:

(G)    Emilio Q. Daddario - Chairman
          Subcommittee on Science and Development
          House of Representatives
          U. S. Congress
          Washington, D. C.  20515
          Tel.  (202) 225-2265

Within the Senate, similar efforts in the environmental area have

come from the Committee on the Interior and Insular Affairs.

Information can be obtained from the office of:

(H)    Henry M. Jackson - Chairman
          Committee on the Interior and Insular
            Affairs, Senate
          U. S. Congress
          Washington, D. C.  20510
          Tel.  (202) 225-3441

# SECTION D: REFERENCES
## ENVIRONMENT

1. Committee on Science and Astronautics, Environmental Quality, Hearings before the Subcommittee on Science, Research and Development, House, 90th Congress, 2nd Session, U. S. Gov. Printing Office, Washington, D. C. 1968.

   These hearings explore the ways in which the science resources available to the Federal Government are developed in support of national goals for environmental quality. A sequence to the Subcommittee Hearings in 1966 which led to the report, Environmental Pollution, a Challenge to Science and Technology.

2. Committee on Science and Astronautics, "Technology Assessment", House, 90th Congress, 1st Session, U. S. Gov. Printing Office, Washington, D. C., 1967.

   Explored the relationship between "science and society" and between "technology and culture". Expressed the need for increased congressional capability in dealing with the ramifications of technological development.

3. Committee on Science and Astronautics, The Adequacy of Technology for Pollution Abatement, Hearings before the Subcommittee on Science, Research, and Development, Committee on Science and Astronautics, House, 89th Congress, 2nd Session, U. S. Gov. Printing Office, Washington, D. C., 1966 (Two Volumes).

4. Gershinowitz, Harold, "The Environmental Studies Board", The Rockefeller University, New York, N. Y., March 1969

   First formal report on the activities of the Environmental Studies Board (ESB). Includes a brief Summary of ESB's origin, its Charter, the principles under which it has chosen to operate, and a statement on current programs and future plans.

5. Goldman, Marshall I., (ed.), Controlling Pollution: The Economics of a Cleaner America, Prentice-Hall, Englewood Cliffs, New Jersey, 1967.

   A general description of the Nation's pollution problems and an assessment of pollution economies. Current case studies are presented and a description of the Soviet parallel.

6. National Academy of Sciences, "Applied Science and Technological Progress, a report to the Committee on Science and Astronautics, House, Washington, D. C., June 1967.

   A collection of essays by leaders of the American technical community which stresses the need for understanding, prediction, and control of the consequences of technology, industrialization, and urbanization on man's physical and biological environment.

7. National Research Council, Useful Applications of Earth-Oriented Satellites, Report of the Central Review Committee National Academy of Sciences, National Research Council, Washington, D. C. 20418, 1969.

   Summary of a summer study on space applications for the National Aeronautics and Space Agency. The report considers various factors affecting space applications - national, international, social and economic. Available from Printing and Publishing Office, NAS, 2101 Constitution Ave., N. W., Washington, D. C. 20418.

8. National Research Council, Useful Applications of Earth-Oriented Satellites, Summaries of Panel Reports, National Academy of Sciences, National Research Council, Washington, D. C. 20418, 1969.

   Summary of 13 panels; including: Geology, hydrology, meteorology, sensors and data systems, point-to-point communications, economic analysis, and broadcasting.

9. President's Science Advisory Committee, Environmental Evolution Panel, Restoring the Quality of Our Environment, The White House, U. S. Gov. Printing Office, Washington, D. C. 20402, 1965.

   An extensive assessment of the state of the environment and recommended actions to restore it to a healthy condition. The document discusses the effects of pollution of all types, their sources, and plans for action. Subpanel reports on various aspects are included as appendices -- including air problems, solid wastes, and water.

10. Resources For The Future, Inc., Resources, 1755 Massachusetts Avenue, N. W., Washington, D. C. 20036.

    This is the publication, issued three times a year, of Resources For The Future, Inc., a non-profit corporation established in 1952 to advance the development, conservation, and use of natural resources through research and education. This periodical represents a reasonable effort to inform the public of events relating to the use and management of natural resources.

11. Senate Committee on the Interior and Insular Affairs, House Committee on Science and Astronautics, Congressional White Paper on a National Policy for the Environment, U. S. Gov. Printing Office, Washington, D. C., 1968.

    Policy formulation on Federal involvement in environmental quality and control. The product of an informal joint House-Senate colloquium on "National Policy for the Environment", held in July of 1968, which brought together interested executive branch heads and leaders of industrial, commercial, academic, and scientific organizations. Part I covers several aspects of environmental management: The relationship among population growth, environmental determination, and quality of life; the role of ecology; the redirection of research activities; and new approaches for the government to take. Part II explored alternatives for Congressional action while Part III proposed alternative suggestions for appropriate policy-statements. Included in this document is a valuable listing of selected issues and representative legislation introduced in the 90th Congress.

12. Subcommittee on Science, Research, and Development, Environmental Pollution: A Challenge to Science and Technology, Report to the Committee on Science and Astronautics House, 89th Congress, 2nd Session, U. S. Gov. Printing Office, Washington, D. C., 1966.

    The result of a review of Hearings before the Subcommittee describing where the Nation now stands technologically with respect to pollution abatement and what it must do to improve this position. Needed research in Air and Water is set forth in detail, along with overall goals and objectives. Appendix II highlights other reports on environmental pollution.

13. Subcommittee on Science, Research and Development of the House Committee on Science and Astronautics, Managing The Environment", U. S. Gov. Printing Office, Washington D. C. 20402, 1968.

    A Summary of current information from the Hearings, subcommittee consultants, and staff studies on the means by which science and technology can serve the national goals of environmental quality and national progress. The general subjects of pollution control, ecology, and environmental quality have been considered, and recommendations for the proliferation of future activity are made.

14. Task Force on Environmental Health and Related Problems, A Strategy for a Livable Environment, A report to the Secretary of HEW, U. S. Gov. Printing Office, Washington, D. C. 20402, June 1967 ($0.60).

    The Task Force was charged with recommending to the Secretary goals, priorities, and a Departmental strategy to cope with environmental threats to man's health and welfare. Action Goals are provided in the areas of air quality, water quality, waste disposal, population, urban concentration, chemical safety, consumer protection, radiation contro, occupational disease and safety and governmental compliance.

# ENVIRONMENT: AIR POLLUTION

15. Air Quality Act of 1967, Public Law 90-148, 90th Congress, 2nd Session, S. 780, 21 November 1967, U. S. Gov. Printing Office, Washington, D. C. , 1967.

16. Battle Memorial Institute, Summary Report on Study of Unconventional Thermal, Mechanical, and Nuclear Low-Pollution-Potential Power Sources for Urban Vehicles, submitted to Department of HEW, National Center for Air Pollution Control, Battelle Columbus Laboratories, Columbus, Ohio 43201, 15 March 1968.

This report was prepared to provide background information and recommendations required by NCAPC for development of future research and development programs on low-pollution-potential propulsion systems for urban vehicles.

17. Committee on Public Works, Air Quality Criteria, Staff Report for Subcommittee on Air and Water Pollution, Committee on Public Works, U. S. Senate, U. S. Gov. Printing Office, Washington, D. C. , 1968.

An objective analysis of the factors relevant to the development of Air Quality Criteria in line with the policies established by the Clean Air Act of 1967. Includes rationale for standards, health effects of pollution, and present indicators in use.

18. Department of Health, Education, and Welfare, Air Pollution Abatement by Federal Facilities, Second Report of the Secretary of HEW to the U. S. Congress, U. S. Gov. Printing Office, Washington, D. C. , 4 March 1969.

A report required by the Air Quality Act of 1967 describing in detail such progress as has been made toward controlling Air Pollution from sources for which Federal Departments or Agencies have jurisdiction.

19. Department of Health, Education, and Welfare, Progress in the Prevention and Control of Air Pollution, First Report of the Secretary of Health, Education, and Welfare to the U. S. Congress, U. S. Gov. Printing Office, Washington, D. C. , 28 June 1968 ($0.30).

The first of a series of reports required by the Air Quality Act of 1967 describing the progress being made in this country to prevent and control air pollution. Contents include relevant background information , progress toward a regional approach, progress toward effective control of air pollution, additional research and supporting activities. A list of 20 references is included.

20. Department of Health, Education, and Welfare, Progress in the Prevention and Control of Air Pollution, Second report of the Secretary of Health, Education, and Welfare to the U. S. Congress, U. S. Gov. Printing Office, Washington, D. C. , 4 March 1969.

The second in a series of reports required by the Air Quality Act of 1967, updating such information as was reported in the 1968 report to Congress. Contents include control technology R&D, Control Program Support, progress toward a regional approach, federal abatement activities, automative air pollution, air pollution monitoring and measuring.

21. Department of Health, Education, and Welfare, Public Health Service, Consumer Protection and Environmental Health Service, National Air Pollution Control Administration, Guidelines for the Development of Air Quality Standards and Implementation Plans, Washington, D. C. , May 1969.

Intended to facilitate the dealing with air pollution problems on a regional basis. The document outlines requirements of the Air Quality Act of 1967; provides recommendations as regarding standards, implementation plans, and public participation; and describes federal assistance. Useful appendices include Simulation Modeling, List of Air Quality Control Regions, and Regional NAPCA Directors. A list of 33 references is also included.

22. Department of Health, Education, and Welfare, Public Health Service, National Air Pollution Control Administration, Air Pollution Publications: A selected Bibliography with Abstracts 1966-1968, Public Health Service Publication No. 979, U. S. Gov. Printing Office, Washington, D. C. , 1969 ($4. 50).

An annotated bibliography of 992 entries compiled by the Library of Congress Science and Technology Division. Sections include: General aspects, emission sources, atmospheric interactions, measurement, control methods, plants, air quality, legal and administrative aspects, social aspects, basic science and technology. Author and subject indices are provided.

23. Department of Health, Education, and Welfare, Public Health Service, The Federal Air Pollution Program, Public Health Service Publication No. 1560, U. S. Gov. Printing Office, Washington, D. C. , Rev. 1967 ($1. 00).

An informational publication on the federal program. Includes history of the program, research activities, assistance to state and local governments, abatement and prevention of air pollution, control of vehicular pollution and information and education.

24. Department of Health, Education, and Welfare, Public Health Service, The Sources of Air Pollution and Their Control, Public Health Service Publication No. 1548, U. S. Gov. Printing Office, Washington, D. C. , Rev. 1968 ($0. 40).

A general introduction to the air pollution problem and its sources. Facts and figures are presented for motor vehicles, and stationary sources, including industry, power plants, space heating and refuse disposal.

25. Hoffman, George A. , "The Electric Automobile", Scientific American, October 1966, P. 34-40.

Quantitative and Qualitative description of a possible configuration for the electric auto.

26. Little (Arthur D. ), Inc. Prospects for Electric Vehicles: A Study of Low-Pollution Potential Vehicles-Electric, prepared for the Dept. of HEW/National Center for Air Pollution Control, 15 Acorn Park, Cambridge, Mass. 15 May 1968.

27. Metropolitan Washington Council of Governments, "Model Local Air Pollution Ordinance", Washington, D. C. , 1966.

Distributed by U. S. Clearinghouse for Federal Scientific and Technical Information as PB 177 504.

28. Ott, Wayne, John F. Clarke, Guntis Ozolins, Calculating Future Carbon Monoxide Emissions and Concentrations from Urban Traffic Data, Public Health Service Publication No. 999-AP-41, Dept. of HEW, Public Health Service, Cincinnati, Ohio, June 1967.

A technical report outlining methods applied in Washington, D. C. to calculate future and present emissions and ambient concentration of carbon monoxide. The dispersion model used is outlined in Appendix A.

29. Ozolins, Guntis, and Raymond Smith, A Rapid Survey Technique for Estimating Community Air Pollution Emissions, Dept. of HEW, Public Health Service, Division of Air Pollution, Cincinnati, Ohio 45226, October 1966.

The method presented here utilizes information readily available in most communities to provide accurate, yet rapid, estimates of the major air pollutant emissions in urban areas.

30. Panel on Electrically-Powered Vehicles, The Automobile and Air Pollution: A Program for Progress, Report to the Commerce Technical Advisory Board, Department of Commerce, U. S. Gov. Printing Office, Washington, D. C. , October 1968, (Two Volumes).

A comprehensive study of the complex problem of automotive transportation in relation to the current problem of air pollution. Vol. I contains Panel findings on Air Pollution: The Problems and the Risks; Technology and The Control of Automotive Air Pollution; The Role of Industry; and the Role of Government. Vol. II contains supporting subpanel studies and an extensive bibliography of 312 entries.

# ENVIRONMENT: AIR POLLUTION

31. Public Health Service, Proceedings: The Third National Council on Air Pollution, Public Health Service Publication No. 1669, U.S. Gov. Printing Office, Washington, D.C., 1967.

A complete report of the Dec. 12-14, 1966, conference. All aspects of air pollution are discussed, reflected in the eight panel topics: Motor Vehicles; Heat and Power Generation; Industrial Operations; Solid Waste Disposal; State and Interstate Air Pollution Control Programs; Local or Regional Air Pollution Control Programs; Role of Federal Government in Air Pollution Control; Economic and Social Aspects of Air Pollution Control.

32. Smith, Maynard, (ed.), Recommended Guide for the Prediction of the Dispersion of Airborne Effluents, The American Society of Mechanical Engineers, United Engineering Center, New York, N.Y. 10017, 1968.

A technical treatment of atmospheric dispersion effects.

33. Sweet, A. H., B. J. Steigerwald, J. H. Ludwig, "The Need for a Pollution-Free Vehicle", APCA Journal, Vol. 18, No. 2, February 1968.

This article demonstrates the need for a pollution-free vehicle by projecting to 2010 vehicle emission densities for eight urban areas and measures of population exposure to pollution for four cities. Different degrees of control are evaluated as to their relative long-term effectiveness.

# ENVIRONMENT: WATER POLLUTION

34. Clean Water Restoration Act of 1966, Public Law 89-753, 89th Congress, S. 2947, 3 November 1966.

This amendment to the Water Pollution Control Act of 1956 increased annual Federal authorization for construction grants to $450 M in 1968; $700 M in 1969; $1 B in 1970; and $1.25 B in 1971 (M - million) (B - billion). It also eliminated dollar ceilings on construction grants, enabled a municipality to receive between 30% and 55% in Federal grant for water pollution control programs, and authorized funds for: research and demonstration projects on pollution from combined storm and sanitary sewers and separate storm sewers; projects demonstrating advanced waste treatment and water purification methods, and new or improved methods of joint treatment of municipal and industrial wastes; and projects, either by industry or private individuals which help develop or demonstrate new or improved ways to prevent pollution of waters by industry.

35. Federal Water Pollution Control Act Amendments of 1961, Public Law 87-88, 87th Congress, H.R. 6441, 20 July 1961.

An amendment to the Federal Water Pollution Control Act (33 U.S.C. 466a) which provided for a more effective program of water pollution control. Specifically stated were water quality control and storage requirements and enforcement measures against pollution of interstate or navigable waters. Limits for appropriations and grants to states for the following five-year period were also established.

36. Federal Water Pollution Control Administration, Federal Grants for Clean Water, FWPCA Publication Office, 1921 Jefferson Davis Highway, Arlington, Virginia, January 1969.

Lists Federal grants and other financial assistance for clean water administered by the FWPCA. Gives details on purposes, financing basis, methods of distribution, and other information on the various categories of grants and contracts.

37. Federal Water Pollution Control Administration, "Program Review and Evaluation Staff Annual Report, FY-1968", U.S. Dept. of Interior, 1921 Jefferson Davis Highway, Arlington, Virginia, 30 June 1968.

This publication summarizes the Program Review and Evaluation Staff's activities for fiscal year 1968. A list of completed projects is supplied and a review of operations is presented in terms of specific, on-going projects: namely, cost estimate studies, a comprehensive program evaluation, an evaluation of technical programs, a review of regional and past program activities, manpower requirements analyses, program planning and control, and an FY 1970-1974 Program Financial Plan.

38. Federal Water Pollution Control Administration, Research, Development, and Demonstration Projects, U.S. Dept. of Interior, Washington, D.C. 20242, January 1969.

A three-volumed series which gives descriptions of current, active grant and contract projects awarded by three separate divisions within the FWPCA. These booklets provide the grantee's name, project number and title, the Federal funds committed to the project, and a brief description of the project. The various grant types, Sections 5 and 6 of Public Law 660, are outlined and an address for obtaining further information is listed. The three volumes and respective authors are as follows:
   Volume I - Division of Applied Science & Technology
   Volume II - Division of Process Research & Development
   Volume III - Division of Water Quality Research.
All Divisions are located within the Office of Research and Development in the FWPCA.

39. Federal Water Pollution Control Administration, Office of Programs, Plans, and Development, "The Cost of Clean Water", 1921 Jefferson Davis Highway, Arlington, Virginia 1968.

A four-volumed series which estimates the national requirements and the costs of attaining water quality standards:
   Vol. I - A Summary of the major findings and conclusions concerning an ambitious, cost analysis effort on the subject of water pollution.
   Vol. II - Descriptions and analyses of the various subject areas which formed the basis for the cost estimates in the Summary Report.
   Vol. III - Industrial waste profiles: Ten studies of major water-using industries which describes the cost and effectiveness of alternative methods of reducing industrial wastes.
   Vol. IV - State and major river basin municipal tables; includes breakdown of estimated construction costs, sanitary sewers, and operation and maintenance costs.

40. Federal Water Pollution Control Administration, "Water Pollution Control, 1969-1973, the Federal Costs", U.S. Department of the Interior, Washington, D.C. 20240, 1968.

A projected cost estimate of necessary Federal expenditure to effectively combat the water pollution problem in the Nation's lakes and rivers.

41. Federal Water Pollution Control Administration, Office of Research and Development, Water Pollution Control Research, Development, Demonstration, and Training Projects: 1968 Grant and Contract Awards, U.S. Dept. of Interior, Washington, D.C. 20242, 1968.

A Summary of FWPCA's Awards presented for FY 1968-1969. The structure of FWPCA's RD&D program has been constructed in an easy-to-reference, organizational diagram. The Foreward includes a listing of grants and contracts which are available and tells how further information or request forms for the submission of applications can be obtained. Also mentioned are Training Grants and Research Fellowships, offered by FWPCA's Division of Manpower and Training. Awards are given for: Research, demonstrations, storm and combined sewers, advanced waste treatment, industrial waste treatment, training, and fellowships.

# ENVIRONMENT: WATER POLLUTION

42. Federal Water Pollution Control Administration, "Water Quality Standards", FWPCA Publications Office, 1921 Jefferson Davis Highway, Arlington, Virginia, 1969

Defines water quality standards, method of establishing standards, and what results can be expected in improving the quality of America's waters. Describes State and Federal responsibilities in setting, enforcing, and revising standards. Publication may be obtained without charge.

43. International Association on Water Pollution Research, Water Research, Pergamon Press, Headington Hill Hall, Oxford, England, Published Monthly.

This technically-oriented Journal of the IAWPR covers every conceivable topic related to waterways, their uses, the water pollution situation, and programs to eliminate water contaminants. Subscription rates are: Single issue $ 9; non-members $100/annually; educational libraries $40/ annually. Back issues are available; write for "Back Issues Price List" from Pergamon Press Ltd. at 44-01 -21st Street, Long Island City, N. Y. 11101. The Journal aims at publishing original research work in the field of water quality management. Of special concern are papers concerned with the chemistry, biology and technology of water and waste water treatment, studies of the effects of waste discharges into inland waters, the scientific aspects of industrial water and waste treatment and the effects of such wastes on collection and treatment systems and the environment, and the analysis of water and waste by chemical, physical, or micro-biological methods and advancement in instrumentation.

44. Izaak Walton League of America, Inc., Clean Water - It's Up to You. FWPCA Office of Publications, 1921 Jefferson Davis Highway, Arlington, Va., 1968.

Describes pollution problems, pollution laws, and water quality standards. Proposes a community action program for safeguarding local water supplies. Publication was partially financed by an FWPCA Grant.

45. Robert A. Taft Sanitary Engineering Center, "Current List of Water Publications, 1965-1968", Office of Information, Ohio Basin Region, Federal Water Pollution Control Administration, U. S. Dept. of Interior, Cincinnati, Ohio 45226.

A comprehensive listing of studies, reports, and books concerned specifically with the different aspects of water contamination and the necessary corrective sanitation procedures and methods.

46. Water Pollution Control Act of 1956, Public Law 660, 84th Congress, Chapter 518, 2nd Session, Section 890.

It amended the Water Pollution Control Act (33 U. S. C. 466-466j) to include comprehensive programs for water pollution control. Most significant was the authorization given to the Government for making municipal grants which would financially aid the construction of sewage treatment facilities. It also established the Water Pollution Control Advisory Board within the Public Health Services.

47. Water Quality Act of 1965, Public Law 89-234, 89th Congress, S. 4, 2 October 1965.

This law amended the Federal Water Pollution Control Act to establish a Federal Water Pollution Control Administration (FWPCA), to provide grants for research and development, to increase grants for construction of sewage treatment works, and to require the establishment of water quality criteria at a state level. It also doubled maximum construction grants to $2. 4 million for single projects and to $4. 8 million for multi-municipal projects; boosted authorized Federal contributions for waste treatment construction to $150 million per year; and authorized $20 million / year through 1969 for research and demonstration projects on improved methods of controlling discharges from combined sanitary and storm sewers and from separate storm sewers.

48. Water Resources Council, Handbook For Coordination of Planning Studies and Reports, Washington, D. C. 20005, June 1969.

Designed for use by those concerned with the investigation and development of water and related land resources. Provides a summary of coordination policies and procedures, a description of agency areas of interest and responsibility, and information on distribution of investigation notices to agency offices and representatives. This publication is available only from: Office of the Executive Director, Water Resources Council, 1025 Vermont Avenue, N. W., Suite 900, Washington, D. C. 20005.

49. Water Resources Council, "Procedures for Evaluation of Water and Related Land Resource Projects", Washington, D. C. 20005, June 1969.

A review of the policies and procedures followed by Federal agencies in the formulation and evaluation of projects for the use and development of water and related land resources. Contains innovative and pioneering proposals on future water and related land resource programs sponsored by the Federal Government. This report is available only through: Office of the Executive Director, Water Resources Council, 1025 Vermont Avenue, N. W., Suite 900, Washington, D. C. 20005.

50. Water Resources Council, "The Nation's Water Resources - Summary Report", U. S. Gov. Printing Office, Washington, D. C. 20402, 1968. ($0. 65).

This document represents the first national assessment of the Nation's water resources prepared by the Water Resources Council. It describes the Nation's water and related land resources, their use and the associated management problems thereof. Included are findings and recommendations of the Council with respect to national and regional water problems and related land resources problems.

51. Water Resources Council, The Nation's Water Resources (Parts 1-7), U. S. Gov. Printing Office, Washington, D. C. 20402, 1968. ($4. 25).

This account of the Nation's water resources constitutes the results of initial field study work done by the Water Resources Council. The material in these detailed reports is synopsized in "The Nation's Water Resources - Summary Report", which is listed in this bibliography.

52. Water Resources Planning Act, Public Law 89-80, 89th Congress, S. 21, 22 July 1965.

It established the Water Resources Council; encouraged conservation, development, and utilization of water and related land resources of the U. S. on a comprehensive and coordinated basis by the Federal Government, States, Localities, and private enterprise; listed guidelines for comprehensive river basin planning; and provided for promotion and support of research programs and training in the study of water supply and of resources which affect water.

53. American Medical Association Congress on Environmental Health, "Noise Pollution", Department of Environmental Health, AMA, 535 N. Dearborn St., Chicago, Ill. 60610, April 1969.

Five papers were presented by members of the AMA which reflected the state-of-the-art in the medical profession and how successfully it has coped with environmental noise pollution. The complete set of presentations includes: Donald H. Eldredge, M. D., "Noise Induced Hearing Loss - Pathological Effects"; Aram Glorig, M. D., "Medical Aspects of Noise Control" and "Non-Auditory Health Effects"; Lewis S. Goodfriend, "Psycho-Physical Aspects - Non-Transportational Noise Sources"; Karl D. Kryter, Ph. D., Evoluation of Transportation Noise".

# ENVIRONMENT: NOISE

54. American Speech and Hearing Association, "Noise As A
    Public Health Hazard", ASHA office of Public Information,
    9030 Old Georgetown Road, Washington, D. C. 20014,
    1969.

    Proceedings of the American Speech and Hearing Association
    (ASHA) Conference #4 at which over 300 papers by noise ex-
    perts across the country were presented. This document is
    an excellent, state-of-the-art source on medical defects caused
    by various noise sources.

55. Bell, A., "Noise, An Occupational Hazard and Public Nui-
    sance", Public Health Paper No. 30, World Health Organi-
    zation, Geneva, Switzerland, 1966.

56. Committee on Environmental Quality of the Federal Council
    for Science and Technology, "Noise - Sound Without Value",
    U. S. Gov. Printing Office, Washington, D. C. 20402,
    September 1968 ($0.60).

    This report reviews the dimensions of the problem of noise in
    our society and the responsibilities of the Federal agencies
    concerned with noise abatement. Topics treated include air-
    craft noise, surface transportation noise, other outdoor noises,
    indoor noise, and occupational noise. Each topic is covered by
    a description of the present situation, current programs to
    remedy the problem, and recommended Federal actions.

57. Harris, C. M., ed., Handbook of Noise Control, McGraw
    Hill, New York, 1957.

58. "How Today's Noise Hurts Body and Mind", Medical World
    News, 13 June 1969.

    An introduction to the effects different noise levels have on
    the human body. The findings of several prominant physicians
    are recounted; the different medical defects resulting from
    specific decibel levels are described. This article is ideal
    for gaining initial background knowledge in the hazardous
    health effects of noise. Special concern is expressed for
    man's continuous exposure to increasing noise levels. Neuro-
    sensory hearing loss, physiological harm, and suspected
    psychological and emotional damage resulting from noise
    are treated.

59. Kryter, K. D., "Acceptability of Aircraft Noise", Journal
    of Sound and Vibration, 5:364, 1967.

60. National Aeronautics and Space Administration, "Noise:
    Effects on Man and Materials - A Selected Bibliography",
    300 - 7th St., S.W., Washington, D. C. 20546, 15 Feb. 68

    A 32-page annotated bibliography listing references which deal
    with the effect of noise on men and materials, where noise is
    defined as unwanted sound. Most of the noises dealt with are
    audio-acoustic in nature. There is some reference to elec-
    tronic noise.

61. "Noise And Sonic Boom In Relation to Man", Report to the
    Secretary of the Interior of the Special Study Group on
    Noise and Sonic Boom in Relation to Man, Washington, D. C.
    20240, November 1968.

    This report concerns the Special Study Group's investigation
    of sonic boom generation and transmission, the effects it has
    on living organisms, and the economic and legal considerations
    that must be acknowledged in future decision-making on the
    sonic boom problem.

62. Wilson, Sir Alan, Noise, Her Majesty's Stationery Office,
    Sales Section, British Information Office, 845 - 3rd Ave.,
    New York, N. Y. 10022 ($2.60).

# ENVIRONMENT: SOLID WASTE

63. American Public Works Association, Committee on Solid
    Wastes, Refuse Collection Practice, 3rd ed., Public
    Administration Service, Chicgo, Illinois, 1966.

    A textbook-like survey of refuse collection practices. Chapter
    topics include: Problem description, cost factors, methods
    and equipment, transportation, financing, management, and
    accounting. Appendices provide selected data, typical ordi-
    nances, and chapter-related bibliographies.

64. American Public Works Association, Solid Waste Collection
    and Disposal Facilities Needed. 1966 to 1975, American
    Public Works Association Institute for Solid Wastes,
    Chicago, Illinois, 1966.

    A report for the Subcommittee on Economic Progress of the
    Joint Economic Committee, U. S. Congress. Outlines
    10-year waste management needs.

65. Association of Bay Area Governments, Bay Area Regional
    Planning Program, Refuse Disposal Needs Study, Berkeley,
    California, July 1965 (Two Volumes).

    Part of the Federally-financed Regional Planning Program,
    this study outlines refuse management practices in the Bay
    Areas, determines future needs, and recommends future
    action. The "Supplemental Report" documents current prac-
    tices in refuse man agement and presents a county-by-county
    discussion of needs and trends.

66. Bureau of Mines and IIT Research Institute, Proceedings of
    the Symposium: Mineral Waste Utilization, Chicago, Ill,
    1968.

    Topics concern the economies of mineral waste utilization,
    Mining and Processing Wastes, Industrial wastes, and
    Special Bureau of Mines Projects. (Available from BuMines).

67. Bureau of Mines, Automobile Disposal: A National Problem,
    U. S. Gov. Printing Office, Washington, D. C., 1967.

    This report presents information accumulated by Bureau of
    Mines in a fact finding survey of the auto wrecking industry,
    the ferrous scrap-processing industry and other factors in the
    junk automobile situation in 54 case study districts. General
    observations and conclusions are followed by the area studies
    and a limited bibliography. Numerous illustrations are pro-
    vided.

68. Bureau of Mines, "Wealth Out of Waste", Department of the
    Interior, Washington, D. C.

    An informational brochure describing the Bureau of Mines
    Programs in Solid Waste Utilization. A general problem
    definition and data is followed by discussion of reuse of in-
    cinerator residue, Mine dumps, scrap autos, and fuel re-
    sources. R&D programs are outlined. The primary concern
    is with wastes from mining and mineral processing.

69. Department of Health, Education, and Welfare, Public Health
    Service, Proceedings: The Surgeon General's Conference
    on Solid Waste Management for Metropolitan Washington,
    Public Health Service Publication No. 1729, U. S. Gov.
    Printing Office, Washington, D. C., 1967 ($0.75)

    Topics of the 3-day conference include: Present Practices
    and Needs in the Metropolitan Area; Technology Today,
    including transportation, land reclamation, refuse reduction
    and reuse; Development of a Regional Solid Waste Disposal
    Plan.

# ENVIRONMENT: SOLID WASTE

70. Kenahan, Charles B., et. al., <u>Composition and Characteristics of Municipal Incinerator Residues</u>, Department of Interior, Bureau of Mines, Report of Investigations 7204, Washington, D. C., 1968.

This report describes the first phase of the Bureau of Mines research in reclaiming the metal and mineral values contained in municipal incinerator residues. Data is provided on the results of sampling and analysis at the Bureau's College Park Metallurgy Research Center, with statistics. A limited bibliography is included.

71. National Research Council, <u>Waste Management and Control</u>, Publication 1400, National Academy of Sciences, National Research Council, Washington, D. C., 1966.

A report to the Federal Council for Science and Technology by the NRC Committee on Pollution attempting to determine areas in which science and technology can assist in reducing and controlling Pollution. Extensive Appendices discuss the pollution problem; criteria, instrumentation and monitoring; transport systems; abatement technology; and public policy. Air, water, and land pollution are considered.

72. Public Health Service, <u>Role of Packaging in Solid Waste Management 1966 to 1976</u>, Public Health Service Publication No. 1855, U. S. Gov. Printing Office, Washington, D. C.

73. Public Health Service, <u>Solid Waste Handling in Metropolitan Areas</u>, U. S. Gov. Printing Office, Washington, D. C. 20402, 1966.

74. Regional Plan Association, <u>Waste Management</u>, Regional Plan Association, Inc., 230 West 41st Street, New York, N. Y. 10036, 1968.

A report of the second regional plan regarding the generation and disposal of solid, liquid, and gaseous wastes in the New York region. This long-range study projects to the Year 2000. It includes illustrations and statistics.

75. Schultz, George Park, <u>Managerial Decision-Making in Local Government Facility Planning for Solid Waste Collection</u>, A Thesis presented to the Graduate School of Cornell University for the Degree of Doctor of Philosophy, Department of City and Regional Planning, Cornell University, Ithaca, N. Y. January 1968.

This study attempts to increase the effectiveness of facility planning for solid waste collection systems through careful analysis and synthesis of appropriate methodologies for decision-making. Particularly valuable is the extensive bibliography on solid waste problems in general and analytical techniques in particular.

76. <u>Solid Waste Disposal Act</u>, Public Law 89-272, Title II, Section 201, 87th Congress, S. 306, October 20, 1965, U. S. Gov. Printing Office, Washington, D. C. 20402, 1965.

77. <u>Solid Waste Disposal Act Amendment of 1968</u>, Senate Report No. 1447, 90th Congress, 2nd Session, U. S. Gov. Printing Office, Washington, D. C. 20402, 1968.

78. Urban Action Clearinghouse, <u>County-Wide Plan Controls Dayton Area Pollution Problem</u>, Case Study No. 11, Chamber of Commerce of the United States, 1615 H Street, N. W., Washington, D. C. 20006, 1968 ($1.50).

This case study describes the development of a coordinated solid waste disposal program for the City of Dayton, surrounding towns, and industrial plants in the County. The plan utilizes incineration to rid the County of air pollution and health hazards previously associated with solid waste.

79. Wiley, John S., <u>Composting of Organic Wastes - An Annotated Bibliography</u>, U. S. Dept. of HEW, Public Health Service, Bureau of State Services Communicable Disease Center, Savannah, Ga., April 1960.

A somewhat dated but extensive bibliography of 388 entries on composting of organic solid wastes.

# ENVIRONMENT: HEALTH CARE

80. Belknap, Ivan, & John G. Steinle, <u>The Community and Its Hospitals -- A Comparative Analysis</u>, University of Texas, Austin, Texas, 1963.

81. Blum, Henrik L. and Associates, <u>Notes on Comprehensive Planning for Health</u>, Comprehensive Health Planning Unit, School of Public Health, University of California, Berkeley, Calif. 94720, October 1968.

This book is divided into four parts: Part I Environment for Planning; Part II Planning to Determine Goals; Part III Planning to Achieve Goals; and Part IV Special Concerns and Areas of Planning. This book also contains a Community Health Study Outline, a glossary of terms and a selected Bibliography of Bibliographies and Data Sources. This book is a very complete and valuable reference for any health planning study.

82. Conant, Ralph W., <u>The Politics of Community Health</u>, Report of the Community Action Studies Project, National Commission on Community Health Services, Washington, D. C., 1968.

This 136 page report attempts to determine the appropriateness and political feasibility of metropolitan or regional areas for administering health policy and coordinating services. It examines the transferability of health planning experiences between communities. The study also reviews the effectiveness of communication among health interests.

83. Department of Health, Education, and Welfare, <u>Delivery of Health Services For The Poor</u>, U. S. Gov. Printing Office, Washington, D. C. 20402, December 1967, ($0.75).

An analysis of the personal health care needs of the poor. This 135 page report contains background data on who are the "poor", what is their health status, how do they receive their health services, and what major current health care programs affect them.

84. Department of Health, Education, and Welfare, <u>Proceedings of The White House Conference on Health</u>, U. S. Gov. Printing Office, Washington, D. C. 20402, November 1965, ($2.00).

A 608 page book containing the transcript of the conference including the results of panel discussions on Health Professions Education, Health Care, and Health Protection.

85. Department of Health, Education, and Welfare, <u>Report of the National Conference on Medical Costs</u>, U. S. Gov. Printing Office, Washington, D. C. 20402, 1968, ($1.25).

A compilation of papers and panel discussion results presented at the National Conference on Medical Costs on June 27-28, 1967, in Washington, D. C. This conference brought together more than 300 of the Nation's health leaders, representing both providers and consumers of health services.

86. Department of Health, Education, and Welfare, <u>Report of Secretary's Advisory Committee on Hospital Effectiveness</u>, U. S. Gov. Printing Office, Washington, D. C. 20402, 1968.

Secretary John W. Gardner assigned this Advisory Committee to study: "Ways to improve the internal efficiency of the hospital", "The extent to which the hospital should serve as the organizing focus of a new and more efficient system for the delivery of health care", "Considerations of the community mix of health care facilities", and "The formula for reimbursement to hospitals and other health care institutions by third-party payers". This Report is the result of that study and lists the 11 recommendations of the Committee.

# ENVIRONMENT: HEALTH CARE

87. Department of Health, Education, and Welfare, A Report to the President On Medical Care Prices, U. S. Gov. Printing Office, Washington, D. C. 20402, February 1967, ($0.20).

A 38 page Report to the President that covers the following points: Medical Care Price Trends, Physicians' Fees, Hospital Costs and Charges, and Drug Prices. The Report attributes price rises to the pressure of rising demand for medical services, the slow growth in the supply of physicians, rising wage costs in hospitals without increases in productivity, and the increasing complexity of medical care provided to patient. The approach recommended in this Report to moderate rising prices is to use our medical resources more efficiently.

88. Fein, Rashi, The Doctor Shortage, An Economic Diagnosis, The Brookings Institution, Washington, D. C., 1967.

This 210 page book assesses the "doctor shortage" and projects the future demand and supply. It assesses alternative way of meeting the growth in demand. The author concludes that increases in efficiency through new patterns of organization and development of new types of personnel may offer substantial returns. The book discusses the distinction between health, medical, and physicians' services on one hand, and manpower on the other, taking into account the growth and change of the population as well as the impact of Medicare. Possible sources of increased productivity are analyzed and arguments in favor of group practice are assessed.

89. Health Is A Community Affair, Report of the National Commission On Community Health Services, Harvard University Press, Cambridge, Mass. 1967.

A significant appraisal of the personal and environmental health services that will be needed in the years ahead, with authoritative recommendations for action to achieve better health for all. A synthesis of six task force explorations and a report on community action studies drawn from 21 communities extending across the country and ranging in population from 30,000 to 3,500,000.

90. Health Services Research Branch, Federal Health Programs Service, U. S. Public Health Service, "Health Evaluation Center", U. S. Public Health Service Hospital, 3100 Wyman Park Drive, Baltimore, Md. 21211.

An 8 page booklet on a multiphasic health screening system and clinic.

91. Hospital, Regal Art Press, Troy, New York, 1966.

The result of a 12 week, study and design effort by 9-fourth year Architecture Students of Rensselaer Polytechnic Institute. The problem was to design a community health complex for the Troy, New York area. Nine separate designs were proposed. To obtain a copy of this report, write to either: Student Publications, School of Architecture, Rensselaer Polytechnic Institute, Troy, N. Y. 12181, or; Health Services Research, U. S. P. H. S. Hospital, 3100 Wyman Park Drive, Baltimore, Md. 21211.

92. "Kaiser Foundation Medical Care Program: Annual Report", Public Relations Department, Kaiser Foundation Medical Care Program, 1924 Broadway, Oakland, Calif. 94612, 1965.

This final report has a good article on the history and organization of the Kaiser Foundation Medical Care Program.

93. "Kaiser Foundation Medical Care Program: Annual Report", Public Relations Department, Kaiser Foundation Medical Care Program, 1924 Broadway, Oakland, Calif. 94612, 1966.

An excellent section on regional planning is presented in this report. It tries to outline the problem, discusses the desirability of regional planning, considers government involvement, and emphasizes regional planning dangers.

94. "Kaiser Foundation Medical Care Program: Annual Report", Public Relations Department, Kaiser Foundation Medical Care Program, 1924 Broadway, Oakland, Calif. 94612, 1967.

This annual report has an excellent article on health manpower and is divided into 8 sections: The Lack of Physicians, Demand for Health Services, Growing Impact of Government, Health Care and the Poor, A Medical Middle-Class, Technology, Patient as a Resource, and Organization.

95. Mann, Floyd C. & Basil S. Georgopoulos, The Community General Hospital, The Macmillan Co., New York, 1962.

96. National Advisory Commission on Health Facilities, A Report to the President, U. S. Gov. Printing Office, Washington, D. C. 20402, December 1968, ($0.45).

An 85 page report tothe President covering such areas as: From Facilities to Systems, Today's Health Care Patterns, and Requirements for Comprehensive Health Care Systems. This report also has a short annotated bibliography.

97. National Commission On Community Health Services, Comprehensive Health Care, A Challenge to American Communities, Report of the Task Force on Comprehensive Personal Health Services, Public Affairs Press, Washington, D. C., 1967.

The Task Force developed its recommendations in the context of three basic requirements to the provision of comprehensive personal health services: the key role of the personal physician, access to one standard of medical service, and associations of physicians. The recommendations are concerned with community planning, need for the personal physician, modes of access and integrated system of care, training of personal physicians, supporting facilities. Comprehensive personal health services.

98. National Commission on Community Health Services, Financing Community Health Services and Facilities, Report of the Task Force on Financing Community Health Services and Facilities, Public Affairs Press, Washington, D. C., 1967.

This 171 page Task Force Report considers the prevailing levels of community health services, their cost, mechanisms and sources of financing, and the respective fiscal capacities of the several sources of payment. The recommendations relate to the financing of health department activities, expenditures for hospital care, hospital construction and planning, and water pollution control.

99. National Commission on Community Health Services, Health Care Facilities: The Community Bridge to Effective Health Services, Report of the Task Force on Health Care Facilities, Public Affairs Press, Washington, D. C., 1967.

Viewing the whole system in which health facilities operate, this Report stresses the need for each community's health facility system to be responsive to changing concepts and approaches to personal health care.

100. National Commission on Community Health Services, Health Manpower: Action to Meet Community Needs, Report of the Task Force on Health Manpower, Public Affairs Press, Washington, D. C., 1967.

The Task Force's recommendation are presented in this 168 page report and relate to effective planning for recruitment, education, use of personnel by Government and voluntary agencies at all levels, and private and public financial support.

# ENVIRONMENT: HEALTH CARE

101.  Public Health Service, Department of Health, Education, and Welfare, Hospital Administrative Research, P.H.S. Pub. No. 930-C-8, U.S. Gov. Printing Office, Washington, D.C. 20402, Ap. 1967, ($0.35).

Material presented in this publication describes some of the activities, as a part of the Hill-Burton Program, which are contributing to progress through hospital administrative research. An annotated list of research and demonstration projects sponsored by the Hill-Burton program is presented in the last chapter of this report. Also included in this listing are publications resulting from these studies.

102.  Public Health Service, Department of Health, Education, and Welfare, Principles for Planning the Future Hospital System, P.H.S. Publ. No. 721, U.S. Gov. Printing Office, Washington, D.C. 20402, 1959, ($1.25).

This book is a compilation of 16 workshop documents which evolved from four conferences, co-sponsored by the American Hospital Association and the U.S. Public Health Service. The meetings were conducted in April and May of 1959 in Chicago, Illinois; New Orleans, La.; Salt Lake City, Utah; and Washington, D.C.

103.  Public Health Service, Department of Health, Education, and Welfare, United States Statistics On Medical Economics: Present Status and Recommendations for Additional Data, P.H.S. Publ. No. 1125, U.S. Gov. Printing Office, Washington, D.C. 20402, January 1964 ($0.75).

Eight major aspects of health economics are discussed in the body of this report; a chapter is devoted to each. In the order of their consideration, these topics are: Manpower Resources, Facilities, Utilization of Services, Unit Price to Consumers, Expenditures by or on Behalf of Consumers, Insurance and Prepayment Aspects of Medical Care, and Quality Measurements Significant to Health Economics. A brief explanation of the significance of the topic and rationale for its inclusion is given at the beginning of each chapter. Existing prime sources of data are then outlined and the general status of data collection in this field is briefly indicated.

104.  Public Health Service, Electronics for Hospital Patient Care, P.H.S. Publ. No. 930-D-25, Health Facilities Planning and Construction Service, Health Services and Mental Health Administration, Public Health Service, Dept. of Health, Education, and Welfare, 7915 Eastern Ave., Silver Spring, Md. 20910.

Contains some useful information pertaining to the hazards involved in the use of electronic and related electric equipment. It also includes a report of a study of present practices of electronic patient monitoring equipment and needs for new developments.

105.  Public Health Service, "Hill-Burton Is...", P.H.S. Publ. No. 930-F-13, U.S. Gov. Printing Office, Washington, D.C. 20402, 1969.

106.  Public Health Service, Hill-Burton Program 1946-1966: 2 Decades of Partnership, P.H.S. Publ. No. 930-F-9, U.S. Gov. Printing Office, Washington, D.C. 20402, August 1966, ($0.15).

107.  Public Health Service, Hill-Burton Program 1946-1966: 2 Decades of Partnership for Better Patient Care, P.H.S. Publ. No. 930-F-8, U.S. Gov. Printing Office, Washington, D.C. 20402, August 1966 ($0.45).

108.  Public Health Service, Hospital Electrical Facilities, P.H.S. Publ. No. 930-D-16, Health Facilities Planning and Construction Service, Health Services and Mental Health Administration, Public Health Service, Dept. of Health, Education, and Welfare, 7915 Eastern Ave., Silver Spring, Md. 20910.

This publication gives up-to-date references to applicable codes and standards and reflects changes in current practices that are needed to conform with recommended design practices that should be followed in the construction of hospital facilities.

109.  Public Health Service, Hospital Emergency Service: Criteria For Organization, P.H.S. Publ. No. 930-C-3, U.S. Gov. Printing Office, Washington, D.C. 20402, 1963.

110.  Public Health Service, Hospital Outpatient Services, P.H.S. Publ. No. 930-G-7, U.S. Gov. Printing Office, Washington, D.C. 20402, 1963.

111.  Report of the National Advisory Commission on Health Manpower, Vol. I, U.S. Gov. Printing Office, Washington, D.C. 20402, November 1967, ($0.45).

This Report is divided into three parts: Introduction, Health Manpower and Health Services in the Future, and Improving the Health Care System. This Report attempts to deal not only with the number of health personnel needed but also deals with the problems of using present health professionals and facilities more efficiently.

112.  Representative Construction Costs of Hill-Burton Hospitals and Related Health Facilities, Dept. of Health, Education, and Welfare, Public Health Service, Health Services and Mental Health Administration, Health Facilities Planning and Construction Services, Silver Spring, Md. 20910, Biannually (January-June).

This publication is designed to meet a need for up-to-date cost data on the construction of hospitals and other health, facilities. Although the data do not reflect all construction activity in the hospital field, they do provide a realistic overall view of general hospital building cost trends for the Nation as a whole. The data cover representative cost construction projects approved under the Hospital & Medical Facilities Survey and Construction Program -- more popularly known as the Hill-Burton Program.

113.  Somers, Herman M., & Anne R. Somers, Doctors, Patients, and Health Insurance: The Organization and Financing of Medical Care; The Brookings Institution, 1775 Mass. Ave., N.W., Washington, D.C. 20036.

114.  Somers, Herman M. & Anne R. Somers, Medicare and the Hospitals: Issues and Prospects, The Brookings Institution, 1775 Mass. Ave., N.W., Washington, D.C. 20036, September 1967.

This book is an attempt to deal with the issues that arose concerning the nature and extent of the impact of Medicare on the Nation's hospitals. The book is divided into three parts: Part I introduces the protagonists by describing the legislative and administrative background of the program and a general overview of the American voluntary hospital. Part II focuses on selected major issues that cover a broad spectrum of hospital and financing issues. Part III undertakes to weave together major themes developed earlier and to project present trends into a picture of the American hospital and Medicare a decade or so ahead.

# WASHINGTON, D.C. AREA INFORMATION SOURCES

There are a great many information sources of various types in the Washington, D.C. area which might be of use to interdisciplinary systems studies at universities and to individual researchers concerned with problems in the urban sector. This chapter outlines several general sources which maintain extensive data and information holdings on a wide variety of subjects and also make referrals to additional services and printed references.

A considerably more extensive description of available information centers, in the Washington area both general and specific, can be obtained from six basic references:

1. A Directory of Information Resources in the United States - Federal Government (ref. 5).

2. A Directory of Information Resources in the United States - Physical Sciences, Biological Sciences, Engineering (ref. 6).

3. Government Publications and Their Use (ref. 8).

4. Library and Reference Facilities in the Area of the District of Columbia (ref. 4).

5. Statistical Services of the U. S. Government (ref. 1 ).

6. United States Government Organizations Manual 1969-70 (ref. 7 ).

## CLEARINGHOUSE FOR FEDERAL SCIENTIFIC AND TECHNICAL INFORMATION

The Clearinghouse was established as the Government's first effort at getting the results of Government-sponsored research and development reports in all disciplines into the hands of private industry and other interested users. The Clearinghouse is the center in the Government for the collection of unclassified R & D reports from other agencies, including unclassified Department of Defense, NASA, and Atomic Energy Commission Reports. The Clearinghouse announces the reports, and reproduces and sells them at nominal cost ($3.00 per hard copy, $0.65 per microfiche copy).

Current holdings include about half a million documents, to which about 50,000 reports are added each year. In addition, the Clearinghouse publishes and sells the following documents to inform Government, industry and private users of its recent acquisitions:

a.  U. S. Government Research and Development Reports:
    published twice a month, describing over 1,000 documents
    arranged by subject matter, which have just been released
    through the Clearinghouse.

b.  Government-Wide Index to Federal Research and Development
    Reports: published bimonthly, listing reports by subject,
    personal author, corporate source, and accession numbers
    of all reports announced in U. S. Government Research and
    Development Reports.

The Clearinghouse also provides references and inquiry services to Government agencies and the general public, including inquiries on document availability, and searches for documents in specific areas of interest:

Clearinghouse for Federal Scientific and
Technical Information
5285 Port Royal Road
Springfield, Va. 22151
Tel. (703) 321-8500

It should be noted that many of the studies referenced in this document are distributed by the Clearinghouse, particularly those performed by private contractors for Federal agencies. Reports unavailable from the authors themselves may well be retained by the Clearinghouse.

## THE NATIONAL REFERRAL CENTER FOR SCIENCE AND TECHNOLOGY

The Library of Congress National Referral Service for Science and Technology (NRC) may be described as the "information desk" of the scientific and technical community. It does not provide technical details in answer to inquiries or furnish bibliographic assistance. It functions rather as an intermediary, directing those who have questions concerning scientific and technical subjects to organizations or individuals who have specialized knowledge in these fields and are willing to share this knowledge with others.

In answer to requests for guidance and assistance, the center provides names, addresses, telephone numbers, and brief descriptions of appropriate information resources. "Information resources" has been broadly defined to include professional societies, university research bureaus and institutions, and individual experts as well as more traditional sources of information, such as technical libraries, information and document centers, and abstracting and indexing services.

Referral services are available without charge. No specific forms are required. Requests may be made by writing or calling:

> National Referral Center for Science
> and Technology
> Library of Congress
> Washington, D.C. 20540
> Tel. (202) 967-8265

The Center welcomes registration by any organization having knowledge or expertise that it is willing to share with others. A registration form is available for this purpose but it is not mandatory. Those who wish to register may call (202) 967-8341, or write to NRC at the address above.

NRC publishes three very important manuals (ref. 4, 5, 6).


## U. S. GOVERNMENT PRINTING OFFICE (GPO)

The Government Printing Office executes or monitors the printing and binding of publications for every establishment of the Federal Government, sells and distributes Government publications, and supplies stationery to all Government agencies. The Office of the Superintendent of Documents provides information regarding catalogs, availability, and sales prices of Government publications printed by the GPO and designed by the originating department for public sale. A few general references on GPO holdings worth noting include:

a. Monthly Catalog of U. S. Government Publications: a comprehensive listing of all publications issued by the various departments and agencies of the U. S. Government. It is compiled by the Library of the Division of Public Documents, which according to law must receive one copy of each publication authored by any Federal bureau or branch. (Yearly subscription $6.00).

b. Price Lists of Government Publications: Periodically, the GPO publishes a listing of its current stock of publications embracing each of several topic areas, complete with order numbers and prices. They are distributed free of cost. Price lists of particular interest with respect to urban problems include:

- PL 25 Transportation, Highways, Roads, and Postal Service
- PL 36 Government Periodicals & Subscription Services
- PL 59 Interstate Commerce
- PL 62 Commerce
- PL 70 Census Publications
- PL 72 Homes
- PL 86 Consumer Information

These, as well as all other documents printed by the GPO, can be obtained from:

The Superintendent of Documents
Government Printing Office
Washington, D. C.  20402

A large number of references included in this document are GPO publications and may be obtained through the Superintendent of Documents for the price quoted (where available).

SCIENCE INFORMATION EXCHANGE (SIE)

The Exchange is a Clearinghouse for information on scientific research in progress from all available sources: Government, industry, and private institutions. It complements the services of technical libraries by providing information about research in progress between the time a project is proposed or started and the time results are made available in published form.

The SIE compiles information on current and proposed research projects in all areas of science, including life, physical, medical, engineering, agricultural, behavioral, and education sciences; geographical distribution of research grants; automatic computer indexing and retrieval; comparative indexing techniques; computer dictionaries.

The Exchange maintains synoptic records of current research projects, including name of supporting agency, names of the principal and associate investigators, location of work, level of effort, dates of active work, and 200-word descriptions of research in progress. It also maintains computer and manual indexes to projects.

The Exchange answers questions from individual investigators regarding the names of researchers working in specific fields, the locations of such activity, and the supporting agencies. The system is capable of compiling all research records related to a specific topic or any combination of items to answer questions relating to program management or investigator interests. Also, in response to queries, the SIE will perform a manual or computer search, as the case requires.

The SIE is located at:

> 1730 M Street, N. W.
> Rm. 300
> Washington, D. C. 20036

## BUREAU OF THE CENSUS

The Bureau of the Census maintains vast files of statistics in the fields of demography, agriculture, business, foreign trade, public health, housing, education, and transportation. A substantial amount of this data is stored on punch cards and magnetic tape and is available to the user in that form. The Bureau also holds from 1,200 to 6,000 statistical publications issued yearly since 1950.

The Bureau of the Census Catalog (quarterly, cumulative to annual issue, with monthly supplements) lists census publications, available unpublished tabulations, punched cards, and computer tapes, and describes the Bureau's various services and the policies governing special work (ref. 2).

The mailing address of the Bureau of the Census is:

U. S. Department of Commerce
Washington, D. C. 20233

## DEFENSE DOCUMENTATION CENTER (DDC)

The Defense Documentation Center is the central depository for documents generated by the research, test, and evaluation activities of the Department of Defense and its contractors, subcontractors, and grantees. The DDC files contain some 850,000 documents, and the Center also operates data banks containing information on contractor performance evaluations, contractor cost reductions, and research and development facilities.

Documents in the collections are available, without charge, to all executive agencies and to their contractors and grantees approved for DDC services. Nearly half of the collection is computerized for rapid searching, and bibliographic searches are made in response to authorized queries. Unclassified documents in the DDC system are announced and indexed in the Clearinghouse's U. S. Government Research and Development Reports.

Information as to the use of the Defense Documentation Center is available from:

> Defense Supply Agency
> U. S. Department of Defense
> Cameron Station
> Alexandria, Va. 22314
> Tel. (202) 698-1865

## NASA SCIENTIFIC AND TECHNICAL INFORMATION DIVISION

The Division serves as NASA's primary technical information resource in answering inquiries and making referrals. It provides machine-prepared bibliographies for NASA personnel, contractors, and grantees, based on materials abstracted in its two semimonthly abstracting publications: Scientific and Technical Aerospace Reports (STAR) and International Aerospace Abstract (IAA). Further information about NASA machine-search capabilities may be obtained from:

> NASA Scientific and Technical Information Facility
> Machine Search Branch
> P. O. Box 33
> College Park, Maryland 20740

## CONGRESSIONAL RECORD

The Congressional Record has been published continuously, beginning with the first session of the 43rd Congress in 1873. The Record is published in three forms:

1. The daily Record, which appears on the morning after the day to which it relates.

2. The paper-bound biweekly Record, which is simply an assemblage of the daily issues.

3. The permanently bound Record, which contains the proceedings for each session and constitutes an individual, numbered volume (Volume I recounts the special session of the 43rd Congress; subsequent volumes have been numbered accordingly).

An Index to the Record is issued every two weeks. At the end of the session, however, a new index is prepared for the forthcoming bound Record since the paginations of the daily Record and the hardbound volumes do not correspond. This discrepancy owes to the omission of passages from the daily Record which are not considered germane to congressional proceedings. Consequently, the session index can be used as a key to material in the appendices of the daily Record.

Most university libraries subscribe to the Congressional Record and its indexes.

# REFERENCES: INFORMATION SOURCES

1. Bureau of the Budget, Statistical Services of the U. S. Government, Office of Statistical Standards, Bureau of the Budget, Executive Office of the President, U. S. Gov. Printing Office, Washington, D.C. 20402, Rev. 1968.

   Describes the organization and operation of the statistical system of the Federal Government, various forms of presentation, and the meaning of certain indicators. Principal statistical programs are outlined, and significant publications by each of the Federal agencies are listed and described.

2. Bureau of the Census, Bureau of the Census Catalog, U. S. Gov. Printing Office, Washington, D. C. 20402, Quarterly.

   The Publications Section of the catalog lists available Bureau of the Census publications, while statistics stored on punched cards and magnetic tape are listed in the Unpublished Materials Section. The catalog is published quarterly with annual compilations.

3. Council of Social Science Data Archives, Social Science Data Archives in the U. S., 1967. Published by Council of Social Science Data Archives, 605 West 115th St., New York, N. Y. 10025, September 1967.

   Social science data archives are depositories of data that scholars, policy-makers, and others may use for scholarly research or for other purposes. Through the Council, the member archives exchange information about new data sources, methods of data management and retrieval, and promising lines of secondary analysis. In addition, the Council is a vehicle for the exchange of information and experience among persons conversant with the new methods of managing, retrieving, and analyzing social science data by computer.

4. Library of Congress, Library and Reference Facilities in the Area of the District of Columbia, Seventh edition, U. S. Gov. Printing Office, Washington, D. C. 20402, 1966, ($1.00).

   This book describes the libraries that offer service to the public and those possessing unique or specialized collections even though they serve a restricted clientele. Where the collection is restricted, qualified researchers can generally arrange to use the material through the librarian. The statement on regulations indicates the conditions under which permission may be obtained. A subject index is also included.

5. National Referral Center for Science and Technology, A Directory of Information Resources in the United States - Federal Government, U. S. Gov. Printing Office, Washington, D. C. 20402, June 1967, ($2.75).

   This directory is based on the register of information resources that has been built up since the Center was established in 1962. All appropriate Federal organizations, as well as information resources sponsored in whole or in part by the Federal Government, are represented. A subject and government organization indexes are also included.

6. National Referral Center for Science and Technology, A Directory of Information Resources in the United States - Physical Sciences, Biological Sciences, Engineering, U. S. Gov. Printing Office, Washington, D. C. 20402, Jan. 1965, ($2.25).

   The entries in this directory are listed in alphabetical order by organizational name. In cases where several information resources are parts of a single organization, such as university or Government agencies, the individual units are entered alphabetically under the main entry; cross-references have been introduced to aid in locating specific units. In the subject index, the full names of the information resources are given below each pertinent subject term to allow for rapid scanning and identification.

7. Office of the Federal Register, National Archives and Records Service, General Service Administration, United States Government Organization Manual 1969-1970, U. S. Gov. Printing Office, Washington, D. C. 20402, ($2.00).

   This manual is the official organization handbook of the Federal Government. It contains sections describing the agencies of the legislative, judicial, and executive branches. It also contains brief descriptions of quasi-official agencies and of selected international organizations. Included as supplemental information are charts of some of the more complex agencies, brief hisotries of agencies abolished or transferred since 1933, lists of Government publications, and references showing where agency rules are published in the Code of Federal Regulations.

8. Schmeckebier, Laurence F. & Roy B. Eastin, Government Publications and Their Use, The Brookings Institution, 1775 Mass. Ave., N.W., Washington, D. C. 20036, 1961.

   The purpose of this volume is to describe the basic guides to government publications, to indicate the uses and limitations of available indexes, catalogs, and bibliographies, to explain the system of numbering and methods of titling, to call attention to certain outstanding compilations or series of publications, and to indicate how publications may be obtained. Although this book cites many publications by title, it is not a catalog, a bibliography or a checklist. It is an aid to the acquisition and utilization of the publications.

# APPENDIX A

## HOUSING MANUFACTURERS LISTING

The following list of manufacturers was reproduced with the permission of the Department of Housing and Urban Development (HUD) from Volume III of the In-Cities Experimental Housing Research and Development Project Phase I Reports. The basic report is clearly outlined in the annotation of (ref. 31) in Chapter IV and the complete document, manufacturers list included, is available from the Clearinghouse for Federal Scientific and Technical Information. HUD's stock of these reports is extremely limited, which suggests that the Federal Clearinghouse is clearly the better source for obtaining copies of the Phase I Report and the Collateral Literature Survey volume (ref. 54 in Chapter IV). The Clearinghouse price is $3.00/bound volume, and $0.65 for microfiche. Orders should be made by accession number: Vol. I, P. B. 184121; Vol. II, P. B. 184122; Vol. III, 184123; Vol IV, 184124; and the Collateral Literature Survey, P. B. 184164.

Process:    Off-Site Prefabrication and Assembly
Structure:  Box
Material:   Metal

THE BEHRING CORPORATION, 2800 East Oakland Park Blvd., Fort Lauderdale, Florida 33306; MODIFLEX HOMES, prefabricated galvanized steel frame housing modules for detached and attached construction; prototype stage.

COMPREHENSIVE DESIGN GROUP, 17 Compton Terrace, Canonbury, London N 1.; CANNISTER HOUSING; stressed steel panel stackable housing units for two- and three-story construction; conceptual.

DIVCO WAYNE INDUSTRIES, INC., 680 Fifth Avenue, New York, New York 10019; steel frame stackable housing units for two- and three-story construction; prototype stage.

HIRSHEN/VAN DER RYN, 731 Virginia Street, Berkeley, California 94710; KIT HOUSE; steel framed box, in-fill walls and utility core unit; adaptable to self-help labor; one-story construction; conceptual.

HOUSING RESEARCH, INC., Michigan City, Indiana; FACTORY-FAB; steel frame housing units stackable up to three stories; uses Armco Steel Corp. "Steelox" panels; prototype stage.

HURIHOM, INC., 24150 Hesperian Blvd., Hayward, California 94545; steel frame stackable housing modules for low- and high-rise construction; prototype stage.

JONES AND LAUGHLIN STEEL CORPORATION, 3 Gateway Center, Pittsburgh, Pennsylvania 15230; steel frame module concepts for all building types.

HARRY KARLSSON, Byggneds AB, Sweden, LUNNAVILLA; wood and steel, two-section modules for single family detached construction; no U.S. projects.

CENTER FOR MANAGEMENT TECHNOLOGY, 59 E. 54th Street, New York City 10022; ACCORDIAN HOUSE; "fold-out" wood-frame preassembled house; shipped with panels folded around service core; single family detached construction; conceptual.

THE COMMODORE CORPORATION, 2410 Dodge Street, Suite 3000, Omaha, Nebraska; stackable wood-frame housing units for attached construction; conceptual.

COMMUNITY PRIDE, INC., 6723 South Western Avenue, Los Angeles, California 90047; ECONOFAB Homes; wood frame stackable housing units for one- and two-story construction; conceptual.

EDWARD DIEHL ASSOC., 23 Lexington Avenue, Cambridge, Massachusetts; DEAD RIVER HOUSING; wood frame housing module for detached and attached construction; prototype stage.

GLEN DEVELOPMENT COMPANY, 100 22nd Street, N. W. Washington, D. C. 20037; wood frame housing modules with site assembled pitched roof forms for one-and two-story construction; one project in Amherst, Massachusetts.

GUERDON INDUSTRIES, INC., P. O. Box 230, Vicksburg, Mississippi 39180; MAGNOLIA HOMES; wood frame stackable housing modules for two-story attached construction; in production.

INTERDESIGN, INC., 475 Summit Avenue, St. Paul, Minnesota 55102; UNITIZED HOUSING; wood frame and plywood panel housing modules; units can be stacked up to three stories; conceptual.

MARLETTE HOMES, INC., 3305 Wilson Street, Marlette, Michigan 48453; prefabricated wood sectionalized modules; single family detached housing; in production.

MLTW/MOORE TURNBULL, 1146 Chapel Street, New Haven, Connecticut; wood frame stackable housing modules for two- and three-story attached construction; conceptual.

MODULAR CONSTRUCTIONS, INC., P. O. Box 447, Old Bridge, New Jersey 08857; wood frame modular townhouses; one prototype has been built.

MUCKLOW PLAN, LTD., Waterfall Lane, Old Hill, Staffordshire, England; stressed skin plywood stackable housing modules for 2-3 story construction; in production in England; no U. S. projects.

NATIONAL HOMES CO., 401 Earl Avenue, Lafayette, Indiana; wood frame stackable housing units for two-story attached construction; in production.

PEERLESS MANUFACTURING CO., 4301 Bluffton Road, Fort Wayne, Indiana 46807; STACKHOUSE; wood frame housing modules for two-story attached construction; in production.

MODULUX, INC., 38505 Cherry Street, Newark, California 94560; steel framed modules for 1-3 story construction; in production.

PAUL RUDOLPH, 26 West 58th Street, New York, New York; steel frame stackable housing modules for low-rise construction; conceptual (also concepts for high-rise construction using suspended modules).

PERKINS AND WILL PARTNERSHIP, Architects, 309 West Jackson Blvd., Chicago, Illinois 60606; (P.L.U.S.) PERSONAL LIVING UNIT SYSTEM; steel frame housing modules for all building types-detached through high-rise; conceptual.

SIERRA SHELL HOMES, 1858 Almaden Road, San Jose, California, MOD-CAP (modular capsule housing); steel frame housing modules for one- and two-story construction; prototype stage.

STEEL COMPANY OF CANADA, LTD., 3 Windermere, Toronto, Canada; steel framed stackable housing units for two-story attached construction; prototype stage; no U.S. projects.

TRYGVE HOFF AND ASSOCIATES, 1922 East 107th Street, Cleveland, Ohio 44106; steel frame stackable housing modules for high-rise construction; conceptual.

UNIHAB, INC., Box 424, Canal Street Station, New York, New York 10013; steel frame housing modules for low- and high-rise construction; conceptual.

ZELL AND GARCIA, INC., 3011 Haddington Drive, Los Angeles, California 90064; PARKHOUSE concept; prefabricated and finished light weight steel frame housing modules installed in high-rise structural steel frame; conceptual.

ZIEGELMAN AND ZIEGELMAN, Architects, 167 Townsend, Birmingham Michigan 48011; INSTA-BUILDING; metal framed stackable housing modules for two- and three-story construction; prototype stage.

Process:    Off-Site Prefabrication and Assembly
Structure:  Box
Material:   Wood

ALUMINUM COMPANY OF CANADA, LTD., 200 University, Toronto, Canada; wood frame, aluminum siding, sectionalized housing units for single family detached construction; prototype stage; no U. S. projects.

ANN ARBOR COLLABORATIVE, 336 1/2 South State Street, Ann Arbor, Michigan; wood frame stackable housing units for two-story attached construction; prototype in Detroit.

JOHN BEMIS, Acton, Massachusetts; ACORN house; "fold-out" sandwich panel housing unit; shipped with panels folded around service core; appropriate for one-story construction; conceptual.

PORTAKABIN LTD., Ouseacres, Boroughbridge Road, York, England; wood framed, mobile home modules for one- and two-story construction; in production in England; no U. S. projects.

REDMAN INDUSTRIES, 7800 Carpenter Freeway, Dallas, Texas 75247; wood frame stackable housing modules for two-story construction; prototype project has been completed in Detroit.

RITZ-CRAFT HOMES, P. O. Box 400, Shamokin, Pennsylvania; wood frame stackable housing units for attached two-story construction; prototype in Detroit.

ROYCRAFT INDUSTRIES, INC., 114 West First Street, Chesaning, Michigan; sectionalized wood frame housing units for single family detached housing; in production.

SANFORD INDUSTRIES, INC., P. O. Box 1177, 951 Southwest 12th Avenue, Pompano Beach, Florida 33061; SANFORD CUBICLE; wood frame housing units for attached and low-rise construction; conceptual.

SLIDUS STRUCTURES, Vancouver, Canada; wood frame stackable housing units for two-story attached and detached construction; in production in Canada; no U. S. projects.

STEPHENSON DEVELOPMENTS LTD., Grosvenor Works Leeds Road, Huddersfield, Yorkshire, England and G. H. BURGESS & CO., Stains Road, Hounslow. Middlesex, England; wood panel mobile home units on steel skids; temporary one-story construction; no U. S. projects.

STIRLING CUBET CORPORATION, 1150 East River Road, Avon, New York; HOMEX; wood framed stackable housing modules for two-story attached construction; in production.

U. S. PLYWOOD, 777 Third Avenue, New York, New York 10017; SEATTLE WORLD'S FAIR ATRIUM HOUSE; wood panel mobile home units arranged by fours to form an atrium; one-story attached construction; prototype.

| | |
|---|---|
| Process: | Off-Site Prefabrication and Assembly |
| Structure: | Box |
| Material: | Reinforced Concrete |

DON BEDDOE, Box 114, Dana Point, California 92629; APARTMOBILE; reinforced concrete housing modules inserted in structural frame for high-rise construction; conceptual.

BUILDING BLOCK MODULES, INC., 114 West 14th Street, Oakland, California 94607; precast reinforced concrete stackable housing modules for low- and high-rise construction; six unit prototype has been constructed.

CONBOX A/S, Filstedvej 12, 9000 Aalborg, Denmark; precast reinforced concrete housing modules placed in independent structural frame; 2-4 story construction; no U. S. projects – 500 units in Denmark.

GENERAL MATRIX CORPORATION, 257 Newtonville Avenue, Newton, Massachusetts 02158; THE MATRIX SYSTEM; reinforced concrete modules fabricated on or off site by pneumatically applied concrete on an expanded steel frame and mesh formwork; attached and low-rise construction; prototype stage.

ILLINOIS INSTITUTE OF TECHNOLOGY RESEARCH INSTITUTE, Technology Center, Chicago, Illinois; precast reinforced concrete stackable housing units for high-rise construction; conceptual.

WILLIAM MORGAN, A.I.A., 1611 Ocean Blvd., Atlantic Beach, Florida; INTERPOD; precast reinforced concrete housing modules – stacked and suspended – for high-rise construction; conceptual.

RENFRO ASSOCIATES, 1224 Broadway, Santa Ana, California; precast reinforced concrete housing modules connected to structural service core; low- and high-rise construction.

SKANSKA CEMENTDJUTERIET, Malmo 1, Sweden; CORPUS System precast reinforced concrete stackable housing modules for low-rise construction; no U. S. projects.

STRESSED STRUCTURES, INC., 3333 Banock, Continental National Bank Bldg., Denver, Colorado; UNIMENT; precast reinforced concrete stackable housing units for low- and high-rise construction; prototype project in Richmond, California.

SUSPENDED STRUCTURES, INC., 47 Kearny Street, San Francisco, California 94108; precast reinforced concrete housing units suspended from slipformed core tower; high-rise construction; conceptual.

SYSTEM LOCARN LTD., 24 York Road, Hitchin, Herts, England; precast and assembled reinforced concrete stackable housing modules for two- and three-story construction; no U. S. projects.

TRUSCON, Manchester, England; precast and preassembled U-shaped box units for low- and high-rise construction; used in England; no U. S. projects.

WILLIAM AND LAMPARD, Grove Ferry Hill, Canterbury, Kent, England; W. L. RING System; precast reinforced concrete rings stacked checkerboard fashion to form two- and three-story construction; prototype stage.

H. B. ZACHRY CO., P. O. Box 21130, San Antonio, Texas 78221; precast reinforced concrete stackable housing modules for low- and high-rise construction; in production.

| | |
|---|---|
| Process: | Off-Site Prefabrication and Assembly |
| Structure: | Box |
| Material: | Plastic |

AEROJET GENERAL CORPORATION, P. O. Box 15847, Sacramento, California 95813; INTERSPACE BUILDING SYSTEM, filament wound reinforced plastic housing units for attached and low-rise construction; conceptual.

HERCULES INC., 910 Market Street, Wilmington, Delaware 19899; filament wound plastic housing modules; conceptual.

ARTHUR QUARMBY, Carlton House, 44 New North Road, Huddersfield, Yorkshire, England; PAVILION HOUSING; fiberglass reinforced plastic room modules; room sized units can be stacked or joined for two- or three-story construction; octagonal; in prototype stage.

| | |
|---|---|
| Process: | Off-Site Prefabrication – On-Site Assembly |
| Structure: | Bearing Panel |

ADVANCED PRODUCTS DEVELOPMENT CO., INC., P. O. Box 116, Warden, Washington 98857; APCO HOMES; wood faced foam plastic core load bearing sandwich panel system for single family detached construction; in production.

AMERICAN BUILDING AND CONSTRUCTION CO., INC., 1025 Vermont Avenue, N. W., Washington, D. C. 20005; U. S. franchisers for the COIGNET system; precast reinforced concrete bearing panel system for high-rise construction; many European projects – none, as yet, in U. S.

BELLAIRE PRODUCTS, INC., Tallevest, Florida; Aluminum faced paper honeycomb core load bearing sandwich panel system for single family detached construction; in production.

THE BINKLEY COMPANY, Suite 211, 100 St. Francois Street, Florissant, Missouri; all-steel frame and panel system for single family detached construction; prototype stage.

BRAMALEA CONSOLIDATED DEVELOPMENT, LTD., 70 Bramalea Road, Bramalea, Ontario, Canada; North American contact for SKARNE system precast reinforced concrete bearing panel system for high-rise construction; no U. S. projects.

JOHN H. BRENNEMAN, Princeton, New Jersey; BRENLOC; modular wall, floor and ceiling panels fastened together with grip-splines; appropriate for single family detached construction; prototype stage.

CAMUS, LTD., 12 Bloomsbury Way, London, WC1, England; U. S. contact: ECODESIGN, 1106A Massachusetts Avenue, Cambridge, Massachusetts; CAMUS system; precast reinforced concrete panel system for high-rise construction; in use in Europe – no U. S. projects.

CEBUS U. S. LIMITED, P. O. Box 308, Laurel, Maryland 20810; U. S. licensee for French CEBUS system; precast reinforced concrete bearing panel system for high-rise construction; no known U. S. projects.

CERTAIN-TEED PRODUCTS CORP., Broad Axe Offices, 25 Shippack Pike, Ambler, Pennsylvania 19002; post and panel system with asbestos cement extrusions for single family detached construction; prototype in Austin, Texas.

COMPOSITE STRUCTURES, INC., Berkeley Research and Development Div., 43 Village Court, Orinda, California 94963; BERKELEY "BENT-PLATE" SYSTEM; plywood insulated wall and roof panel assemblies for two-and three-story construction; conceptual.

COMSTRUCT, INC., P. O. Box 813, Lincolnton, North Carolina; wood faced paper honeycomb core sandwich panel system for single family detached construction; prototype has been constructed.

DUES DEVELOPMENT CORPORATION, 135 West Dorothy Lane, Dayton, Ohio; DUES BUILDING SYSTEM; reinforced concrete bearing panel system for low- and high-rise construction; in production.

DURASTRUCT, 229 West Fifth Street, Winston-Salem North Carolina 27102; reinforced concrete bearing panel system for single family detached to low-rise construction; two prototype units have been constructed.

ENDURE PRODUCTS, INC., 2375 Northwest Station, Miami, Florida 33147; aluminum faced, honeycomb core sandwich panel system for one-story single family detached construction; in production.

ERBEST HOMES, England; wood and concrete panel system for single story detached dwellings; medium weight concrete floor and wall units; timber roof units; no U. S. projects.

GO-CON CONCRETE LIMITED, 17 Woodstock Street, London W1, England; U. S. contact: R. K. WHITE CONSTRUCTION COMPANY, Akron, Ohio; reinforced concrete bearing and non-bearing panels system pressed at rapid speed by GO-CON concrete press, low- and high-rise construction; in production in England; no U. S. projects.

DONALD L. GRIEB ASSOCIATES, 777 West Glencoe Place, Milwaukee, Wisconsin 53217; plastic bearing wall homes; single family detached; four prototypes built.

HALL HOMES, P. O. Box 17887, Atlanta, Georgia 30316; prefabricated wood frame panel package for single family detached housing; in production.

HUFSCHMIDT ENGINEERING COMPANY, Highway 164, Sussex, Wisconsin 58089; reinforced concrete bearing panel system for two- and three-story construction; conceptual.

IMPRESA GENERALE COSTRUZIONI MBM, s.p.a., Trezzano sul Naviglio, Milano, Italy; U. S. contact: ASSOCIATED SYSTEM PLANNERS AND DESIGNERS, INC., 370 Lexington Avenue, New York, New York; BALENCEY system precast reinforced concrete load bearing panel system with cast in place floor slabs; appropriate for high-rise construction; not yet in production in U. S.; many European projects.

INDUSTRIAL LAMINATES CORP., 1806 East Fourth, Austin, Texas 78702; expanded polystyrene core sandwich panels; site assembled; prototype constructed for the Auston-Oaks project sponsored by HUD and University of Texas.

A. JESPERSEN AND SON INTERNATIONAL A/S, 18 Nyropsgade, DK – 1602, Copenhagen V, Denmark; JESPERSEN SYSTEM; precast reinforced concrete crosswall system for low- and high-rise construction; no U. S. projects.

KEMAXCO, INC., P. O. Box 36191, Houston, Texas; reinforced concrete bearing panel system for one- and two-story construction; 500 single family units built in Mexico but no U. S. projects.

KINGSBERRY HOMES CORP., 5096 Peachtree Road, Chamblee, Georgia; prefabricated wood frame panel package appropriate for one- and two-story attached and detached construction; in production.

CARL KOCH & ASSOCIATES, INC., 35-36 Lewis Wharf, Boston, Massachusetts 02110; TECHCRETE; precast reinforced concrete bearing panel system for low- and high-rise construction; in production.

LOCKHEED AIRCRAFT SERVICE COMPANY, P. O. Box 33, Ontario International Airport, Ontario, California; PANEL-LOCK System precast reinforced concrete bearing panel system for one-story construction; 80-unit development in Puerto Rico and prototype unit in Austin, Texas; assembly possible by unskilled labor.

MILLER, BUCKLY AND COIGNET, LTD., Trident House, Station Road, Hayes, Middlesex, England; U. S. contact: AMERICAN BUILDING AND CONSTRUCTION CO.; COIGNET System; precast reinforced concrete bearing wall system for high-rise construction; no known U. S. projects.

MYERS BROTHERS CONSTRUCTION, Box 65557, Los Angeles, California 90065; TT PANEL HOME; wood sandwich panel and extruded metal frame system for one-story construction; prototype stage.

NATIONAL FOREST PRODUCTS ASSOCIATION, Technical Services Division, 1619 Massachusetts Avenue, N. W., Washington, D. C. 20036; UNICOM; shop fabricated modular wood frame system for single family detached construction; conceptual.

WILLIAM OLD (RESIFORM) LTD., Old's Approach, Tolpits Lane, Watford, Hertfordshire, England; RESIFORM; fiberglass reinforced plastic bearing panel system for attached and low-rise construction; experience in Britain, but no known U. S. projects.

PANELFAB, INC., Northeast 1463 Street, North Miami, Florida; metal faced paper honeycomb core, sandwich panel system for one-story construction; in production.

PINTER CONTRACTING CO., 230 Park Avenue, New York, New York 10017; modified LARSEN-NIELSON System; reinforced concrete bearing panel system for high-rise construction; not in production in U. S.

PORTLAND CEMENT ASSOCIATION, Old Orchard Road, Skokie, Illinois 60076; RESEARCH VII AND RESEARCH I HOUSING; precast reinforced concrete bearing panel systems for attached and low-rise construction; prototypes have been built.

PRECAST CONSTRUCTORS, LTD., England; P.A.C. SYSTEM; precast reinforced concrete bearing panel system for high-rise construction; no U. S. projects.

PRECON INDUSTRIES, INC., 2339 Inwood Road, Dallas, Texas; PRECON (L.T.V.); precast reinforced concrete panel system for single family detached construction; conceptual.

REEMA CONSTRUCTION, LTD., Milford Manor, Salisbury, England; precast reinforced concrete bearing panel system for attached and low-rise construction; no U.S. projects.

RHEEM MANUFACTURING COMPANY, 7600 South Kenzie Avenue, Chicago, Illinois 60652; "all-steel" frame and panel system for single family detached construction; prototype stage.

ROCKY MOUNTAIN PRESTRESS, INC., P. O. Box 1434 Inglewood, California; precast reinforced concrete bearing panel system for low- and high-rise construction; prototype stage.

ROHR INDUSTRIES, P. O. Box 878, Chula Vista, California 92012; asbestos cement faced sandwich panel system with load bearing steel studs for one- and two-story construction; conceptual.

SAM INDUSTRIES, INC., 4199 Eighth Avenue South, St. Petersburg, Florida; wood faced honeycomb core sandwich panel system for single family detached construction; in production.

SKANSKA CEMENTDJUTERIET, Malmo 1, Sweden; ANGLE-ELEMENT system; precast reinforced concrete wall/floor system for low-rise construction; many European projects — none in U. S.

SOUTHERN CAST STONE CO., Sutherland Avenue, Knoxville, Tennessee; prefabricated concrete block wall system for single family detached construction; prototype stage.

STAHL INDUSTRIES INC., 746 Golfview Avenue, Youngstown, Ohio; STAYLITE PANEL HOMES; urethane foam core load bearing sandwich panels for single family detached construction; prototype constructed in Jamaica — panels in production in U. S:

STRESCON INDUSTRIES, INC., 3501 Sinclair Lane, Baltimore, Maryland 21213; BISON WALL FRAME; precast reinforced concrete bearing wall system for low- and high-rise construction; no U. S. projects as yet.

STRUCTURAL DESIGN AND RESEARCH, 26 Vineland Street, Brighton, Massachusetts 02135; INTEGRACAST; reinforced concrete bearing panel system for low- and high-rise construction; conceptual.

DON STULL ASSOCIATES, 10 Milk Street, Boston, Massachusetts; INFIL; precast reinforced concrete bearing panel system for in-fill sites between existing row houses

SUNDH LTD., 31 Sow Street, Finsbury Square, London ECZ, England; Swedish precast reinforced concrete load bearing panel system with cast in-place floors for high-rise construction; no U. S. projects.

TRACOBA, 254 Rue de Bercy, Paris 12, France; U. S. contact: PAUL WEIDLINGER, Consulting Engineer, 777 Third Avenue, New York, New York 10017; TRACOBA No. 1; precast reinforced concrete bearing panel system for high-rise construction; many European projects — none in U. S.

TO 8B, Czechoslovakia; precast reinforced concrete bearing panel system for low- and high-rise construction; many European projects — none in U. S.

UELAND AND JUNKER, Architects, 1718 Sansom Street, Philadelphia, Pennsylvania 19103; precast reinforced concrete bearing panel system for two-story attached construction on in-fill sites between existing row houses and apartments; conceptual.

THE URBAN DESIGN GROUP, 43 Mill Street, Newport, Rhode Island 02840; (I.C.C.) INTERMODAL CONSTRUCTION CONCEPT; fiberglass faced, urethane core sandwich panel and structural frame system for attached and low-rise construction; conceptual.

LARRY VITA, Fort Lauderdale, Florida; "waste paper" house; one-story paper product bearing wall unit; prototype stage.

WATES, LTD., 1260 London Road, London SW 16, England; precast reinforced concrete bearing panel system for high-rise construction; many European projects; none in U.S.

HARRY WEESE AND ASSOCIATES, 10 West Hubbard, Chicago, Illinois; FIRNKAS System; precast reinforced concrete bearing panel system for two- and three-story attached housing; developed for the Fort Lincoln New Town project; conceptual.

ALFRED A. YEE AND ASSOCIATES, INC., Structural Engineers, Ala Moana Bldg., Suite 810, Honolulu, Hawaii; DOMINO; precast reinforced concrete bearing wall system for high-rise construction; one project has been constructed.

Process:    Off-Site Prefabrication — On-Site Assembly
Structure:  Structural Frame

ALUMBER COMPANY OF AMERICA, INC., 11 Hazelwood Circle, Willingboro, New Jersey 08046; aluminum structural framing system for single family detached construction; assembly is possible with unskilled labor; prototype stage; construction of units in New Jersey and Puerto Rico on an experimental basis.

DON BEDDOE, Box 114, Dana Point, California 92629; PIPEMOBILE; steel structural frame system for high-rise construction; conceptual.

DAVID B. CHESKIN CO., 407 South Dearborn Street, Suite 1600, Chicago, Illinois 60605; precast reinforced concrete structural frame system for low- and high-rise construction; conceptual.

COMPONOFORM, INC., 15 Brattle Street, Cambridge, Massachusetts 02138; precast reinforced concrete rigid frame system for high-rise construction; in production; recent application in Boston.

CONSTRUCTION SYSTEMS PTY. LTD., 1200 Hay Street, West Perth, Australia; UCON SYSTEM; precast reinforced concrete framing system appropriate for low- or high-rise construction; no U.S. projects.

ECONOSTRUT SYSTEMS, 650 California Street, San Francisco, California 94108; steel frame and sandwich panel system with interchangeable components; one- and two-story construction; in production.

GROUPEMENT d'ETUDE pour une ARCHITECTURE INDUSTRIALISEE, 31 Avenue Charles de Gaulle, 95-Montmorency, France; GEAI System steel column and space frame system for construction up to five stories high; first project being built in France; no U.S. projects.

INDULEX ENGINEERING LIMITED, 17 Woodstock Street, London W.1, England; steel frame system with plastic composite panel wall cladding; high-rise construction; many European projects — none in U.S.

INTERPACE, 2855 West Pomona Blvd., Pomona, California; (U.R.B.S.) UNIVERSITY RESIDENTIAL BUILDING SYSTEM; precast reinforced concrete structural frame system for low- and high-rise construction; conceptual — developed in conjunction with the Portland Cement Association.

JORGEN AND KAJ SCHMIDT, Rosenvaenget Alle 20, Copenhagen, Denmark; T.V.P. System; precast reinforced concrete frame and hollow-core slab system; low- or high-rise; used in Denmark and England, no U.S. projects.

T. Y. LIN AND ASSOCIATES, 15 Vandewater Street, San Francisco, California; DYNACORE; lightweight reinforced concrete framing system for low- and high-rise construction.

MASSACHUSETTS INSTITUTE OF TECHNOLOGY, Cambridge, Massachusetts; STAGGERED TRUSS SYSTEM; high-rise steel frame system with story-high trusses; 17-story housing project for the elderly in St. Paul, Minnesota.

MATHEWS AND MUMBY LTD., Oldham Street, Denton, Manchester, England; reinforced concrete structural frame system for low- and high-rise construction; no U.S. projects.

MINISTRY OF PUBLIC BUILDINGS AND WORKS, Thames House South, London SW 1, England; NENK System; structural steel framing system with various cladding materials for all buildings below five stories; no U.S. projects.

NEAL MITCHELL ASSOCIATES, INC., 149 Putnam Avenue, Cambridge, Massachusetts; lightweight reinforced concrete interlocking column, beam and slab system for attached and low-rise; demonstration units have been built in Lancaster, Pennsylvania and at HUD-University of Texas project in Austin, Texas.

MAGIC HOMES, INC., P. O. Box 6093, Homewood, Alabama 35209; HAIG MODULAR CONSTRUCTION SYSTEM; aluminum frame system for single-family detached housing; in production.

MODULAR MANUFACTURING CO., 721 Monterey Blvd., San Francisco, California 94127; aluminum frame system for single family detached dwellings; assembly of components can be done by unskilled labor; prototype has been built.

NOVOA, INC., Sargento Luis Medina No. 390, Apto. 1-ext. Roosevelt, Hato Ray, Puerto Rico 00918; precast reinforced concrete structural frame and in-fill panel system for one- and two-story construction; many projects in Puerto Rico — none in continental U.S.

OWENS-KLEINE STRUCTURES, LTD., P.O. Box 10, Darleston, Wednesbury Staffs, England; structural steel frame with reinforced concrete floor slabs for high-rise construction; prototype stage.

PORTLAND CEMENT ASSOCIATION, Old Orchard Road, Skokie, Illinois 60076; precast reinforced concrete staggered truss framing system for high-rise construction; conceptual.

SCHERRER-BAUMANN AND ASSOCIATES, 1224 North Broadway, Santa Ana, California 92701; BAUMANN SPACE SYSTEM; prefabricated expandable, self-locking structural steel space frame for detached, attached and low-rise construction; conceptual.

W. J. SIMM SONS AND COCKE LTD., Haydon Road, Sherwood, Nottingham, England; SIMMCAST; precast reinforced concrete frame and panal system for low- and high-rise construction; projects in England — none in U.S.

STRESCON INDUSTRIES, INC., 3501 Sinclair Lane, Baltimore, Maryland; DYNA-FRAME; precast reinforced concrete structural frame for high-rise construction; in production.

TURNER AND NEWALL LTD., 77 Fountain Street, Manchester, England; T & N HOUSE; structural steel frame system for two-story construction; prototype stage — development in England.

UNIVERSAL PRECISION STRUCTURES, Germany and 10 Dorland Ct., 106 W. Hill, London SW 15, England, hollow reinforced concrete floor/ceiling slab with a steel socket case into each corner and a hollow steel column with tapered spigots which fit into slab sockets; appropriate for low- and high-rise housing; conceptual.

U.S. STEEL, 525 William Penn Place, Pittsburgh, Pennsylvania; U.S.S. SELF HELP SYSTEM; lightweight structural steel framing system for two- and three-story construction; one prototype has been built; components may be assembled by unskilled labor.

TAGE WIBERG AB, Gothenborg, Sweden; TECHBUILT; modular bolted steel frame system for one- and two-story construction; unskilled labor can erect; many European projects – none in U.S.

Process:    On-Site Prefabrication and Assembly

BUILDING AND CONSTRUCTION CO., LTD., Penarth Road, Cardiff, Glamorgan, England; CAUVET System; loadbearing reinforced concrete panel system fabricated on-site in steel molds; low- and high-rise; no U.S. projects.

CONCRETE FABRICATORS CO., 1109 East Bayseed Avenue, Denver, Colorado 80209; CON-FAB System; reinforced concrete bearing panel system fabricated on-site by a portable precasting machine; prototype machine is available.

DOW CHEMICAL COMPANY, Plastic Products Division, Midland, Michigan 48640 Spiral Generation, Polystyrene core panel system prefabricated on-site for single family detached construction; test structures have been built in form of domes.

FOLDCRETE INTERNATIONAL, INC., 166 Geary Street, San Francisco, California 94108; FOLDCRETE; reinforced concrete box cast on site in flat "folded-out" position; low- and high-rise construction; prototype stage.

GENERAL ELECTRIC CO., Community Systems Development Division, Lincoln Towers, P.O. Box 1661, Louisville, Kentucky 40201; on-site fabricated "L-shape" panel system for one- and two-story and attached construction; conceptual.

GESELLSCHAFT FUR FERTIGBAU, Technik M.B.M., Dortmund, West Germany; KESTING System; reinforced concrete bearing panel system for low- and high-rise construction; fabricated on-site by mobile precasting machine; no U.S. projects.

LUNDGREN AND MAURER, A.I.A., 3108 North Lamar Blvd., Suite 301, P.O. Box 4555, Austin, Texas; on-site precast lightweight reinforced concrete bearing panel system for attached and low-rise construction; conceptual.

McNAMARA AND ASSOCIATES, 8 East Taylor Street, Savannah, Georgia 31401; SLIP-STACK BUILDING SYSTEM; on-site fabricated reinforced concrete L-shaped wall-floor components for low- and high-rsie construction; conceptual.

PETERSON COMPANY, 7701 Forsyth Blvd., St. Louis, Missouri 63105; U.S. contact for the ESTIOT System; on-site precast reinforced concrete bearing panel system for high-rise construction; projects in Europe and Africa; none in U.S.

MOSHE SAFDIE, 1315 Maisonneuve West, Montreal, Canada; HABITAT; site cast reinforced concrete stackable housing modules; project in Montreal Expo '67; no U.S. projects constructed.

STANFORD RESEARCH INSTITUTE, Menlo Park, California; ROLLING SHOP; on-site shop concept for detached and attached construction; conceptual.

TRAN-ZANE SYSTEMS, INC., Buffalo, New York; on-site fabrication concept applicable for all types of construction except hihg-rise; conceptual.

ZETLIN, DESIMONE, CHAPLIN AND ASSOC., New York, NY, site prefabricated steel frame and gypsum wall housing modules suspended between slip-formed concrete cores; high-rise construction; conceptual.

Process:    In-Place Fabrication

AIRFORM CONSTRUCTION, 5927 Franklin Avenue, Los Angeles 28, California; reinforced concrete dome structures for single-family detached housing fabricated in-place using inflatable "balloon-forms" and gunnite; prototypes built in Africa and Mexico – none in U. S.

ARCHITECHNICAL PRODUCTS, INC., 342 Madison Avenue, New York, New York 10017; FERAN INDUSTRIALIZED CONSTRUCTION SYSTEM (F.I.C.S.); reinforced concrete bearing wall system cast in-place using steel expandable "tunnel" forms; high-rise construction; prototype forms are being produced.

CHANEN CONSTRUCTION COMPANY, INC., 3426 North 29th Avenue, P.O. Box 11327, Phoenix, Arizona 85017; concrete block in-place construction of single family detached housing; prototype home constructed in Austin-Oaks '68 experiment.

DICKER STACK-SACK INTERNATIONAL, 2600 Fairmont Avenue, Dallas, Texas; reinforced concrete bearing wall construction fabricated in-place by wetting down steel reinforced "stacked sacks" of dry cement and aggregate; one- and two-story construction; in production.

ECODESIGN, 1106A Massachusetts Avenue, Cambridge, Massachusetts; U.S. representative for French SECTRA system; reinforced concrete bearing wall system for high-rise construction; fabricated in-place with the use of steel "tunnel" form techniques; no U.S. projects.

FOREST PRODUCTS LABORATORY, Madison, Wisconsin, NU-FRAME system rationalized in-place wood construction for single family detached construction; conceptual.

INLAND STEEL PRODUCTS COMPANY, 4101 W. Burnham Street, P.O. Box 393, Milwaukee, Wisconsin 53201; STEELCOR SYSTEM; steel frame, metal lath and sprayed in situ concrete bearing wall system for single family detached housing; in production.

MIDWEST APPLIED SCIENCE CORPORATION, 1205 Kent Avenue, P.O. Box 2157, West Lafayette, Indiana; MOPFU; foamed in-place epoxy resin wall construction for one-story building; conceptual.

R. D. MONROE CONSTRUCTION COMPANY, Cloverleaf Building 11, Suite 311, 6901 West 63rd Street, Shawnee Mission, Kansas; SLIP-FORM INTERNATIONAL; reinforced concrete bearing wall construction fabricated in-place using slipform techniques; low- and high-rise construction; in production.

PROF. M. SALVADORI, Division of Architectural Technology, Columbia University, New York, New York; (T.P.I.) TOTAL PROGRESSIVE INDUSTRIAL; poured in-place reinforced concrete bearing wall system multistory construction; conceptual.

SOUTHEASTERN FOREST EXPERIMENT STATION, Forestry Sciences Laboratory, Housing Research, Carlton Street, Athens, Georgia 30601; URRAL HOME; wood frame rationalized conventional construction for single-family detached rural housing; conceptual.

WILLIAM THORNTON AND SONS, LTD., 38 Wellington Road, Liverpool, England; PROMETO System; reinforced concrete bearing wall system formed in-place by using shutters lifted by Prometo jacks; high-rise construction; used in England – no U.S. projects.

TRACOBA, 254 Rue de Bercy, Paris 12, France; U.S. contact: PAUL WEIDLINGER, Consulting Engineer, 777 Third Avenue, New York, New York 10017; TRACOBA No. 4; reinforced concrete bearing wall high-rise construction formed in-place using tunnel shuttering techniques; many European projects – none in U.S.

U-FORM SYSTEMS INTERNATIONAL, 10111 Capital, Oak Park, Michigan 48237; U-FORM; reinforced concrete bearing wall system poured in-place between permanent urethane plastic forms which act as insulation as well as formwork; appropriate for up to six-story construction; a prototype wall has been built.

VIN-LOX CORPORATION, 1352 Northwest 29th Street, Miami, Florida; reinforced concrete bearing wall construction fabricated in-place by spraying air entrained concrete on to steel frame and mesh forms; one- and two-story building; in production.

MANUFACTURERS LISTING – SUBSYSTEMS AND COMPONENTS

Service Cores

AMERICAN STANDARD, 40 West 40th Street, New York, New York 10018; BATHROOM APPLIANCE CONCEPT; prefabricated bathroom plumbing "wet" wall for construction up to ten stories high; prototype stage.

BORG-WARNER, Plumbing Products Division, 200 South Michigan Avenue, Chicago, Illinois 60604; prefabricated stackable kitchen-bathroom core units including all wiring and plumbing; produced for "Instant Rehab" project in New York.

THE COMMODORE CORPORATION, Suite 3000, 2410 Dodge Street, Omaha, Nebraska 68131; prefabricated core unit including kitchen, bathroom. water heater, furnace and electrical entrance; prototypes produced for Austin-Oaks '68 experiment.

CRANE MANUFACTURING COMPANY, 1285 Bayshore Blvd., San Francisco, California; UNETTE PACKAGED BATHROOM; prefabricated fiberglass reinforced polyester bathroom units; in production.

EDWARD DIEHL ASSOC., 23 Lexington Ave., Cambridge, Massachusetts; DEAD RIVER HOUSING, prefabricated kitchen bathroom service core combined with vertical circulation; prototype stage.

HIRSHEN AND VAN DER RYN, 731 Virginia Street, Berkeley, California 94710; prefabricated kitchen, bathroom and utility room service core; conceptual.

HOUSING RESEARCH, INC., P.O. Box 286, Michigan City, Indiana; prefabricated kitchen, bathroom and utility room service core; conceptual.

IDACO LUMBER COMPANY, 3233 Peralta Street, Oakland, California; wood frame prefabricated kitchen-bathroom core units; at present, the units are being produced for single family detached homes.

MANUEL C. KITE, 350 Arballo Drive, San Francisco, California 94132; prefabricated kitchen unit; conceptual.

WILLIAM OLD (RESIFORM) LTD., Old's Approach, Tolpits Lane, Watford, Hertfordshire, England; prefabricated kitchen and bathroom core units for attachment to exterior of housing units; in production in England – no U.S. projects.

PACKAGE DESIGN SYSTEMS, 22245 Thorofare Road, Grosse Ile, Michigan 48138; prefabricated package bathrooms, kitchens and utility rooms; prototype stage.

ROHR INDUSTRIES, P.O. Box 878, Chula Vista, California 92012; prefabricated modular bathroom core units; conceptual.

WAUSAU HOMES, INC., Wausau, Wisconsin; prefabricated service core for single-family detached construction; in production.

Heating, Ventilating and Cooling

CALIFORNIA HEAT PUMP CORPORATION, 835 North Hollywood Way, Burbank, California 91505: centralized electro-hydronic air-conditioning system using water to air heat pumps; for high-rise construction; in production.

CONTINENTAL BEAUTYBASE CO., 200 Main Street, Baltimore, Maryland 21222; electric hydronic baseboard heater; in production.

DAY AND NIGHT MANUFACTURING COMPANY, 855 Anaheim – Puente Road, La Puenta, California 91747; GENFLEX; GLASSFLEX; flexible duct systems; in production.

EMPIRE STOVE COMPANY, Belleville, Illinois 62222; EMPIRE CLASSIC AIRE; wall mounted, direct vent, sealed combustion, forced air furnace with baseboard extensions; for peripheral and multi-room applications; in production.

GENERAL ENVIRONMENT CORPORATION, 555 West St. John Street, San Jose, California 95110; GENFLEX; NORFLEX; modular air distribution duct kits; in

INTERNATIONAL OIL BURNER CO., 3800 Park Avenue, St. Louis, Missouri 63110; electric hydronic baseboard heater; in production.

LEAR SIEGLER, INC., Holly Division, 4361 Firestone Blvd., South Gate, California; prefabricated heating and air-conditioning package shipped in kit form; includes vertical fan coil unit, steel soffit and plenum, remote condensing unit, registers, etc.; conceptual; (in production products include counterflow heating systems).

NATIONAL GYPSUM COMPANY, Buffalo, New York; PANELECTRIC; electric radiant ceiling system; in production.

THE SINGER COMPANY, 62 Columbus Street, Auburn, New York 13021; ENERGY CONSERVATION CONDITIONING SYSTEM; all electric heating and cooling system for high-rise construction using water to air heat pumps; in production. (Also, electric hydronic boiler systems and radiant heating systems.)

UNITED STATES GYPSUM, Chicago, Illinois; THERMALUX; electric radiant heating system using CELLOTHERM heating elements by CHEMELEX, Danbury, Connecticut; in production.

WEIL-McCLAIN COMPANY, INC., Michigan City, Indiana 46360; electric hydronic baseboard heater and gas fired boilers; in production.

WESTINGHOUSE ELECTRIC CORPORATION, 3 Gateway Center, Box 2278, Pittsburgh, Pennsylvania 15230; various electric heating and cooling systems including counterflow systems, hydronic heating, baseboard heating, etc.; in production.

EDWIN L. WIEGAND COMPANY, 7500 Thomas Blvd., Pittsburgh, Pennsylvania 15208; CHROMALOX TETON COUNTERFLOW; electric wall heater with three way heat delivery; in production.

## Electrical

FEDERAL PACIFIC ELECTRIC COMPANY, 50 Paris Street, Newark, New Jersey 07101; ground fault circuit interrupters and baseboard heater, wireway and receptacle assemblies; in production.

HARVEY HUBBEL INC., Bridgeport, Connecticut 06602; ground fault circuit interrupter; in production.

INTERNATIONAL TECHNOLOGY, INC., 7324 Westmore Road, Rockville, Maryland 20850; baseboard power distribution system with nonmetallic conductors; prototype stage.

I.T.E. IMPERIAL CORPORATION, 1900 Hamilton Street, Philadelphia, Pennsylvania 19130; ELECTROSTRIP; receptacle strip with integral metallic conductor; in production.

JOHNSON PLASTIC CORPORATION, P.O. Box 100, Munn and Stafford Roads, Chagrin Falls, Ohio 44022; JOHNSONITE R-W SURFACE RACEWAY; plastic baseboard wireway and receptacle assembly; in production.

KAISER ALUMINUM, 300 Lakeside Drive, Oakland, California; nonmetallic sheathed cable; aluminum conductor; in production.

LEAR SIEGLER, INC., Lighting Products Division, Toledo, Ohio; electrical wiring system in prefabricated kit form including meter box, conduit wiring, raceways, wiring devices, fixtures, etc.; conceptual.

NELCO CORPORATION, 930 South Central, Kent, Washington; baseboard heater with integral wireway and installed receptacles; in production.

H. K. PORTER CO., INC., Electrical Division, 640 Dubuque Street, South San Francisco, California 94080; surface mounted metal raceway; in production.

RUCKER CO., Electronics Division, 747 Bancroft Way, Berkeley, California 94710; SAFETY SENTRY; ground fault circuit interrupter; in production.

WESIX ELECTRIC HEATER COMPANY; 1611 Adrian Road, Burlingame. California 94010; baseboard heater, wireway and receptacle assembly; in production.

WIREMOLD CO., Hartford, Connecticut 06110; metal baseboard wireway and receptacle assembly; in production.

## Plumbing

### Systems

COPPER DEVELOPMENT ASSOCIATION, 405 Lexington Avenue, New York, New York 10017; SOVENT System; one stack drainage plumbing system for high-rise buildings; in production.

WALLACE MURRAY CORPORATION, 650 Washington Road, Pittsburgh, Pennsylvania 15280; LILJENDAHL System; vacuum toilet and sewer system; developed in Sweden; no U.S. projects.

### Fixtures

OWENS CORNING FIBREGLAS, Home Building Products Division, Toledo, Ohio 43601; fiberglass reinforced plastic bathtubs and shower stalls; in production.

SUPERIOR LAMINATES, INC., 1250 North Parker Street, Orange, California 92667; fiberglass reinforced plastic bathtub-wainscot units and shower stalls; in production.

UNIVERSAL-RUNDLE CORPORATION, New Castle, Pennsylvania; UNI-BATH, UNI-SHOWER; fiberglass reinforced plastic bathtub and shower stall units with enclosing walls; in production.

### Pipe

ALABAMA PIPE COMPANY, P.O. Box 309, Anniston, Alabama; "no-hub" cast iron drain, waste and vent piping; in production.

B. F. GOODRICH CHEMICAL CORPORATION, 3135 Euclid Avenue, Cleveland, Ohio 44115; polyvinyl-chloride (PV.C.) drain waste and vent pipe; in production.

BORG WARNER CORPORATION, 200 South Michigan Avenue, Chicago, Illinois 60604; Acrylonitrite-butadiene-styrene (A.B.S.) drain, waste and vent pipe; in production.

CELANESE PLASTICS COMPANY, 142 Parsons Avenue, Columbus, Ohio 43215; Acrylonitrite-butadiene-styrene (A.B.S.) drain waste and vent pipe; in production.

UNITED TECHNOLOGY CENTER, Techite Department, P.O. Box 5222, Sunnyvale, California 94088; TECHITE pipe; reinforced plastic mortar pipe; in production.

## Enclosure

### Floors

AMERICAN PLYWOOD ASSOCIATION, 1119 "A" Street, Tacoma, Washington 98401; plywood floor and wall construction concepts for one- to three-story construction; conceptual.

DUES DEVELOPMENT COMPANY, 135 West Dorothy Lane, Dayton, Ohio 45429; eight foot wide hollow core precast, prestressed concrete floor slab; in production.

NATIONAL LIME ASSOCIATION, 4000 Brandywine Street, Washington, D.C. 20016; grade slabs formed by lime soil stabilization; technique is in use.

POTLATCH FORESTS, INC., Lewiston, Idaho 83501; "T-Joist" plywood floor system and wood frame plenum floor systems; prototype stage.

REID AND TARICS, 1019 Market Street, San Francisco, California; and the AMERICAN IRON AND STEEL INSTITUTE, 633 Third Avenue, New York, New York; steel composite action duct-beam system; conceptual.

ROCKWIN CORPORATION, 13440 East Imperial Highway, Santa Fe Springs, California 90670; FILIGREE prefabricated floor systems: "wide element" slab – permanent precast concrete form containing entire reinforcement of floor and composite floor construction – reinforced concrete "T-ribs" with concrete masonry blocks installed between; in production.

UNITED STATES GYPSUM COMPANY, 101 South Wacker Drive, Chicago, Illinois 60606; prefabricated metal edge wire mesh reinforced gypsum floor plank; in production.

### Walls

ADVANCE PANEL, 3163 Olive Highway, Oroville, California; prefabricated plywood or metal faced, styrene core sandwich panels for single family detached construction; in production.

ALUMINUM STRUCTURES COMPANY, 2515 Laurel, Wilmette, Illinois, 60091, prefabricated extruded aluminum solid surface load bearing wall for one and two story construction; conceptual.

ARMCO STEEL CORPORATION, Metal Products Division, Middletown, Ohio; STEELOX wall systems; fiberglass insulated, metal faced exterior panels; in production.

BUILDER'S EQUIPMENT COMPANY, P.O. Box 7143, Phoenix, Arizona 85011; THOMAS-WALL panels; prefabricated concrete block wall panels formed by block laying machine; prototype stage.

CEDAR-CREST HOMES, Oakland, California; prefabricated solid wood core load bearing wall panels for single family detached construction; in production.

CENTAUR ENGINEERING, Division of Marbon Chemical, P.O. Box 447, Mount Clemen, Michigan 48043; foam casting of plastic panels – not developed for housing; in production.

DOW CHEMICAL COMPANY, Plastics Products Department; Midland, Michigan 48640; TREADLINE; high strength adhesive mortar for fabricating masonry walls; in production; also, SARABOND; polymer mortar additive to increase bond strength in masonry wall construction; in production.

ESSO INTERNATIONAL, New York City, New York; BMX BLOCK; building block made from mixture of heavy oils and soil pressed and heat polymerized; conceptual.

GROUTLOCK CORPORATION, P.O. Box 466, Canton, Ohio 44701; self-aligning concrete clock wall system; in production.

HARRY KINGSMILL, 6710 – 9th Street North, St. Petersburg, Florida 33702; MODUMATIC building units; lightweight insulated, metal faced modular "building blocks" for bearing and nonbearing wall construction; for one- and two-story construction; conceptual.

JOHNS MANVILLE, Building Products Division, 215 Market Street, San Francisco, California 94105; "expandible partition" composed of prefabricated gypsum wallboard facings separated by equally spaced paperboard webs; in production; also, TRANSITOP curtain wall system with aluminum mullions and cement-asbestos faced sandwich panels; in production.

MASON AND HANGER, Silas Mason Co., Inc., 33 South Hogan Street, Jacksonville, Florida; INTER-LOCK 3; concrete block construction units with interfitting edges and surfaces; one- and two-story construction; conceptual.

MODERN CRAFT ENTERPRIZES, P.O. Box 5037, Poland, Ohio 44514; wood frame plenum wall system for single family detached construction; conceptual.

PERMAWALL MANUFACTURING COMPANY, 14 Pedder Street, Albion, Brisbane, Q4010, Australia; U.S. contact: Henry Fleishman, 115 East 92nd Street, New York, New York; prefabricated plywood, aluminum or asbestos board faced, polyurethane core sandwich panels for walls and roofs of one- and two-story construction; in production in Australia; no U.S. projects.

LEWIS B. PRICE, 4112 East Kilmer, Tucson, Arizona 85711; poured in place or prefabricated rigid polyurethane foam core sandwich panel partitions; faced with treated lath paper and vinyl finish; prototype stage.

THE STANLEY WORKS, New Britain, Connecticut 06050; prefabricated sandwich panel system with metal joinery for single-family detached construction; prototype stage.

UNIROYAL, 1230 Avenue of the Americas, New York, New York 10026; ROYALEX; vacuum formed plastic nonloadbearing sandwich panel; in production.

UNITED STATES GYPSUM COMPANY, 101 South Wacker Drive, Chicago, Illinois 60606; STRUCTICORE; prefabricated integral stud gypsum panel partitions; in production.

UNIVERSAL BUILDING PRODUCTS CORPORATION, 1025 Vermont Avenue, N.W., Washington, D.C.; INNSETT concrete block wall system laid without exposed mortar joints; in production.

VELFAC/FELUX A/A, Maskinej 4, Soburg, Denmark; timber frame nonloadbearing modular exterior curtain wall units for attached and low-rise construction; in production in Europe — no U.S. projects.

See also Advanced Products Development Co., Inc.; Bellaire Products, Inc.; Comstruct, Inc.; Endure Products, Inc.; Industrial Laminates Corp.; Panelfab, Inc.; Sam Industries, Inc., and Stahl Industries, Inc., under off-site prefabrication — on-site assembly — bearing panels.

## Miscellaneous

### Finishes and Coverings

ARMSTRONG CORK COMPANY, Lancaster, Pennsylvania; CASTILIAN; wide roll (6 ft to 12 ft) vinyl flooring with hydrocord back; in production.

GAF CORPORATION, Floor Products Division, 1139 Lehigh Avenue, Whitehall, Pennsylvania; wide roll (up to 12 ft) resilient vinyl floor covering; in production.

KAISER GYPSUM COMPANY, INC., Kaiser Center, 300 Lakeside Drive, Oakland, California; tough surface veneer plaster system; in production.

NATIONAL GYPSUM COMPANY, Buffalo, New York; KAL-KOTE; high strength, hard surface veneer plaster; in production.

UNITED STATES GYPSUM COMPANY, 101 South Wacker Drive, Chicago, Illinois 60606; MASTICAL; low consistency, high strength gypsum cement floor leveling underlayment; in production.

### Openings

ADOR CORPORATION, Subsidiary of Rusco Industries, Inc., 2401 West Commonwealth Avenue, Box 4159, Fullerton, California 92634; adjustable metal frame replacement window and surround with wall panel assembly; for rehabilitation projects; in production.

FILON CORPORATION, 12333 South Van Ness Avenue, Hawthorne, California 90250; fiberglass reinforced plastic glazing; in production.

GENERAL ELECTRIC COMPANY, 235 Montgomery Street, San Francisco, California; LEXAN; high strength transparent polycarbonate glazing; in production.

W. R. GRACE & CO., Dewey and Almy Chemical Division, 62 Whittmore Avenue, Cambridge, Massachusetts 02140; BITUTHENE; self-adhering polyethylene asphalt waterproofing membrane; in production.

IDA PRODUCTS COMPANY, 3001 Miller Street, Detroit, Michigan 48211; aluminum frame replacement windows for rehabilitation; in production.

SEASON-ALL INDUSTRIES, INC., Indiana, Pennsylvania 15701; aluminum replacement windows for rehabilitation; in production.

VINYLAST CORPORATION, 3019 East Manhattan, Toledo, Ohio; all-vinyl replacement window; for rehabilitation; in production.

### Vertical Transportation

DOVER ELEVATOR COMPANY, P.O. Box 2177, Memphis, Tennessee 38102; preassembled elevator penthouse components; conceptual.

METAL SERVICE COMPANY, INC., Subsidiary of Washington Aluminum Co., Inc., Baltimore, Maryland 21227; prefabricated and pre-erected adjustable steel stairways; in production.

OTIS ELEVATOR COMPANY, 1 Beach Street, San Francisco, California 94133; preassembled elevator equipment; conceptual.

PICO SAFE STAIRS CO., 4628 42nd Place, Hyattsville, Maryland 20781; prefabricated steel stairs; in production.

### Foundations

AMERICAN IRON AND STEEL INSTITUTE, 150 East 42nd Street, New York, New York 10017; steel floor joist foundation system; in production.

AMERICAN PLYWOOD ASSOCIATION, 1119 "A" Street, Tacoma, Washington 98401; treated wood foundations for detached and attached construction; conceptual.

J. H. BAXTER & CO., 1700 El Camino Real, San Mateo, California 94402; wood pole structural foundation platform for detached and attached construction; in production.

POTLATCH FORESTS, INC., P.O. Box 3591, San Francisco, California; prefabricated treated wood foundation walls for single family detached construction; prototype.

### Waste Disposal Systems

AEROJET GENERAL CORPORATION, Environmental Systems Division, 9200 East Flair Drive, El Monte, California 91734; CENTRALSUG SYSTEM; vacuum refuse collection system for high-rise buildings; in production.

JOSEPH GODER, INC., 2483 Greenleaf Avenue, Elk Grove Village, Illinois 60007; programmed attendant free incinerator system; high-rise construction; in production.

LEAR SIEGLER, INC., 3171 South Bundy Drive, Santa Monica, California; OMNIVAC System; vacuum refuse collection system; in production.

### Utility Installation

COORDINATED UTILITIES, INC., No. 1 Hiller Drive, Oakland, California 94618; HILLER COORDINATED SYSTEM; underground installation technique of both telephone and powerlines, used for housing project in Berkeley.

PARSONS, Division of Koehring Company, 200 North 8th Avenue East, Newton, Iowa 50208; cable laying machines for underground utility installation; in production.

WOODLAND MANUFACTURING COMPANY, 155 West Main Street, P.O. Box 1235, Woodland, California 95695; EL TOPO; cable laying machine for underground utility installation; in production.

CELLULAR CONCRETE COMPANY, P.O. Box 481, Old Lyme, Connecticut 06371; SIPOREX; lightweight cellular concrete; used extensively in Sweden; no U.S. projects.

CONSOLIDATED SERVICES, 3311 Charles Street, Rockford, Illinois 61108; wall sandwich material composed of aluminum siding, paper and wire, and "vonco" plaster which was developed by Dow Chemical Co., Freeport, Texas; in production.

FMC CORPORATION, Riverside Division, P.O. Box 552, 3075-14th Street, Riverside, California 92502; THE MONSTER; mechanical nailing machine for automated prefabrication of wood frame wall and roof panels; in production.

FRIGIDAIRE, Division of General Motors Corporation, Dayton, Ohio 45401; LAUNDRY CENTER; vertically stacked combination washer-dryer unit; in production.

SAMI A. KLINK, Division of Machines and Structures, Renselaer Polytechnic Institute, Troy, New York; FYCRETE; concrete reinforced with glass fiber rods; cheaper and stronger than steel reinforced concrete; patent pending.

LEAR SIEGLER, INC., Borroughs Division, Kalamazoo, Michigan; prefabricated modular steel storage units — closets and cabinets; conceptual.

McGRAW-EDISON COMPANY, Power Systems Division, P.O. Box 100, Franksville, Wisconsin 53126; ARMETER System; automated water, gas and electric meter reading and billing system; ready to market.

MORGEN MANUFACTURING CO., Box 160-6A, Yankton, South Dakota 57078; adjustable scaffolding for masonry construction; in production.

NATIONAL CONCRETE MACHINERY COMPANY; Division of Irl Daffin Associates, Inc., Keller Avenue and Fruitville Pike, Lancaster, Pennsylvania 17604; CONCRETE MOBILE; combination materials transporter and mobile concrete mixing plant; in production. (Also, mobile cement gunning machine and concrete pumps.)

JAMES P. ROMAULDI, Director, Transportation Research Institute, Carnegie-Mellon University, Pittsburgh, Pennsylvania; concrete reinforced with steel fibers; in development.

STANDARD PRESSED STEEL CO., 12352 East Whittier Blvd., Whittier, California 90607; prefabricated steel double faced closet and room dividers; conceptual.

SYNCROFLO, INC., 5300 Belmont Road, Downers Grove, Illinois; preassembled tankless water pressure booster system; for high-rise construction; in production.

SYNTERCRETE, INC., 59 - 30th Street, San Francisco, California; process for mixing concrete which increases curing time and flexural strength and reduces costs; development stage.

U.S. FOREST SERVICE, Forest Products Marketing Laboratory, Princeton, West Virginia; MARCRAFT floor leveling system; wooden screeds held in place by rigid urethane foam to form base for laying a new floor over a sagging floor; for rehabilitation; development assistance by Gusmer Coatings Co., Inc., of Woodbridge, New Jersey and Union Carbide Co. of South Charleston, West Virginia.

THE VIKING CORPORATION, Hastings, Michigan; FIRECYCLE System: automatic fire suppression system using electrically controlled sprinklers which automatically turn on and off when needed; in production; also: Factory Mutual Research Corporation, Norwood, Massachusetts — innovative concepts on fire protection.

# SYSTEMS DESIGN IN ENGINEERING

**WILLIAM BOLLAY,** Visiting Professor and **BRUCE B. LUSIGNAN,** Assistant Professor, Stanford University

AS THE SCIENTIFIC and technical capacities of mankind have expanded, so have the complexities of the systems he is able to build. While the engineering talent required to build the Egyptian pyramids or the Roman aqueducts was substantial, it was far less than that required to build the airplanes or communications systems of the 1930's and 1940's. And these systems in turn required only a very small fraction of the systems design efforts needed for the Apollo moon programs, communications satellites, or supersonic aircraft of today.

In early projects it was possible for single geniuses to grasp all the essential engineering principles and guide the project alone. Today's projects, however, require such a wide range of detailed knowledge that no single person can encompass it. Therefore, today's systems design is done by teams, each of whose members ideally has a basic understanding of all areas of the design and a deep understanding and expertise in at least one specialty area. In some projects, teams composed entirely of engineers are sufficient; however, in an increasing number of projects, technical advances make contributions to scientific, economic, and social problems and teams must include experts from these areas as well. Systems engineers in such teams then also need to be aware of fields outside of engineering.

Since a majority of engineers at the bachelor's or master's level and a large percentage at the doctor's level will be involved in design of such complex systems or subsystems, universities and colleges should include appropriate material in their curricula. The hardest part of educating a systems engineer, that is, training him in depth in a specialty area, is usually covered quite adequately in normal courses. However, other essential areas have been. overlooked until recently, with the result that many engineering graduates have begun their careers only partly prepared. They had the highly sophisticated mathematical tools, often more sophisticated than those of older engineers in industry, but lacked the ability to apply these tools efficiently to the real-world problems. Part of the lack was the inability of engineers to converse with other engineers or specialists and part was an inability to synthesize and optimize an engineering design.

## Systems Design Courses

To overcome these shortcomings, Professor Bollay introduced a Systems Engineering course at M.I.T. in 1962 and a second course at Stanford in 1963. In these courses students form a team to complete a preliminary design of a complex engineering system. New design problems are chosen each year to match the expected enrollment of students and to have real potential value if solved properly. Background information and engineering "know-how" is supplied by over 20 guest speakers from government, industry, and university. At the end of the course, one semester at M.I.T. and two quarters at Stanford, a verbal presentation is given and a 300-400 page. report is published. Details of the course organization and cost ($15,000 to $20,000 per year, including faculty salaries) are contained in Reference 1.

From early experimental projects, both courses now form an integral part of M.I.T.'s and Stanford's engineering curricula. Three years ago M.I.T. started a second course in the area of civilian technology directed by Professor Dwight Baumann. Recognizing the value of such courses, NASA funded the authors in the summer of 1966 to acquaint other professors with the techniques used. The following year NASA repeated the program at Stanford and started two new programs in connection with Auburn University and the University of Houston. These programs are conducted cooperatively with NASA Centers, the Ames Research Center with Stanford, The Marshall Space Flight Center with Auburn, and the Manned Space Flight Center with Houston. NASA is again funding these three Summer Training Programs in Systems Engineering in the summer of 1968.

Many universities and colleges now include such systems design courses in their curricula. Many of these have been started and more will be started in the next academic year as a direct result of the programs described above. Similar courses have also been started in other institutions with the encouragement and financial support of private industry. The academic community is aware of the growing importance of complex engineering systems in today's world and is taking steps to ensure that future engineering graduates are prepared to cope with these systems.

The topics of the first two courses directed by Professor Bollay and the other five studies at Stanford directed by both authors are listed below. Two of these studies, ICARUS and SAINT, were carried out by faculty teams at the NASA Ames-Stanford summer programs.

MITROS (MIT 1962-63): A line-scan camera satellite in equatorial orbit transmitting cloud cover data directly to small stations.

SWAMI (Stanford 1963-64): Polar satellites collecting weather data from free-floating buoys and balloons and relaying it to a central ground station.

SAMPLER (Stanford 1964-65): A Mars exploration system, including an orbiting vehicle and two landing craft.

SPINMAP (Stanford 1965-66): Design of space and ground systems to observe weather parameters, by balloon, buoy, and satellite for two-week forecasts.

ICARUS (Stanford-Ames 1966): An advanced spacecraft to observe the solar wind within 0.2 AU of the sun.

ASCEND (Stanford 1966-67): Communications and educational TV satellite and ground system for Brazil, India, and Indonesia.

SAINT (Stanford-Ames '67): Satellites to supply all international and regional communications needs in all the mid 1970's.

The results of these studies are reported in detail in References 2-8. In what follows examples from these reports will illustrate some important aspects of systems engineering.

## Synthesis and Analysis in Systems Engineering

In the military and space fields, systems engineering is usually divided into four phases (Ref. 9):

1. *The Conceptual Phase,* during which specifications are formed which represent significant technical advances, but advances that are attainable with available time and money.

2. *The Project Definition Phase,* in which alternative approaches are identified and evaluated and, the optimum chosen. This usually includes detailed theoretical and simulator studies and cost and time analysis.

3. *The Acquisition Phase,* in which detailed design and development is completed, and the system is built, delivered, installed, and acceptance-tested.

4. *The Operational Phase,* which includes operation, maintenance, modification, and updating of the system.

The first two phases are most critical to a system design. By the time the third phase is underway, so much has been invested in the details of planning and production that any changes are tremendously expensive; any technical errors must be corrected with "quick fixes"; and any further optimizations of the system are normally rejected as too costly. The problem formulation and the system optimization then are the most important and most challenging to the systems engineer and are also the phases most readily treated by a university course.

These phases become a succession of synthesis and analysis, forming solutions to system and subsystem requirements and evaluating the performance of the different solutions. The procedure can be illustrated by an example from the ASCEND educational TV satellite, Table 1. Listed on the left of the table are the various subsystems of ASCEND. The lines to their right represent the possible alternatives for each subsystem,

**TABLE 1**
**Some System Alternatives of the ASCEND Study**

| Subsystem | | Alternatives | | | | | | |
|---|---|---|---|---|---|---|---|---|
| Launch Systems: | 1st Stage | Scout \| Thor \| Atlas \| Titan I \| Titan III \| Saturn I \| Saturn V \| | | | | | | |
| | 2nd Stage | Scout \| Delta \| Agena \| Centaur \| Saturn SIV \| | | | | | | |
| | Kick Stage | FW4S \| X–259–A3 \| TE–364–3 \| | | | | | | |
| Orbit: | Altitude | 100 nautical miles – – – – – – – – – – Synchronous – – – – – – – – – – – – – – – – Escape | | | | | | | |
| | Accuracy | 0 – – – – – – – – – – – – – – – – – – – – – – – – – – – – – – – – – – ∞ (ft) | | | | | | | |
| Orientation: | Direction | random \| 1 axis \| 2 axis \| 3 axis \| | | | | | | |
| | Scheme | gravity gradient \| fully active \| spin \| stabalite \| | | | | | | |
| | Accuracy | 0 – – – – – – – – – – – – – – – – – – – – – – – – – – – – – – – – – 360° | | | | | | | |
| Thrust: | Level | 0 – – – – – – – – – – – – – – – – – – – – – – – – – – – – – – ∞ (lbs) | | | | | | | |
| | System | resistojet \| ion \| cold gas \| electrolysis \| hot gas \| | | | | | | |
| Power System: | Level | 0 – – – – – – – – – – – – – – – – – – – – – – – – – – – – – – ∞ (watts) | | | | | | | |
| | Primary System | radioisotope \| reactor \| thermoelectric \| fuel cell \| battery \| solar cell \| | | | | | | |
| | Secondary System | battery \| fuel cell \| none \| | | | | | | |
| Thermal: | High Limit | 0 – – – – – – – – – – – – – – – – – – – – – – – – – – – – – – ∞ (°K) | | | | | | | |
| | Low Limit | 0 – – – – – – – – – – – – – – – – – – – – – – – – – – – – – – ∞ (°K) | | | | | | | |
| | Control | passive \| louvers \| heat pipes \| | | | | | | |
| Spacecraft Antenna: | | omnidirectional \| cylindrical \| earth oriented \| country oriented \| | | | | | | |
| | | \| \| \| \| | | | | | | |
| TV Broadcast Signal: | Power | 0 – – – – – – – – – – – – – – – – – – – – – – – – – – – – – – ∞ (watts) | | | | | | | |
| | Frequency | 0 – – – – – – – – – – – – – – – – – – – – – – – – – – – – – – ∞ (Hz) | | | | | | | |
| | Modulation | AM \| AM–SSB \| FM \| FM–SSB \| digital \| | | | | | | |
| | No. Channels | 1 \| 2 \| 3 \| 4 \| 5 \| 6 \| 7 \| 8 \| 9 \| 10 \| 11 \| · · · · · · · · · · · · · · · · · | | | | | | | |
| Spacecraft Structure: | Material | steel \| aluminum \| titanium \| fiberglass \| plastic \| | | | | | | |
| | Form | plate \| skin & stringer \| truss \| honeycomb \| waffle \| shell \| | | | | | | |
| | Configuration | many ways of putting together the various subsystems \| | | | | | | |
| Ground Antenna: | Type | parbola \| horn \| lens \| yagi \| slot array \| | | | | | | |
| | Size | 0 – – – – – – – – – – – – – – – – – – – – – – – – – – – – – – ∞ (ft) | | | | | | | |
| | Material | aluminum \| expanded metal \| plastic \| steel \| | | | | | | |
| Ground Receiver: | Noise Temperature | 0 – – – – – – – – – – – – – – – – – – – – – – – – – – – – – – ∞ (°K) | | | | | | | |
| | Circuit | transistor \| tunnel diode \| paramp \| cooled paramp \| mixer diode \| | | | | | | |

either several different approaches or, in some cases, choice from a continuous range of some parameter. The systems engineers must identify the various possible solutions and then determine the best.

Creativity and imagination play their major role in identifying the possible solutions. In industry, engineers additionally draw on their past experience, on the current literature, and on handbooks. In the course the students usually draw more on their creativity and imagination, but also draw on the experience of the guest speakers, on current literature, on handbooks, and on their previous course experience (although often this is quite sparse in the areas of synthesis).

Once the alternatives have been identified or invented, they must be analyzed. For simplicity in Table 1, only about half of the alternatives actually considered in the ASCEND study have been listed. Even so, since theoretically any combination of choices can be made, the alternatives shown represent well over $10^{18}$ different solutions to the ASCEND problem. The goal of the systems design team is to find the best one. It is in this search that the sophisticated analytical tools of the engineer are applied, and they obviously must be applied efficiently if the optimum solution is to be found in a reasonable amount of time. It is this ability to apply the theories that engineering students often lack. Stated another way, engineering students are amply prepared to answer technical questions but true systems engineers must also be able to determine which questions are important to ask.

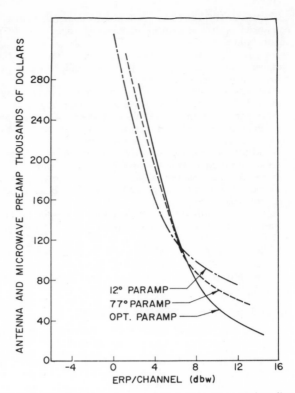

Figure 1. Ground station antenna and front end cost comparison (from SAINT report, Figure 30, page 77, NASA Contract NSR-05-020-151).

### Techniques in Searching for the Optimum System

The search for the optimum system requires a wide range of approaches. Order of magnitude calculations will clearly eliminate some alternatives; others will require detailed theoretical analysis before a decision emerges. Although the chosen system will be analyzed in detail, time usually allows alternative approaches to be analyzed only to a depth sufficient to reject them. Reducing the myraid possible systems to a manageable number of analytical questions involves many appoaches, approaches best taught by example in a systems course and impossible to describe completely in an article of this length. However, several of the most useful techniques can be illustrated with the following example.

Figure 1 shows a decision graph from the SAINT study of communications satellites. On the abcissa is the satellite's effective radiated power (ERP). On the ordinate is the cost of the ground antenna and the amplifier necessary for the various satellite power levels. Curves are shown for three different amplifiers. Note, for instance, the curve for the optimized paramp. At a high ERP, most of the total cost is due to the amplifier and little to the antenna; as the ERP drops however, larger and far more expensive antennas are needed and total cost rises sharply. With the 12° paramp, costs at high ERP's are more since this amplifier is more expensive than the optimized paramp. However, this amplifier is also more sensitive and therefore can use a smaller antenna. This favors the 12° paramp as the ERP is lowered and the

antenna costs become important in the total cost. A composite curve formed from the 12° paramp curve from 0 to 6 dbw ERP, the 77° paramp from 6 to 7 dbw and the optimized paramp from 7 to 16 dbw, gives the minimum antenna-amplifier cost for any ERP.

This curve represents an intermediate step in the system definition. Communications and information theory have been used to relate the satellite power to amplifier performance and antenna size, and cost data provides the standard for comparison. Note that this curve does not itself represent a choice of amplifier, of antenna size, or of ERP. What it does represent is a reduction of three "independent" variables to only one independent variable, ERP; choice of amplifier type and antenna size now depend on the choice of ERP. In the next step, this minimum antenna-amplifier cost curve will be multiplied by the number of ground stations and added to a satellite cost vs ERP curve to get the combined system cost vs ERP. This combined curve has a minimum, which then dictates the optimum choice of ERP, which in turn dictates the choice of amplifier (the lowest curve in Figure I at the given ERP), which in turn specifies the antenna size needed for the given ERP and amplifier.

Although each step in each system analysis is different, this example illustrates several important concepts. First, a method is shown that combines the consideration of discrete alternatives, the amplifiers, with consideration of a continuous alternative, the antenna size. It also illustrates the importance of identifying the strategic parameter linking two subsystems, in this case effective radiated power (ERP) joins satellite to ground receiver. It also shows the use of a "parametric" calculation; since the ERP had not yet been defined, the best ground systems had to be found for a range of this parameter.

This example also reflects the importance of identifying the analytical depth necessary for a decision. Two other amplifier types were considered in the study but were eliminated very early when an approximate analysis showed them to be non-optimum. While they could have been analyzed in depth along with the others, the time invested would have been wasted. In the ASCEND study, the system to control the satellite's orientation also illustrated this point. Here, initial calculations were quite sufficient to eliminate one contender, but detailed analysis was necessary to make the choice between the remaining two.

In the student projects, a wide range of analytical depth is encountered. In some analyses, theories normally taught in the senior year of college have been adequate. In most analyses, however, students have had to use theories learned or being learned in first and second year graduate courses. Several studies have also required construction of subsystems to verify a design concept and experimentation to confirm a theoretical prediction.

In practice, one cycle of synthesis and analysis is never sufficient, and the system is actually configured and analyzed four or five times during the optimization process. The first cycles are usually more approximate and serve to bring out the interdependence of the subsystems, to identify areas that will require deep theoretical derivations, amassing of data, and experimental testing, and to eliminate many obviously inferior alternatives. They also stimulate creativity by pinpointing the needs for invention, showing where standard solutions are poorly suited to the problem or where recent advances in theory have not yet been applied. In these early stages, many wild and wonderful schemes come from the students' imaginations. In the final cycles of analyses and optimizations, the wild schemes are rejected and the true breakthroughs are refined for application in the system.

### Importance of Interspecialty Interaction

In all phases of the study, interaction of the different members of the team is extremely important. In each analysis usually several different fields are represented; and the better the communication among the specialists in these fields, the better are the chances of finding the optimum solution.

In the MITROS study, for instance, a line-scan camera was conceived and analyzed cooperatively by different students working on the orbits, satellite orientation, camera system, communications link, and ground receiver and display. Similarly, the SAMPLER spacecraft's power supply and communications antenna were combined into a single efficient structure by mechanical engnieers configuring the system, aeronautical engineers calculating orbit parameters and spacecraft stability, and electrical engineers designing communications and power systems. (The need to theoreti-

cally calculate and experimentally verify the radio reflectivity of solar cells even established rapport between electrical engineers from the dc and from the RF ends of the frequency spectrum). In the ICARUS spacecraft, two weeks of constant trade-off discussions involving the entire engineering team evolved an extremely efficient configuration which met stringent structural, thermal, power, stability, and communications requirements.

While interaction between different engineers is essential, so is interaction between engineers and scientists on many projects. On SAMPLER, for instance, a team of mechanical and electrical engineers and two biologists worked together to design a biochemical laboratory to detect life on Mars. On SPINMAP, engineers, physicists, and meteorologists working together designed a computer system to generate two-week weather predictions and a satellite sensor system to measure the atmospheric data needed for the computer.

In the ASCEND study, it was obvious that communication between engineers and non-technical specialists was also of great value. In this ETV satellite study, cooperation between education, mass communications, business and engineering students produced decisions on the number of channels needed. It also defined the place of ETV in the educational programs and budgets of Brazil, India and Indonesia. Similarly, business majors in the SPINMAP study evaluated the national and international benefits of two-week weather forecasts to determine the justifiable development pace of the weather prediction system. Finally, in both ASCEND and SPINMAP, international law students joined the team to define the international environment in which these systems would be implemented.

In these studies, the non-technical and science specialists worked with the engineers through all the cycles of the system design. In this way, the system "users" had a strong influence on the engineers throughout. The reverse was also true; and as the design progressed, the "users" were able to modify their own specifications to take advantage of emerging engineering capabilities or compensate for difficulties the engineers encountered. In the design of new systems, such interaction between user and designer is extremely important if the team is to find the optimum solution.

### Student Benefits from Systems Engineering Course

The primary purpose of the systems engineering courses at M.I.T. and Stanford has been educational. These design projects have been intended to teach the students what is necessary for them to be effective members of systems design teams. Most of the necessary concepts have been described above. These skills and some other educational benefits might be summarized as follows:

1. The students learn to apply the advanced science and engineering theories learned in other courses to the solution of real problems.
2. The course broadens the student's understanding of all areas of engineering and in some related fields of science, social science, economics, and politics.
3. The students learn to organize their analysis, not to

find just any solution but to find the optimum solution to a problem.

4. The course teaches the students to work as a team with specialists from other areas in a unified effort toward a common goal.

5. Through guest speakers and visits to industry the students obtain a broad preview of the world in which they will pursue their careers.

6. The course provides an excellent introduction to a new problem on the technical frontier. This can form the basis of a research topic for an advanced degree or contribute to the student's effectiveness in a particular position in industry or government.

7. The course offers the students opportunity for creative engineering during the period of their life when they have acquired the basic scientific tools and have the greatest imagination and inventive capability. It develops more enthusiasm for engineering and also shows the students how they as engineers can make major contributions toward solving world problems.

## Practical Value of the Reports

In designing the systems engineering course, it was decided to choose real unsolved problems and provide the students with much of the background information through guest speakers. This decision has had two effects. First, it has provided great motivation to the students and made them more attuned to the real world. Secondly, it has given the reports practical value, as can be illustrated by the following examples.

Both the SWAMI and SPINMAP reports have been closely reviewed by NASA systems groups and rated high and excellent in scope and quality when compared with industry studies costing more than $100,-000. The SWAMI data collection system is essentially the same as the subsequent EOLE system now being implemented by the French. The SPINMAP analysis of weather prediction benefits was quoted extensively in a report of the Congressional Committee on Science and Astronautics as "the first reasonably detailed figures" available to them. The SPINMAP sensing satellite system is presently being given serious consideration for inclusion in advanced weather programs. The ASCEND study conclusions that ETV with satellites will cost less than $1 per student per year are being carefully studied by the governments of Brazil, India, and Indonesia and by appropriate departments in the United States.

These successes would be impossible without the guest speakers who come from the important levels of government, industry, and university to share their experience and ideas with the students. In one way the student team serves to meld the individual contributions of these experts into a unified system design. In another way, the speakers serve to bring realism to the imaginative schemes of the students.

While space science has dominated our course topics, university systems studies are, of course, also applicable to civilian technology. They can make worthwhile contributions either where new science and technology have created opportunities or where existing science and technology can be better applied by taking a broader systems approach. Application of new technology has characterized the transportation systems design of Professor Baumann's class at M.I.T. (see "The Glideway System" by Professor Baumann

elsewhere in this issue). A recent systems analysis by the Institute for Defense Analysis (Ref. 10) shows how existing technology can be used much more effectively in combating crime.

Similar systems engineering studies might well be carried out on many critical national problems. Reference (11) describes the opportunities for such systems engineering studies in the fields of urban planning, urban transportation, building systems design, and area and regional development. Other opportunities exist in such fields as the school and educational technology; industrial development of Latin America, Africa, or the Middle East; international information systems; smog elimination; etc. The Office of Invention and Innovation of the U. S. Department of Commerce has provided the initial impetus to stimulate universities into undertaking such system studies on public sector problems. It is hoped that other governmental R&D organizations may also consider this powerful approach as a technique for focusing the attention of university students on these critical problems which their generation will have to solve. Grants to universities having qualified staff would both help support an important educational activity and also provide new technical concepts for the solution of these pressing problems.

## References

1. *Principles, Techniques and Approach Used in Conducting Program in Space Systems Engineering.* NASA-Stanford University Training Program, Administrative Report, summer 1966. Prepared under NASA Contract NSR-05-020-151.

2. *MITROS—A Preliminary Design and Feasibility Study of an Equatorial Weather Satellite System.* An Experiment in Systems Engineering Education at the Massachusetts Institute of Technology, spring term 1963.

3. *SWAMI—An Analysis and Preliminary Design Study for a Global Meteorological Data Collection System.* An Experimental Appproach in Space System Engineering at Stanford University, 1964.

4. *SAMPLER—An Analysis and Preliminary Design Study of a 1971 Mars Probe.* Stanford University, School of Engineering, 1965.

5. *SPINMAP—Stanford Proposal for an International Network for Meteorological Analysis and Predictions.* Stanford University, School of Engineering, 1966.

6. *ICARUS—Preliminary Design of an Advanced Solar Probe.* Stanford University, School of Engineering, 1966. Prepared under NASA-Stanford Summer Training Program in Space Systems Engineering under NASA Contract NSR-05-020-151.

7. *ASCEND—Advanced System for Communications and Education in National Development.* Stanford University, School of Engineering, 1967.

8. *SAINT—Preliminary Design of an International Satellite Communication System.* Stanford University, School of Engineering, August 1967. Prepared under NASA-Stanford Summer Training Program in Systems Engineering under NASA Contract NSR-05-020-151

9. Mitchell, M. D., and Koppel, C. J., *An Introduction to Air Force Systems Management.* Series of 8 booklets, Paragon Design Co., P. O. Box 10636, San Diego, California.

10. *Task Force Report: Science and Technology. A Report to the President's Commission on Law Enforcement and Administration of Justice.* Prepared by the Institute for Defense Analyses, 1967. (Available from Superintendent of Documents, U.S. Government Printing Office, Washington, D.C. 20402. Price $1.25).

11. Bredo, Eric R., *Opportunities for University Work on Public Sector Problems.* Office of Invention and Innovation, Bureau of Standards, U. S. Department of Commerce, Washington, D.C., 1967.                                                                    △

*Reprinted from* JOURNAL OF ENGINEERING EDUCATION, Vol. 58, No. 7, March 1968
© 1968 American Society for Engineering Education

# Interdisciplinary Systems Engineering at M.I.T.

**DWIGHT M. BAUMANN,** Associate Professor, Department of Mechanical Engineering, Massachusetts Institute of Technology

SYSTEMS ENGINEERING is in itself an interdisciplinary activity. It has been said that systems engineering is an *all-at-once solution of a complicated problem.* It is usually implied that the problem is so large or complicated that it even interacts with the environment in which it is placed, and thus the environmental parameters and the variations that will be created by the introduction of a new system must be investigated.

The term *systems engineering* is of rather recent origin and perhaps dates back only to the days of the Manhattan project (3). Present usage has expanded the terminology to the entire field of engineering, and now it is becoming customary to speak of the systems approach as being applied to such areas as sociology and political science. Actually the activities now encompassed by *systems engineering* are the same as the ones formerly described by the simple term *design* or sometimes as engineering design. Some years ago the term design fell into disrepute and, particularly in the school of electrical engineering, the term *systems engineering* came into use to replace it.

The term systems engineering has also been used to describe only the analysis of a system. Whereas systems engineering has been synonymous with all of design, including synthesis and analysis, it includes possible creative acts.

## Teaching Systems Engineering

Systems engineering, creativity, or design—terms all in some way synonymous—has become a discipline and is actually a way of life for a great number of practicing engineers. What is meant by these terms is somewhat more related to art than to science, to wisdom than to knowledge, or to judgment than to proof. A person is not really prepared to work in systems engineering until he has had experience, and at the same time he cannot obtain the experience until he has the job opportunity. The answers to this dilemma have been the various forms of apprentice relationships used through the ages.

One might ask, Why should this real world experience be brought to the classroom? Our answer is that it is extremely crucial that the student be involved in the way which has all of the realism and total responsibility, but where the consequences of failure do not result in refusing the student another chance at a project or system design of this size or complexity. The student may be berated and thus subjected to a valuable learning experience, but he is not fired. The primary reason, thus, is that the university environment allows the luxury of considering the success of the people rather than the success of the project.

A course of this kind provides considerable motivation for the students. Probably also the most severe criticism is the fact that students often spend too much time on the interdisciplinary systems course, with the result that their other activities suffer. However, should not such response be expected because at last a student is allowed to participate in problem solving in a manner for which he has spent most of his life preparing. A systems design course also motivates students to be more diligent in their pursuit of other studies because they see how the science they have learned is applied. Another factor is providing motivation in the satisfaction of a job well done. If one is to be prepared to search for the unknown, to create a new system where none existed before, it is vital that the personal ego be sufficiently charged by previous success to allow the person to continue to participate in the face of probable defeat. The goal of performing that improbable act of solving the unsolved requires a great portion of self-confidence. A delicate balance must, however, be maintained so that overconfidence does not lead to systems designs without sufficient scientific justification and enough alternative courses of action, backstops, and fall back positions to insure at least the partial successes required to justify the expenditure of time and effort. Even yet, the most useful result is often the learning obtained and the discovery of the paths and directions that will not work.

## Format of the Systems Engineering Course

The systems engineering courses at M.I.T. attempt to establish a formal course structure directed primarily towards making available to the students concentrated and condensed experience in a format that is sympathetic to the students rather than to the economic or political constraints of the real world situation. However, the economic or political real world constraints are not ignored; rather this is considered as an opportunity for the students to make mistakes and successes and to be guided from one episode to another, with the primary concern that of the well-being of the student and his educational development. The result is an interdepartmental systems engineering and project management course aiming to give the students an experience that they could heretofore only obtain by working on a large multidisciplinary activity in a real live situation. Most likely such an opportunity would only arise a number of years after graduation, and equally it would take a number of years to go through an actual systems study of equal magnitude. The experience is concentrated and condensed by eliminating some of the noncreative or nonintellectual activities and in some cases even by stipulating that the students would have been able to carry out certain analyses, given sufficient time. The problem, thus, is truncated or some of the answers are supplied by the staff or by visiting experts brought in specially for the purpose of informing the class.

These courses are only for students who have a good basic background in engineering and science. They

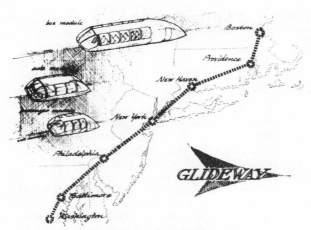

Figure 1. High-speed transportation vehicles

Figure 2. Metropolitan capsule transportation

augment and motivate their study of science, but never replace it. The systems engineering courses discussed here are really a form of apprenticeship. A team of skilled faculty is required to perform in this kind of teacher-student relationship. One would not expect to find a non-artist teaching art, or to find an inexperienced architect or surgeon teaching architecture or surgery; therefore, why should systems engineering be any different?

## Development of the Interdisciplinary Course

The interdisciplinary systems course at M. I. T. is the direct descendant of a course on information systems developed as an interdisciplinary course in 1962 by Professors W. W. Seifert, Y. T. Li, W. E. Vandervelde, C. L. Miller, and H. M. Paynter. The course, organized under the title Special Studies in Information Systems as a joint offering of the Departments of Civil, Mechanical, Electrical, and Aeronautical and Astronautical Engineering, was listed by a separate subject number in each department. It carried the designation of Grad (A): 2, 4, 6—meaning two hours lecture, four hours laboratory, six hours preparation per week.

In this first experiment, the students were allowed to choose from a number of projects, each dealing somehow with information processing. Lectures were given on some of the standard systems sciences, such as modeling, error analysis, design of experiment, noise, modulation, filtering, etc. Four specific cases considered in 1962 were: information processing in electric power systems, testing of thin shell structure of models, instrumentation of a man spaced vehicle, and range safety instrumentation for a specific missile range. The class was divided into groups, and each group selected a topic on which they worked for the entire term. At the middle of the term made a progress report, and at the end of the term each group made an oral presentation to the class and submitted a comprehensive written report describing the results of their study.

In 1963 Visiting Professor William Bollay and the author joined the groups and together all participated in changing this first systems course. Professor Bollay brought a wide experience from the aerospace industry where he had been president of his own firm. Professor Baumann had been working on the development of

undergraduate courses in mechanical design and creative engineering. The previous results of the course convinced the staff that a single project would be more effective, particularly if it were broad enough to include topics of interest to each of the various disciplines. A meteorological satellite system in an equatorial orbit was chosen as the term project for the interdisciplinary course in the spring of 1963. A procedure was evolved in which the students took active control of the project, elected their own group leaders and planned the progress of the project under the full-time, direct supervision of Professor Bollay as the Faculty Coordinator with participation by the rest of the interdisciplinary faculty. Professor Rene Miller's Space Systems Engineering Course was combined with the project at this time.

Some of the experiences of revolving group leadership, having three group reporting periods, and a final presentation to invited guests that had been tried in the undergraduate mechanical engineering design courses were also integrated into the program. The stage was set for the actual participation in an experience in planning and executing a systems design. Special speakers were brought in to fill in the background knowledge needed by the group, and the client was defined as a group of outside experts who would be invited for a one-day presentation by the class. A group report was made mandatory. Results of this first group project were published as a document entitled, *MITROS, A Preliminary Design and Feasibility Study of an Equatorial Weather Satellite System* and were presented to an audience of over a hundred visiting engineers and scientists on the last day of class. Bollay (2) has discussed this experience and similar courses now taught at Stanford and elsewhere.

In the spring of 1964 the topic was an Advanced Orbiting Astronomical Observatory (AOAO). Again an interdepartmental group for Electrical, Mechanical, Nuclear, Civil, Naval Architecture and Marine Engineering, Management, and Aeronautical and Astronautical Engineering cooperated; and again the previous format, report, and presentation scheme

## Social Engineering Interdisciplinary Projects

Since the spring of 1965, two sections of the systems engineering course have been given each second term. One section has maintained a primarily astronautical

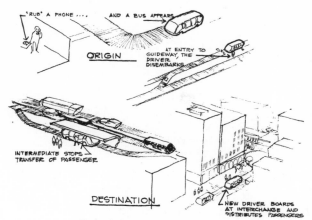

Figure 3. Computer-routed minibuses

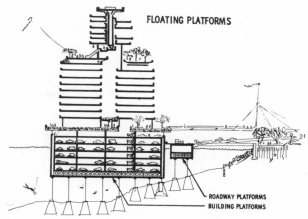

Figure 4. Construction on floating platforms

character; the other has developed into transportation systems, urban systems, and associated societal engineering areas.

The societal engineering section has been redefining the course title and description to reflect both the systems design and the project management laboratory aspects of the course. An important feature of the interdepartmental systems courses as practiced since 1963 has been the technical management training obtained by the student group leaders and project managers. As the group structure changes several times each term, reflecting phases of the projects, a large percentage of the class has opportunity for direct involvement in technical management. Formal and semiformal presentations are required periodically, all participants giving one or more presentations. Because of the broadened nature of the topics, faculty and students from the Departments of Architecture, City Planning, Political Science, Economics, Mathematics, and Industrial Management have joined with the engineers. The exact make-up of the faculty team varies from year to year, depending on the problem being studied. The student reports are now published and distributed by the M.I.T. Press, with any royalty payments going to the support of the secretarial and speaker travel costs for the next class.

The 1965 project was the development of a high-speed ground transportation system for the Northeast Corridor (4). Figure 1 shows the three types of vehicles outlined by the study: a bus-like vehicle, a family-sized vehicle, and an auto-carrying vehicle. Locations, costs, demands, and political feasibilities were studied and presented for the proposed project.

In 1966 the project was Metran (5), an integrated, evolutionary transportation system for a metropolitan area. This study produced the PERC system: a personalized capsule, horizontal elevator system that could be mounted on the second story facade of core city buildings. Figure 2 shows PERC installed on Washington Street in downtown Boston. Also developed was the Genie concept of dynamically routed and scheduled minibuses that respond to a telephone call via a central computer (Figure 3). Several of the Department of Housing and Urban Development contractors have since carried on further studies of this system and are recommending several trials of Genie buses as a distribution system for line haul mass

transit. The Metran report envisioned the Genie system as an evolutionary mechanism, with the Genie vehicles becoming dual-mode buses. The drivers would deliver them to an automated guideway that would carry the vehicles and passengers downtown while the drivers took another vehicle to pick up or deliver another load. The automated guideway, a continuation of the undergraduate Mechanical Engineering Commucar Project (1) was also investigated.

In 1967 project Romulus (6) investigated the feasibility of an industrial consortium's building a partially floating (Figure 4) adaptable, harbor island, subcity for 100,000 people on a square mile. Investigated here were such concepts as modular housing units in a megastructure, movable buildings, domed areas, and grade separation between all pedestrians and the transportation systems. The project being studied in 1968 is a combined airport-seaport for the outer harbor of Boston.

Each of these recent projects has made significant contributions to the state of the art in that in each case they have been the first comprehensive reports to appear. While the results and the reports are not highly polished, they should first be considered as student efforts, unique learning experiences for a group of graduate students. The Interdisciplinary Systems Design and Project Management Laboratory courses are strongly recommended as effective teaching methods.

### References

1. Baumann, D. M., Blanco, E. E., and Mann, R. W., "Commucar—An Intra-Urban Transportation System," *1966 National Transportation Symposium,* The American Society of Mechanical Engineers, New York, N.Y., 1966.
2. Bollay, William, "M.I.T. and Stanford Project in Systems Engineering—An Educational Experience in Creative Design," *Journal of Engineering Education,* Vol. 56, No. 10, pp. 378-380, June 1966.
3. Dommasch and Laudeman, *Principles Underlying Systems Engineering,* Pitman Publishing Corporation, 1962.
4. *The Glideway System,* An Interdisciplinary Systems Design Project by Students at M.I.T., M.I.T. Press, Report No. 6, 1965.
5. *Metran,* An Interdisciplinary Systems Design Project by Students at M. I. T., M.I.T. Press, Cambridge, Mass., Report No. 8, 1966.
6. *Project Romulus,* An Interdisciplinary Systems Design Project by Students at M.I.T., M.I.T. Press, Cambridge, Mass. To be published, 1968. △

*Reprinted from* JOURNAL OF ENGINEERING EDUCATION, Vol. 58, No. 7, March 1968
© 1968 American Society for Engineering Education

# APPENDIX C

Grateful acknowledgement is given to the following people whose cooperation and time spent on interviews, correspondence, and telephone conversations contributed significantly to this document's completion.

In the field of <u>transportation</u>:

Robert E. Barraclough - Office of Transportation Data Research, DOT
Arthur A. Carter - Bureau of Public Roads, DOT
James E. Densmore - Office of the Assistant Secretary for Research
        and Technology, DOT
Thomas H. Floyd - Urban Mass Transportation Administration, DOT
Charles R. Foster - Office of Noise Abatement, DOT
Carl F. Izzard - Bureau of Public Roads, DOT
Richard Kraft - Bureau of Public Roads, DOT
David R. Levin - Bureau of Public Roads, DOT
Harold W. Merritt - Urban Mass Transportation Administration, DOT
William L. Mertz - Bureau of Public Roads, DOT
Gordon M. Murray - Urban Mass Transportation Administration, DOT
Harter M. Rupert - Bureau of Public Roads, DOT
C. L. Shufflebarger - Bureau of Public Roads, DOT
Paul W. Shuldinger - Federal Railroad Administration, DOT
Joseph Stowers - Office of Economics and Systems Analysis, DOT
Richard L. Strombotne - Office of the Assistant Secretary for Research
        and Technology, DOT
Asriel Taragin - Bureau of Public Roads, DOT
Harley J. Unger - Office of Transportation Data Research, DOT
James Verdier - Assistant on Urban Affairs to Congressman Henry
        Reuss, Representative from Wisconsin
Edward J. Ward - Federal Railroad Administration, DOT
Arthur L. Webster - Office of Economics and Systems Analysis, DOT
Dr. William W. Wolman - Bureau of Public Roads, DOT

In the field of <u>housing</u>:

Dr. Irwin H. Billick - Office of Assistant Secretary for Research and
        Technology, HUD

Harold R. Denton - Federal Housing Administration, HUD
Robert Dillon - National Academy of Engineering
Porter S. Driscoll - Federal Housing Administration, HUD
Harold B. Finger - Assistant Secretary for Research and Technology, HUD
Mort Isler - Urban Institute
Duane E. Keplinger - Federal Housing Administration, HUD
Joseph H. Lewis - Urban Institute
Duncan MacRae - Urban Institute
James A. McCullough - Federal Housing Administration, HUD
David Pellish - Office of Assistant Secretary for Science and Technology, DOC
Joseph Sherman - Special Assistant to the Assistant Secretary for Research
    and Technology, HUD
Alan Siegel - Office of Assistant Secretary for Research and Technology, HUD
James R. Simpson - Office of Assistant Secretary for Research and
    Technology, HUD
Albert T. Weinstein - Office of Assistant Secretary for Research and
    Technology, HUD
Arthur J. Zeizel - Office of Assistant Secretary for Research and
    Technology, HUD


In the field of the urban environment:

Dr. Gilbert Barnhart - National Center for Health Services Research and
    Development
Henry Caulfield - Water Resources Council
Frank J. Cservenyak - Solid Wastes Research Program, Department of
    Interior
B. J. Driscoll - National Research Council
Donald D. Dunlop - Office of Science Adviser, Department of Interior
Howard E. Fagin - Health Facilities Planning and Construction Service,
    Public Health Service
Daniel R. Flynn - Commerce Technical Advisory Board, DOC
James L. Hamilton - Special Assistant to the Secretary, Department of
    Interior
Dr. James R. Hibbs - Office of Assistant Secretary for Science and
    Technology, DOC
Dr. Allan Hirsch - Federal Water Pollution Control Administration,
    Department of Interior
Edwin L. Johnson - Federal Water Pollution Control Administration,
    Department of Interior
Jack C. Oppenheimer - Consumer Protection and Environmental Health
    Service, Public Health Service
Frederick L. Orthelib - Office of Research and Development, U. S.
    Coast Guard

Wayne R. Ott - Consumer Protection and Environmental Health Service,
Public Health Service

Martin Prochnik - Office of the Science Adviser, Department of Interior

Dr. Paul J. Sanazaro - National Center for Health Service Research and
Development

Robert Shellard - Commerce Technical Advisory Board, DOC

Roger D. Shull - Federal Water Pollution Control Administration,
Department of Interior

Raymond Smith - National Air Pollution Control Administration, Public
Health Service

David D. Stephan - Federal Water Pollution Control Administration,
Department of Interior

Andrew Sumner - Health Services Research Branch, USPHS Hospital,
Baltimore, Maryland

Dr. Myron Tribus - Assistant Secretary for Science and Technology, DOC

Joseph A. Vitale - Office of University Affairs, NASA

Sherman R. Williams - National Center for Health Services Research
and Development